This is a book of varied sho1 flavour. With the exception of tv Navy, they are all about the T1 who worked there on sailing bɛ boats or took their leisure the 'Tidal Tales'.

The stories differ in length. Some are long ones, perhaps suitable for a railway journey, while others are much shorter and probably best suited to reading in bed, just before dropping off.

Within these pages the reader will encounter some of the characters from my first book 'The Third Hand', but there are plenty of new ones. Among others there are; – the unpleasant doyen of a yacht club, an ebullient Dutch skipper, many of the crew of HM Cruiser Barsetshire and Ted, the man who taught me how to sail, who really existed under another name.

As with some of the yarns in 'The Third Hand' many of the stories in this book are loosely based on the truth. It is up to the reader to work out which ones!

THE AUTHOR

Graham Dent has been interested in Thames Barges since the age of 10 and is currently treasurer of the Society for Sailing Barge Research. He is also a Life Member of Leigh-on-Sea Sailing Club and treasurer of the Customs and Excise Sailing Association. He worked for the Port of London Authority for 34 years, including a spell dealing with barge traffic, and has recently retired from HM Customs and Excise, where he spent the last seven years of his career. He is married with two grown-up children and lives in Leigh-on-Sea, Essex.

TIDAL TALES

Graham Dent

ASHRIDGE PRESS

Published by Ashridge Press
20 Oderin Drive, Trafalgar Park, New Waltham, Grimsby DN36 4GJ

ISBN 1 901214 60 5

FOREWORD

This is a book of varied short stories. Some, like 'The Ghost Barge' and 'The Gold Rush' are long ones, perhaps suitable for a railway journey. Others, for example 'Panic' and 'The Skipper of the Scorpion', are much shorter and probably suited to reading in bed just before dropping off. All, however, are on nautical themes since I seem totally unable to write about anything else! Not all the stories are new. Some, notably 'Salvage', 'The Maiden Voyage', 'Panic' and 'The Skipper of the Scorpion' were written several years ago. 'The Maiden Voyage' reached the short list for the Catherine Cookson Prize and all these older stories have appeared elsewhere. Among the more recent ones 'The Wimp on the Fort' was joint Romantic Fiction winner in my own writer's group annual competition.

As I have already stated, all the stories have a maritime theme, but not as in my first book, 'The Third Hand', exclusively in the world of the Thames Barge. London's Dockland, yacht clubs, a fishing fleet and the Royal Navy are all included. Some of the characters from 'The Third Hand' appear but there plenty of new ones. The reader will meet, among others, the unpleasant doyen of a yacht club, an ebullient Dutch skipper, many of the crew of HM Cruiser Barsetshire and Ted, the man who taught me how to sail, who really existed under another name.

Several people have help this book come to fruition and I would like to thank Colin Moore, the well known Leigh-on-Sea artist for the cover picture. Having acquired my own computer, I needed help with it and my son Alex, son-in-law Jason and friends Colin Bellamy and Nick Hann were of great assistance in this. Finally I would like to thank my family for their encouragement and forbearance! – G.E.D.

CONTENTS

The Ghost Barge:

THE GHOST BARGE

PROLOGUE – JACK DOWNING, 1966

That evening we retired gratefully to the public bar of the King's Head. We had had a strenuous day at Upshore aboard Daisy Maud, which we were rerigging as a yacht barge. Even Ellie, who was far too pregnant to undertake much practical work, had kept us supplied with snacks and tea all day.

There was not much wrong with Daisy Maud's accommodation as she had been a housebarge at Small Gains Creek on the Thames, but since the barge was more or less going to be their home, Bill and Ellie wanted a different arrangement. So Bill and I with a couple of others who had already departed for home, had been knocking down old cabin partitions and erecting new ones.

On deck the real experts, Zeke, Tommy, Ike and Ned, all of them once part of Daisy Maud's racing crew in 1939, had manoeuvred the barge's main mast into its tabernacle and then assessed what standing rigging would be needed. This was a far harder task, for there had been a snowstorm in the middle of the day which had left a slushy deposit on the decks, making moving about hazardous. But this didn't seem to worry the four men, all of whom had sailed on barges professionally, although none of them was young, especially Zeke who was around eighty.

So we were all pleased when the pub opened and we were able to end our working day. The pub's original three bars – saloon, snug and public – had now been knocked into one but the former public area could still be closed off by a folding door and the others all had happy memories of this space, which had not changed in thirty years. This early in the evening we had it virtually to ourselves and, moreover, Ned's wife, Florrie, had built up a good blaze in the open hearth so, with the exception of Ned who had reverted to pub landlord and joined his wife behind the bar, we gathered around the fire.

"Dunno where 'e gets 'is energy from," said Tommy, taking a deep swig of his beer and ignoring the fact that Ned was at least twenty years his junior. So we toasted ourselves in front of the fire, drinking our beer and eating the roast chestnuts that Ned and Florrie had supplied. Bill, Ellie and I were talking about the programme for Daisy Maud's refurbishment while the others discussed different things. During a lull in the conversation I heard Zeke say: "She ain't finished yet, she'll be arahnd agen, mark me words."

"Who isn't finished?" I asked, my natural journalist's curiosity coming to the fore.

"Why the ghost barge, o' course."

"Ghost barge? What ghost barge?"

"All bargemen knows o' 'er," Tommy replied. "Even at Dunkirk, she was. That's where me an' Ike seen 'er."

"An' she were arahnd in '36 jus' before I lost me leg in the Great Gale," said Zeke. He had lost the lower part of his left leg then, but it wasn't so obvious now as an artificial limb had replaced his original peg leg.

"Sails arahnd all misty and ghostly-like," he went on, "an' no good ever follers her"

"Has she got a name – this ghost barge?" I asked.

"Oh, yus. Macbeth. Shakespeare, aint it?"

This was too good to be true, Macbeth, which actors always called the 'Scottish Play' to avoid bad luck.

"Last sailing barge ever built," said Ike, "mebbe that's summat ter do wiv it."

We thought about this. Then Ellie said quietly: "I've seen her too."

"What yew an' all. Miss Ellie?" said Zeke in surprise, for Ellie's main involvement with barges had been as Managing Director and Chairman of Fowler and Dunn, the family firm of barge owners, now trading as Fowler Motorships, Ltd.

"Yes, on the Medway when I went to see the Thames and Medway Barge Co. launch their first 'Spam Can'."

"What's a 'Spam Can'?" I asked.

"That's wot we called them steel moty barges wot Thames an' Medway reckoned would take over from the sailing barges," said Tommy.

"They was right an' all," said Ike. "All the owners got some'at o' the sort," he glanced at Ellie, "even Fowler and Dunn."

"That's progress," said Ellie, unruffled.

Zeke brought us back to the ghost barge.

"She'll be arahnd agen," he said. "Mark me words."

Ned, who was still behind the bar, remarked that she hadn't been since 1948, when rumours were heard that she'd appeared near Grays shortly before Goldsmiths, the owner based there, sold their fleet of sailing barges, a sad event since they had once been the biggest owner of all.

Shortly after that the party broke up as we were all tired after our day's work – Bill and Ellie to retire to their hotel, the others to their respective homes and me to drive back to Mayfield. On the way I thought about what I had heard that evening. There was no doubt that there was an intriguing tale to be told of this 'ghost barge' and I thought that it had the makings of a good project. At the time I was becoming disillusioned with newspaper work and taking on more freelance commissions. Perhaps there was a story here.

That was two years ago. Now, after much research, I can finally present the tale of the last sailing barge ever built – 'Macbeth', the ghost barge.

1932/3 MACBETH –

THE LAST SAILING BARGE BUILT

In 1931 the steel sailing barge Blue Mermaid was launched at Mistley. Shortly afterwards, a small wooden barge, Lady of the Lea, which was designed principally for the carriage of munitions on the River Lea, also took to the water for the first time. It was generally thought that these two would be the last sailing barges ever built.

But in 1932 it was announced that Nathan Letchworth, a small Upshore owner, had commissioned a new barge to be built at Tolworth on the River Whitewater. The news spread rapidly around the sailing barge fraternity and was widely discussed wherever barge crews foregathered.

"Ain't no point," they said on Starvation Buoys at Woolwich, where barges waited for cargoes from the London Docks. "Ain't much work for barges an' ain't goin' to be much."

In the Crab and Lobster at Gravesend they were more upbeat. "Letchworth must have a good contract," they said.

In the Swan at Mistley, the redoubtable Bully Briggs addressed the company, "'E must be mad. My guvnor knew what 'e was doin' when 'e 'ad Blue Mermaid an' them others afore 'er built. Them's steel, last forever." And, after all, Bully's command, Resolve, was one of them.

At Ipswich, the bargemen suspected ulterior motives. "'E's up to summat," they said. In Kent very little was said and Letchworth's venture was dismissed as another piece of Essex foolishness. But then Kentishmen would say that as there was no love lost between Essex and Kent bargemen.

In Upshore, Letchworth's base, much more was known and widely discussed in the two waterside pubs – the King's Head and the Jolly Fisherman. It was generally believed that Letchworth had received an inheritance. Certainly the owner had recently adopted the pursuits of a country gentleman, shooting game and riding to hounds. This lifestyle could not possibly have been supported by his business enterprises – a run-down farm, a mediocre builders' yard and a fleet of three elderly sailing barges, discarded by their original owners at knock-down prices.

There was also the business of the building of the new barge. Letchworth had, allegedly, offered the contract to Fowler and Dunn, Upshore's principal barge owner, who ran their own barge-building and repair yard. Fowler's promptly declined, claiming that they had enough work of their own. This was patently untrue, as very little barge repairing was going on and the yard's main business, at the time, was building yachts and fishing smacks. The truth was that Isaac Fowler, the firm's principal, wished to add all the local barges, Letchworth's included, to his fleet. Not that Letchworth's old tore-outs would have been much use to Fowler and Dunn, but it would, at least, eliminate some competition, since Nathan held the contract for Upshore's mill, a fairly lucrative business, which Isaac dearly coveted.

A little while later, two further developments started tongues wagging all over again. These were that the new barge was to be built with an auxiliary engine fitted and that her name was to be Macbeth. The first was treated with derision as very few barges had auxiliaries at that time. True, the Thames and Medway Barge Company had fitted a few to their barges, generally at the request of individual skippers, but the consensus of barging opinion was that the low powered engines were only of use 'in a flat calm with a fair tide'.

The name did not, at first, cause much comment since bargemen were not particularly, if at all, well versed in Shakespeare. However, a columnist on the Upshore Gazette was and made the theatrical connection at some length in his next contribution to the paper. This was read by several barge-men and thereafter there was much shaking of heads and sucking of teeth to remarks like: 'No good'll come of 'er.'

Oblivious of all this, Letchworth carried on with his project. After Fowler and Dunn's rejection, he had persuaded a Tolworth boat yard, which happened to be owned by his cousin, to build his barge. This was not this yard's normal function. It had no history as a barge builder, it's previous out-put being pleasure craft and fishing vessels. Neither did it have the capacity to build an 80-foot sailing barge. So a nearby field was rented and the barge more or less built on oil-drums, with a Dutch barn arrangement over it to protect it from the weather. Since the field sloped towards the water and was not enclosed by a sea wall it was thought that launching, which would have to be sideways, would not be a problem.

Letchworth had, indeed, received an inheritance from a deceased aunt. His boatbuilding cousin had also benefited from the will and therefore they were able to come to an 'arrangement' about the barge. The auxiliary engine was only an option that was being considered. All that was intended, for the time being, was to fit engine bearers ready for a future installation.

Building proceeded rapidly, with extra men hired into the yard. Meanwhile further rumours circulated among Upshore's waterfront population – unseasoned timber was being used, the yard's steam chest was inadequate and so on. Some of these assertions may even have been true.

By January 1933, Macbeth was ready to be launched. The critics saw this as a potential disaster. Not that a sideways launch was that unusual, but they felt that this was where the yard's lack of experience would show. In the event all went well, Macbeth sliding smoothly down heavily greased baulks of timber into the water – and she didn't leak, at least any more than any other newly launched sailing barge.

A period of fitting out followed at the yard and then Macbeth was towed to Upshore to receive her sails. This was odd, for although Letchworth had engaged Wilfred Hooker, Upshore's one-eyed sailmaker to make the sails; there was no reason why the sails should not have been delivered to Tolworth. The tow was generally put down to either Letchworth's apparent compulsion to spend money or to his desire to show off his new barge.

At Upshore Macbeth lay at the Town Quay for the fitting of the sails and for the Upshore Gazette and other newspapers to take photographs. Letchworth was making the most of what was almost certainly the last sailing barge to be built. She was also scrutinised by a large crowd of bargemen – not just from Upshore, there were visitors from Colchester and even Bully Briggs popped down from Mistley for a look.

Their attitude was summed up by Captain 'Happy' Day of the Daisy Maud: 'She don't look right.' No one could specify what it was but she just didn't look right. The best guess was that her inexperienced builder had 'got it wrong'.

Letchworth was now faced with a crew problem. The general hostility of the Upshore men meant that none of them would accept a berth on the new vessel, not even the crews of Letchworth's existing barges. Moreover the Upshore attitude had spread around other Essex ports and Letchworth eventually engaged the Twining brothers from Sittingbourne in Kent as crew. Although experienced bargemen, the Twinings had not done much coasting work, generally sailing from London to the rivers Medway and Swale. The importation of Kentish bargemen to sail an Essex barge caused further consternation at Upshore.

Macbeth's first voyage was to the Central Granary at Millwall Dock, London to pick up a cargo of wheat for

Upshore's mill. There were a few hiccups on the trip to London, but nothing major. The voyage back was, in the words of Captain Alf Twining, 'a cracker.'

"She's fast," the skipper told Letchworth. "You oughta think about enterin' 'er for a Barge Match." So perhaps her inexperienced builder had accidentally hit on a winning formula, even if she didn't 'look right'.

About this time two disasters hit the Letchworth enterprise. The mill contract came up for renewal and was promptly secured by Isaac Fowler for Fowler and Dunn. Letchworth managed to arrange a new contract for the carriage of petrol in drums from London to Cliffe in Kent which, although it served to keep his barges in employment, was nothing like as lucrative as the mill contract. The petrol, with a little bit of work for his own company and the odd timber cargo was all he had. The petrol job was short-haul work and was considered by the Upshore chorus to be degrading for alleged coasting barges.

"Should suit them Twinings," said a particularly outspoken critic, "them bein' Kentishmen an' all."

The second disaster was the loss of one of Letchworth's original barges. She was run down and sunk by a steamer in Halfway Reach on the Thames. Although raised by the Port of London Authority, she was found to be beyond reasonable repair and declared a total loss. This was nothing like as serious as the loss of the mill contract as Letchworth hadn't really enough work for four barges and, anyway, he had the insurance money, albeit small, to look forward to. But it meant that Macbeth was used more and more on the petrol run. And far worse was to follow.

In those days the carriage of hazardous cargoes on the Thames was not subject to stringent rules and regulations. So apart from an instruction to his crews not to smoke near the cargo, Letchworth took no particular precautions for the carriage of petrol on his little fleet. Whether his one instruction was obeyed or not is not known, but the two brothers on

Macbeth were known cigarette smokers, continually 'rolling their own'.

Thus it was that Macbeth entered the crowded waters of Woolwich Reach on the Thames one bright spring day with a fair north westerly wind. She was well laden with petrol in drums with a small stack of them above her hatch coamings. Because of her short voyage in usually calm waters to Cliffe, only a light tarpaulin was stretched over the deck cargo. The inhabitants of the Reach took little or no notice of her, until an enormous explosion riveted their attention. The forward part of Macbeth was engulfed a huge fireball. Her spars and sails, well alight, came crashing down as the flames spread rapidly aft. Bert Twining, the mate, who must have been up forward, was not seen again but the skipper, Alf Twining, was blown clear, although badly burned. He was rescued by the roadsman from a nearby tier of lighters who, with commendable bravery, had manned his boat to look for survivors.

Quite apart from the blazing wreck of Macbeth, a considerable area of the surface of the Reach was now covered with burning petrol. The tier of lighters, recently vacated by their heroic roadsman, quickly became engulfed. The breeze took the flames towards the south shore where the wooden piles of several wharves began to burn.

Those vessels that could, mainly tugs and powered coasters, rapidly abandoned Woolwich Reach. However, the Woolwich Free Ferry, which had been about to depart from its southern terminal gamely set off for the north shore, narrowly avoiding a patch of burning fuel. When she reached the northern terminal the service was suspended, which was just as well for the next casualty was the southern ferry pier. Here the blaze was particularly severe, the flames engulfing two fire appliances, which had arrived to fight the flames. The firemen fled for their lives.

By now several hundred yards of the foreshore of Woolwich Reach were on fire, together with the tier of lighters. The fire chief began to fear for the safety of Woolwich Arsenal, where many types of munitions were stored. But, in time, his men, backed by personnel and appliances from many other brigades and fire-floats to tackle the offshore blazes, had the fires under control.

What was left of Macbeth sank in the shallow water on the south side, where the PLA Salvage Department later dispersed it. Captain Twining was taken to hospital, where it was feared that he would not survive his burns. Fortunately there had been no further casualties.

Some days later, Nathan Letchworth, depressed by the events at Woolwich and expecting the bailiffs or police to knock on his door at any time, placed the barrel of his sporting rifle in his mouth and blew his brains out.

There were no barges under way on the River Whitewater that night, but fishermen returning to Upshore with their catches reported seeing a ghostly barge loom out of the night. "All fiery she was," they said.

The saga of the ghost barge had begun.

1936 – THE GREAT GALE

Captain Ezekial Brown, normally known as Zeke, of the Dulcie, was undoubtedly one of Fowler and Dunn's top barge skippers. Renowned for his fast passage making and general good seamanship, he had several times formed part of the racing crew in the firm's entries in the annual Barge Matches on the Thames and Medway and at Upshore, his home port, with considerable success. A bachelor, barges were his one passion in life.

It irked him considerably to be trapped in Yarmouth by bad weather, particularly in the company of his present mate. This young man, Matt Earnshaw, was a committed socialist, if not communist. His only conversation, other than barging matters, was of his politics and one further matter – the rapid loss of Zeke's hair.

"It's coming out in handfuls, skipper," he said repeatedly. "You oughta get sommat done about it."

Not that Zeke could fault Matt as a barge mate. The lad was conscientious, as experienced as a nineteen-year old could be and, most importantly, a good cook. Altogether, apart from his conversation, an excellent barge mate.

Zeke was sensitive about his hair-loss and not the slightest bit interested in politics so he tended to avoid Matt as much as he could, taking long walks along Yarmouth sea-front. When funds permitted he repaired to that favourite pub of bargemen, the Druid's Arms, where he joined the skippers of other trapped barges for a pint or two.

Thus it was that Zeke was in the pub with a number of skippers from Grays on the Thames. The subject under discussion was, almost inevitably, the weather. One of the Grays men, who looked about eighty years old, was regarded by the others as some sort of weather prophet.

"That's a-goin' ter get better," he said.

"Not much sign of it," stated one of the others.

"That's as maybe," retorted the old man. "Me rheumatics sez that'll get better."

Behind the bar the landlord tapped his barometer.

"Glass is goin' up," he said hopefully.

"Ah, but when is it goin' to get better," said the critic. "An' 'ow long for. We need a long good spell to get south."

These men, thought Zeke, are hoping to go all the way south to the Thames. Me, I'd settle for as far as Harwich in one go. Do the rest later. Probably the old boy's right, he's been at sea all his life and the barometer's going up. A window in the weather will do. I'll go for Harwich.

"We'd better get ready to go," he said to Matt on his return to the barge. "Sounds like there's goin' ter be a lull, at least."

"Owners should give us some sort of forecast," the mate grumbled. "It's us workers what takes the risks."

Oh God, thought Zeke, politics even with the weather now.

"You lose any more hair in that pub, skipper?"

Zeke went down to the cabin and slammed the hatch behind him.

* * *

In the end, Zeke decided to sleep on the subject of the weather problem and see what it was like in the early morning. He was on deck at 5.30a.m. studying the situation. It wasńt at all bad, he decided. Although it was overcast there was no real movement in the clouds. The wind was westerly, not perfect for

Harwich, but the tide would turn shortly and help push the barge down towards Orfordness. On the strength of all this he went ashore and ordered a tug.

As the elderly paddle tug towed Dulcie through Yarmouth harbour there was no sign of life aboard the other barges, apart from the old man from the pub the previous day.

"We ain't comin'," he hailed. "Me rheumatics sez that won't be no good."

Superstition, thought Zeke.

Once Dulcie had been dropped by the tug, she made good progress to the southward and was off Lowestoft by the time she had settled down to her rig of mainsail, foresail, topsail and mizzen. Zeke did not consider that further sails were necessary and might prove a nuisance if there was a squall.

"We ain't doin' bad at all," he told the mate, who, now they were at sea, had ceased to talk of politics and hair loss. They sailed on in companionable silence for a while.

"Take 'er a minute, will yer?" Zeke said to Matt, moving away from the wheel. "Jus' keep on course. I'm off ter 'ave a look at our glass."

Dulcie had a barometer in the cabin. Zeke tapped it and was alarmed at what he saw. The pressure was falling rapidly. Ah well, thought Zeke, we're committed now, maybe we'll be in Harwich before it gets too bad. When he returned to the deck Matt was staring astern with a puzzled expression.

"That's funny, skipper," he said. "I could have sworn there was another barge a-followin' us just now."

"Who was it?" asked Zeke, with as much nonchalance as he could muster.

"Dunno. She was a bit hazy-like, looked as though she 'ad smoke an' that comin' outa 'er."

"You must 'ave imagin' it," said Zeke firmly, but he was worried for he too had glimpsed the apparition as his head came out of the cabin hatch and Zeke knew all about what the fishermen had seen on the night of Nathan Letchworth's suicide. Was this a warning or a portent of doom?

21

* * *

Matt came on deck with two steaming mugs of tea.

"Think them others left Yarmouth, skipper?" he asked.

"Course they did. Only takes one. They'd 'ave seen us tow out, had a good dither among themselves, then sailed directly. But most o' them are slow old things, so they'll be hours behind us."

They could now clearly see the promontory of Orfordness. Zeke was still worried however. He blew on his tea, took a gulp and then said to Matt: "That wind's gorn funny. Trying ter go southerly. That's no good to us. Freshening, too. Take the mizzen off 'er, will yer?"

Take off the mizzen, he thought, bargeman's first reef.

Half an hour later the wind was definitely southerly and much fresher. Spray and some wave tops were coming aboard up forward.

"Get the topsail off 'er, Matt," Zeke yelled to Matt, who was up forward. "Topsail, second reef and this wind's pushing us away from the land, away from Harwich. Good job we're not a loaded barge, water would be all over the place by now."

With the topsail off, the barge sailed easier, but the wind was still rising. A squall ripped through the rigging. If we had the topsail up, thought Zeke, we would have lost the topmast for sure. We've got to stay on this tack whatever or we'll never get an offing for Harwich. Matt came aft and managed to get a cigarette alight, no mean feat in the wind. He didn't smoke much of it, for it quickly burnt away to nothing.

"I could do with some of the mainsail brailed up," yelled Zeke above the wind. "Daren't risk it, though. Too much could go wrong with the brails an' that. We'll keep on. You jus' stand by ter 'elp me with the wheel."

The barge surged on, needing both men at the wheel at times. If we keep going like this, Zeke mused, we're going to end up in Belgium, but at least we'll be safe. Sooner or later Iím going to have to get her about and try for Harwich. A little while later he thought he detected a lessening of the wind. He quickly gave Matt instructions on the handling of the foresail: "Ease her over gently on the bowline. If that sail goes over with a bang, it'll likely split. An' for Gawd's sake keep one 'and for yerself."

The scheme nearly worked but at the last minute a particularly large sea threw the barge's head off. She fell back on the original tack.

Belgium here we come. No, don't think like that. Look for a quiet patch and try again.

"Now! Lee-oh!" he shouted at Matt who, soaked to the skin, was still up forward. A lull had come. This time the barge came round. Matt scrambled aft.

"We mustn't make too much leeway," Zeke told the mate. "Drop the starboard leeboard halfway down. That'll help."

Zeke was right to be concerned. If the barge made too much leeway she would miss Harwich Harbour. True, to leeward were two rivers, the Deben and the Alde, but both had difficult entrances among shifting sands and Zeke had been to neither river. The lowered leeboard would give the barge more grip on the water and minimise the drift to leeward.

The barge tore on, back towards the land, in what was now definitely a gale. Dulcie was harder to steer now and both men were at her wheel. It began to get dark.

After a while Matt said: "That wind, skipper. I think it's got some east in it."

Zeke nodded his agreement. "Taking off a bit, too, I reckon."

This was good, If the wind was going easterly and becoming only a degree lighter; they would easily make Harwich. Sometime later the lights of Harwich Harbour were plainly in view. The wind, although still strong, had shifted much more into the east. We're all right now, thought Zeke.

"Jus' goin' ter get the leeboard up," he said to Matt. "We don't need it now."

He moved to the nearby crab winch which controlled the

leeboard. As he took the weight on the winch handle some-thing within the winch snapped. The leeboard ran out to its full extent. Zeke lost control of the handle which whipped round and hit him violently on the left shin. Zeke cried out and went down. Matt started forward from the wheel to help his skipper.

"Stay at the wheel," Zeke managed to rasp. He started to crawl painfully towards the wheel, leaving a trail of blood behind him. My left leg's busted, he thought, if I can get to the wheel I can at least hang on to the lower spokes to help Matt. But how are we going to get the sails off her in this breeze? We'll likely pile up some where in the harbour. With this thought he passed out.

But they were lucky. A pilot cutter noticed their plight and, with commendable seamanship, managed to put two men aboard to assist Matt. Once Dulcie was safely anchored in the harbour, with plenty of chain out to prevent the anchor drag-ging, Zeke was removed to hospital. There his leg was found to be too badly smashed to be repaired and it was amputated below the knee.

It was some days before Zeke and Matt knew of the carnage that had happened behind them off Yarmouth. Zeke's friend Happy Day, who took the opportunity of his barge being in Ipswich to visit Zeke in hospital, eventually brought the news. As Zeke had forecast the rest of the fleet had left Yarmouth some hours after Dulcie. Others had joined them from Lowestoft and ports further north.

They did not make good progress and had been caught out by the gale, which was much worse there. A total of seven barges had needed lifeboat assistance. Of these four were blown across the North Sea, three being found in Holland and one in Germany. The other three sank in the Yarmouth area. Some made it into Yarmouth but all had had sails blown out and other damage.

"It was a warning of the gale, then," said Zeke in his hospi-tal bed.

"What was?" asked Happy Day.

"Why, that ghost barge, Macbeth. We seen 'er."

"Aye. 'Appen she'll be seen agen, then."

Once Zeke's stump was properly healed, he had a peg leg fitted. His barging days seemed over, but Fowler and Dunn, in a rare fit of generosity, gave him employment as their ship's husband at Upshore.

As for Matt Earnshaw, true to his socialist principles he went to Spain, where he joined the International Brigade to fight Franco in the Civil War. He never returned. Whether he was the victim of a sniper's bullet or whether he fell in love with Spain (or maybe a senorita) and stayed there is unclear.

1940 – DUNKIRK

"Turn round and report to Ramsgate."

The amplified voice of the sub-lieutenant in charge of the patrol boat came clearly over the still water.

"Only if yer sez please."

A pause. "Turn round and report to Ramsgate, PLEASE! You are urgently needed there."

Tommy Dolby, skipper of the auxiliary sailing barge Hubert put the wheel hard over and chuckled, since he considered that he had scored a point over the Navy.

"What's 'e on about?" asked Ike, the mate. "What'd we want ter go ter Ramsgate fer?"

"'Cos summat's up, that's why. Ain't you noticed them tugs towin' ships' lifeboats an' all them dinky moty-cruisers, what is usually up the Thames? Could be our boys over in France is in trouble."

"We got enough fuel?" There was little or no wind for sailing.

"Jus' about. I took on enough for Upshore to Lunnon, plus a bit extra."

* * *

Hubert reached Ramsgate on the dregs of her fuel. There the Navy completely refilled her tanks and allocated her an extra crew member, Able Seaman White, a cheerful Cockney, who came aboard with a machine gun, a useful addition to the barge's existing armament, one shotgun, usually employed for poaching.

"Call me Knocker," said White, as he erected the gun, "everyone else does."

Tommy returned from shore with their orders. He addressed Ike and Knocker in the cabin, slapping one piece of paper on the table.

"Official requisition by the Navy. Fowler an' Dunn'll love that," he said, referring to the barge's owners. He then read from a larger document. "We're to be towed most o' the way over ter France. 'Ope the tug skipper knows what 'e's doin'. Save our fuel till we're over there. If there were enuff wind I'd bloody sail there. Still we got ter find a place called La Panne an' take soldiers off from there an' dump 'em on bigger ships."

"It's an evacuation, then," said Ike.

"Sounds like it. So we gotta do what we can. 'Ope it's as easy as they makes out."

"But there'll be bombs an' Jerry guns an' all sorts."

"That's what you got me an' me gun for," said Knocker White, unmoved.

* * *

A London lighterage tug, whose skipper knew about towing sailing barges, took them across the Channel, together with a firefloat and an RNLI lifeboat. The tow was cast off just short of Dunkirk Roads and the vessels proceeded under their own steam. There was no difficulty in spotting Dunkirk as a great pall of smoke from burning oil storage tanks and port installations could be seen from miles offshore.

"That don't look good," said Tommy.

They had just crossed the Roads when Ike said: "There's a barge a-sailin' up the Roads." Tommy took a quick glance out of the wheelhouse window, "Yus, can you make out who it is?"

"Nah. Looks like she's copped one, there's all smoke an' that comin' outa 'er. That's funny she's gorn."

"You know what," said Tommy. "Reckon that could be that ghost barge, Macbeth. It's a warnin', not surprised with this caper."

"What's all that about?" asked Knocker, who was enjoying a fag alongside the wheelhouse.

Ike explained: "Well, there's this ghost barge, see, an' us bargemen reckon she appears ter give a warnin' in times of danger. She did it fer the gale in '36. Lot of barges lost that night."

"An' you two just seen 'er?"

"That's right. But it's dangerous 'ere an' no mistake."

Ike and Tommy were both thinking the same thing – I hope that warning's a general one and not for us in particular.

*   *   *

A while later they could see passenger ferries loading troops from Dunkirk's mole.

"Couldn't we go in there, Tom?" asked Ike.

"No mate, big boys only in there. We gotta find this La Panne place up the coast a bit. See what they mean, with our shallow draught we can get right in, pick men up an' then take them off to sommat bigger."

They could see other sailing barges aground on Dunkirk's beaches.

"I 'eard as 'ow some came across early with supplies for the soldiers," said Tommy, "but I reckon none of 'em'll get off there."

"Pride of Upshore's the nearest one," Ike supplied.

"Bloody John Fowler," Tommy pretended to spit on the wheelhouse floor. After his bad behaviour in the 1939 Upshore Barge Match, their former managing director was now an out-cast. They were just past when an enormous explosion nearly threw the crew off their feet. Where Pride of Upshore had been minutes earlier there was now only a great cloud of smoke and debris.

"Oh, my gawd!" exclaimed Tommy in horror, "I reckon they was carrying explosives. Hope the poor buggers were ashore." They were not. John Fowler and his crew had perished.

* * *

Off La Panne, Tommy had a problem – how to embark the troops. Not that many soldiers were ready. He could see large groups of them ashore, but few were near the water s edge. Perhaps the troops, not being seafaring men, did not recognise Hubert, with her strange outline of mast, sprit, sails and box-like wheelhouse as a potential source of rescue. He did not wish to put Hubert aground on a still falling tide – might end up like Pride of Upshore. Neither did he wish to use the barge's boat – it would take an age to transfer men by that means and there was always the danger that the boat might be rushed. To go in as close as they dared and put a ladder over the bows might create similar problems. Knocker White solved the equation for him.

"What about over there, skipper? Someone's built a pier out of lorries an' I can see men standin' on it."

"Oh, yus. We can nose in there all right."

Gingerly Hubert touched alongside the makeshift pier and was immediately boarded by what seemed like hundreds of men. They had some wounded with them who were put in the foc'sle with a medical orderly to look after them. A large sergeant jumped aboard aft, armed with a Bren gun and plenty of ammunition for it.

"I'm yer guardian angel, Sergeant Maloney" he announced in a strong Irish accent and commenced choosing a firing position aft.

"That's our lot. Reversin' off," shouted Tommy above the general hubbub. There seemed no more men on the jetty. He

29

caught sight of his mate among the throng.

"Ike. Sails as well as engine. Let's get outa 'ere, fast."

There was enough breeze to make sailing viable and it would help conserve fuel. The senior officer of the troops, Captain Wade of the Green Howards, came aft and introduced himself. He was very proud that he and his men had built the lorry pier under the supervision of Royal Engineers. The Green Howards, the Engineers and stragglers that they had picked up formed Hubert's passengers. Wade, despite all he had been through, both ashore and in building the pier, still gave an impression of being jaunty and dapper.

"Is there anything I can do to help?" he asked. "I've done some sailing."

Many willing hands were helping Ike set sail.

"No," said Tommy. "Me an' me mate can take care of the sailin'. But there's plenty else, if yer wouldn't mind. First, sorry we can't offer yer all a cuppa tea, but yer wounded's welcome ter all the water we got. So yer can get someone onter that. Second, we're likely be attacked on the way home. 'Appen it'll be aircraft, but we can avoid them, I 'ope, but if that's E-Boats, we can fergit it. So, all your men what's got guns, 'ave 'em ready ter fire. An' last I'd like ter know 'ow many men we've got aboard, jus' fer the record. So get a man onter that, please." Wade went off to do as he was bid, almost saluting as he went. Ike fought his way aft.

"Skipper, wasn't there sommat about takin' troops off ter larger vessels?"

"No way. These are our men an' we're takin' them all the distance." His eyes swept the horizon, ignoring the two Dutch coasters standing off the shore. "'Sides, I don't see no ships, do you?"

* * *

After half an hour they stopped to take twenty men off a broken-down motor cruiser. These, added to the two hundred and

30

fifty reported by the corporal given the task of the original tally, meant that they had two hundred and seventy soldiers aboard.

An hour later the first attack came. Sergeant Maloney spotted an aircraft coming up astern.

"Sure, an' it'll be a Jerry. The RAF boyos aren't around."

"Ready your weapons!" shouted Captain Wade. A forest of rifle barrels sprang above Hubert's main hatch. Tommy, glancing out of the wheelhouse's back window, distinctly saw a bomb leave the plane.

"Fire!" yelled Wade and a fusillade of rifle fire augmented Knocker's machine gun and Maloney's Bren as the aircraft passed overhead. The bomb exploded fifty yards astern, the shock wave pushing the barge forward.

"Bad shot," said Tommy.

"He must be short on bombs," said the knowledgeable Maloney, "Only used one. Sure and he'll use his guns next time."

The plane was banking for another run.

"Reload!" Wade instructed his riflemen.

Next time the German aircraft came in with guns blazing. The same warm resistance greeted it. Something shattered the rear wheelhouse window, brushed hotly past Tommy's cheek and embedded itself in the woodwork. A neat line of holes appeared in the mainsail. Up forward there was the sound of ricochets off metalwork and several men fell. Firing on the main deck died out as the plane disappeared towards the horizon, trailing a thin line of smoke.

"We got her!" shouted Knocker White. Cheering broke out. Fortunately the casualties were all light, as the foc'sle was already full of the original wounded. After a while a motor launch appeared in the distance on a course at right angles to Hubert's.

"I 'ope to Gawd that's one of ours an' not an E-Boat," said Tommy.

"Sure, an' we'll fight him, too," said Maloney.

31

"No chance. They've got guns, torpedoes. The lot."

"'E's an E-Boat, skipper," shouted Knocker White from forward. His recognition of naval vessels was probably better than anyone else's aboard. The E-Boat altered course toward them and increased speed

"'E's seen us," said the ever doleful Ike. "We might as well find summat white ter surrender wiv."

Just then there was an explosion astern followed by a rushing noise overhead. Waterspouts appeared round the E-Boat. Tommy looked through the shattered rear wheelhouse window. A British destroyer was coming up fast from astern and had fired at the E-Boat over Hubert. As Tommy watched her forward gun turrets fired again. More rushing sounds and more waterspouts followed the fast retreating E-Boat.

"Good old Navy!" cried several soldiers.

As the destroyer surged past, no doubt bent on important business elsewhere, she was roundly cheered. There were answering waves from her bridge.

Eventually, with the coast of England in sight, Hubert's engine coughed into silence.

"We still got some fuel," said Tommy, "can't be that."

A couple of Royal Engineers offered to look at the problem. They diagnosed a fuel blockage and commenced taking the fuel lines down. In the meantime Hubert continued under sail alone.

"We're nearer Dover than Ramsgate," Tommy decided, "we'll go in there."

Just as the engineers announced success, a passing trawler offered them a tow into port. Rather than risk the engine, Tommy accepted. The trawler skipper told them that the Dunkirk evacuation was all but over.

"Good. No need ter go agen," said Tommy.

"Gawd, I hadn't thought o' that," Ike added.

Dover was the main debarkation port for the Dunkirk refugees and was absolute pandemonium. To a man Hubert's complement of soldiers queued up to shake hands with

Tommy and Ike, then they stepped on to the quay and were lost in the crowd.

Knocker had jumped ashore as soon as they had come alongside and was saying to anyone who would listen: "We got a Jerry."

When Tommy went ashore a bit later to find someone to report to, he saw Wade and Maloney forming the Green Howards up. They marched away smartly despite their bedraggled appearance. Many had lost items of clothing, some had bandaged wounds, but most had retained their rifles. A WVS lady pressed a mug of tea on Tommy who gratefully accepted, although he was longing for a pint of mild and bitter.

"Ta, luv," he said. "Best drink in the world."

* * *

Many years later, the former Captain Wade, by then a successful London businessman, found Hubert as a dilapidated houseboat on the Upper Thames. He purchased her and turned her into a delightful floating home for his family. Among the guests that they have entertained aboard have been Tommy and Ike, together with Chief Petty Officer 'Knocker' White and Company Sergeant Major Maloney, Military Medal.

1947 – BUSINESS SKULLDUGGERY

The directors of the Thames and Medway Barge Co., Ltd were holding their monthly board meeting. The routine business, minutes of the previous meeting, financial report and so on, had been settled. Now they were left with two special items: New Buildings, which had been on the agenda several times, and a fresh and top secret addition, Possible Take-overs.

New Buildings was an ongoing item – the firm was using Government compensation for its war losses, which had been considerable, to finance a fleet of steel motor barges. They were austerity built in those hard, post-war days, but useful replacements for their lost sailing barges, for they were deemed much faster and more reliable. In the minutes of the meetings they were referred to as 'motorised units'. It was only later when they appeared painted in a particularly hideous salmon shade that the nickname 'Spam Cans' was adopted. Invented by one of Thames and Medwayís wittier bargemen, it became universal, even at Boardroom level.

The Director in charge of Construction reported that the first of these new vessels, which were being built at the firm's own yard, would be ready for launching in a few weeks. The Board agreed that this should be a prestige event, with many local dignitaries invited.

This matter being successfully concluded, the Chairman moved the meeting on to Possible Take-overs. He and the

Managing Director, he explained, had already given this subject much thought. Given the current austere post-war atmosphere, many barge owners were in decline. 'But not our Company (applause).' Most had suffered numerous war losses, not just from enemy action, but by requisition of their barges for duties such as mine watching or tending barrage balloons. Many of the barges on these tasks were now fit only for the scrap heap.

There was, however, one successful company in their line of business. This was Fowler and Dunn of Upshore. They had lost only two barges in the war, Pride of Upshore, which was, in any case, the subject of a dispute between John Fowler and his former family firm and an old vessel called Reed Warbler which was coming to the end of her working life anyway. Admittedly Fowler's had not received much compensation for either, but few of their vessels had been requisitioned for mine watching, etc., as much of their work was in grain and other foodstuffs. This was an area in which Thames and Medway could be more active. As the directors knew Thames and Medway had recently broken into the cement trade by their acquisition of a cement works and there was going to be a huge demand for cement as Europe was rebuilt after the war. Therefore the company would require many units to carry that product. Hence the desire to eliminate competition and acquire more vessels.

With this stirring speech the Chairman handed over to the Managing Director, to run through the history of Fowler and Dunn. The board learnt that the firm had been founded in 1876 by one Richard Fowler to service his several farms in the Upshore area. On his demise, control had passed to his only son, Isaac, who had carefully built up good contracts to carry goods for other merchants. Isaac had brought his two sons, John and Ernest, into the firm as directors. He had also recruited Rupert Dunn, a London shipbroker and the firm's agent in the city, largely for financial reasons. Dunn was now on the verge of retirement and it was anticipated that his shipbroking activities would pass to Fowler and Dunn. This was another area of interest to Thames and Medway.

Older directors would remember an earlier attempt to take over Fowler and Dunn, in 1939. This was abandoned after the death of Isaac Fowler, who would have been an asset to Thames and Medway. Since then, John Fowler had departed under a cloud and Ernest had decided to concentrate on the management of their boatbuilding activities. The day-to-day running of Fowler's had been in the hands of Miss Eleanor Fowler, Isaac's daughter, who had devoted herself to the firm and her young daughter after the unfortunate death of her fiancè in the 1939 Upshore Barge Match. It was felt that, after the strain of the war years, Eleanor might be tired of running the firm and wish to spend more time with her growing daughter. However, she should not be underestimated, for she was a very shrewd young lady. All in all, it was thought that this was the right moment to approach Fowler and Dunn again.

There followed some financial discussion and then the Chairman asked for questions. The most relevant one came from an elderly director who pointed out that in 1939, Fowler and Dunn's men had objected to being taken over by a Kentish firm.

"This is the old Kent-Essex rivalry," replied the Chairman, "and I expect it to raise its ugly head again but, at the end of the day, employees have to do as they are told – or accept the consequences."

This satisfied the questioner and the Chairman then summed up.

"There is no doubt in my mind," he said, "that we should make another approach to Fowler and Dunn. There is also no doubt that the key to this will be Miss Eleanor Fowler, or, as she prefers, Ellie Fowler. To this end I intend to invite her to the launch of our first motorised unit with a view to opening preliminary discussions on a take over. Agreed?" It was carried unanimously.

* * *

Later the same day, Thames and Medway's youngest director, Nigel Ransome, had a surprise confidential meeting with the Chairman.

"Nigel," said the Chairman, without preamble, "about Ellie Fowler. I feel it would help if she was royally entertained during her visit – best hotel in the town, wined and dined, you know the sort of thing. And she will need an escort, near her own age, and that's where you come in – you're the best chap for the job."

Nigel didn't disagree with that. In his early thirties, he could boast a long string of female conquests, although he had, with some skill, managed to remain a bachelor. He had avoided military service during the war and built up many black-market connections. As a result he was never short of petrol for his car and knew where good food and wine could be obtained without too many questions. He was an attractive man, who in the words of one of his many ex-girl friends 'could charm the birds out of the trees.'

"It would be useful," continued the Chairman slowly, "if you could endeavour to end up in the young lady's bedroom. I hear rumours that she was most passionate before her fiancè's death – nude sunbathing, sex in the open air and so on. But she hasn't looked at a man since. May be possible to rekindle the old flame, though, eh?"

Nigel chose his words carefully. "Are we possibly looking at some form of blackmail?" he asked.

"Good heavens, no. But one never knows!"

* * *

If only the conspirators had been able to read Ellie s thoughts at that moment. She was eating a lonely meal in the dining room of her family home. Her daughter Ruth was in bed upstairs, her remaining brother Ernie was out somewhere and

37

the servants had withdrawn. Ellie had had a long and tiring day.

I can't go on like this, she thought. I'm working all day and although I try and keep weekends free for Ruth, I'm not seeing as much of her as I ought. She needs a father figure too; she's obviously having trouble at school. As for me, well, I'm lonely. I can't mourn Bill forever, he's gone. I'm twenty-seven, it's not too late to look elsewhere. I should have done it long ago. God knows there were enough opportunities with all the airmen based around here during the war. I shan't pass up the next opportunity, she resolved.

* * *

Nigel Ransome gave the Ellie matter a great deal of thought. He was alarmed at how little time he would have for the obviously intended seduction, if it worked. Ellie's invite was for the night before the launching and the night after that. Ransome felt that, ideally, he should bring matters to a conclusion the first night, thereby giving the Chairman a clear field for negotiations during the remainder of Ellie's stay. Some ground-breaking was obviously needed. So he wrote Ellie a charming letter saying that he was to escort her during her visit and how much he was looking forward to meeting her. He received a quite glowing letter back; Ellie was very much hoping to enjoy his company. Further correspondence followed and as the launching ceremony approached Ransome felt he already knew Ellie quite well.

* * *

Ellie travelled to the ceremony by train since she was temporarily without a car. Ransome drove to the railway station to meet her, armed with a placard bearing his name, since neither had seen the other before and no photographs had been exchanged.

He was rewarded when a voice said: "Mr Ransome, I presume. Ellie Fowler." The young lady who was holding her hand out to be shaken impressed him. A neat two-piece suit covered her trim figure and short black hair set off pleasant features. A pity about the glasses, though, Ransome thought, still she probably doesn't wear them all the time.

Ellie, too, was impressed, Nigel Ransome had an athletic figure was well groomed and, as she discovered in the car, had an easy but polite manner. Ransome explained that he would take Ellie to her hotel to freshen up and collect her at seven p.m. for a meal. As they pulled up outside the hotel, Ellie thanked him profusely and then, to his surprise, leant over and kissed him on the cheek. My God, thought Ransome, could she have fallen for me already?

* * *

Ellie lay soaking in the bath in her hotel suite. She was pleased with the arrangements. The suite was the best that the hotel could offer and had a view of the river from the bedroom window. When she arrived there had been flowers everywhere. Some were from Thames and Medway, but by far the biggest bouquet was from Nigel Ransome.

He seems a nice man, she mused. Could he be the one? She had vowed that she would not pass up the next opportunity and this could well be it. On impulse she got out of the bath, dried herself quickly and walked through to the bedroom where there was a full-length mirror. Still naked, she studied her body in it. Nothing wrong with that, she thought, good firm breasts, flat stomach, narrow waist, pert buttocks and excellent legs. None of it much used lately, she thought, especially the dark triangle between her legs. Tonight that could change.

She selected her clothing for the evening with great care. She had brought a large number of clothes with her, not knowing what to expect. She chose the skimpiest underwear in her

39

possession and a pair of good stockings that she had obtained on the black market. Ransome had told her that their evening meal would be at a top restaurant that expected evening dress. She had no choice, she had only one long dress with her, but it did show a great deal of cleavage which was just as well. Finally she decided not to wear her glasses.

* * *

They started the evening with drinks in the hotel bar. Ellie, who during Bill's time had been a light beer drinker, had not touched alcohol since his loss, apart from occasional glasses of wine with meals, while it was still obtainable during the war. Throwing caution to the winds, she asked for a gin and tonic while Ransome had a scotch. During this and a second drink that followed, they chatted, mainly of mutual business interests.

A taxi arrived to take them to the restaurant for their meal. They were shown to a secluded alcove where a repast that Ellie had never dreamed possible during post-war austerity was presented. It was accompanied by plenty of wine of which Ellie drank her fill. By the time they reached coffee and brandy, Ransome thought that she was more than a little drunk. She began to talk of her lost fiancè, Bill, something she never normally did with strangers. Her eyes filled with tears.

"You poor girl," said Ransome and, reaching for her hand across the table, pulled her gently forward and kissed her on the lips. After that she cheered up and allowed Ransome to lead her on to the small dance floor. They gyrated round the floor to a slow waltz. She danced close with her head nestling against his shoulder. When we get back to the hotel, Ransome was thinking, I'll suggest a night-cap in her rooms. This was a ploy that had worked many times in previous seductions. There would be no trouble with the hotel staff who had already been well primed. As the waltz finished she held up her lips to be kissed again. Ransome liked the way she responded.

"Let's go," she said.

* * *

There was much more kissing in the taxi back to the hotel and, at one point, Ransome slipped his hand under Ellie's coat and inside the top of her dress. She raised no objection to this. As Ransome paid off the taxi outside the hotel, Ellie stood on the kerb, swaying slightly on her high heels.

"Got a good idea," she said. "Let's get 'nother drink an' take it up to my room." She's playing right into my hands, thought Ransome.

When they arrived in the suite, Ellie led Ransome by the hand into the bedroom. They embraced again and Ransome undid the top buttons of her dress. To his surprise she pushed him down on the bed.

"Wait there, beautiful man," she said.

She walked to the foot of the bed where she undid the rest of the buttons and let the dress float to the floor. She stepped out of it and her shoes and then, raising each foot in turn to the bed, peeled off her stockings as sexily as she could. Sated with food and drink, Ransome lay back and enjoyed the show. Ellie unhooked her brassiere and slowly shrugged it off. Finally she eased her knickers and suspender belt to the floor.

She pirouetted round so that Ransome could admire her assets.

As she did so, she realised that the curtains were not drawn. She made to close them and glanced down at the river. And there she was. The ghost barge Macbeth in all her glory. Everything was suddenly crystal clear to Ellie. My God, it's a warning! This is a trap and I'm falling into it! What on earth am I doing? Bill!

She turned round and sprang on the bed, straddling Ransome, her breasts hanging over him like pendulums, her legs apart. She deftly undid his fly buttons, reached inside and squeezed with all her might, glad that she had long fingernails. Ransome winced with pain.

"Get out," she hissed. "Fuck off now, before I scream rape."

41

Ransome suddenly found himself in the corridor, dress still awry, his eyes watering with the pain in his groin. Ellie went through to the bathroom where she was violently sick in the toilet. A few minutes later she felt better and, still naked, began to pack.

* * *

Next morning, after hearing that Mr Ransome was unwell, Thames and Medway sent one of their managers to the hotel to collect Ellie for the launching. He was informed that she had left sometime earlier.

Ellie was sitting on the second of three trains that would convey her back to Upshore. Now sensibly dressed in slacks and a sweater, she was reflecting on the events of the previous night, She wasn't sure what grubby little plot Thames and Medway had been hatching, but she had a pretty fair idea. It will be a long time before I have anything more to do with them, she thought. I don't need them, I can manage on my own and I'll think of some way of making it up to Ruth. And I must not be impatient; the right man will come along one day. Why, Bill might still be alive somewhere. And I have the ghost barge to thank for saving me from committing an act of folly.

It didn't occur to her that Macbeth's appearance might have been a warning to the barge world in general of the vessels later to be known as 'Spam Cans'.

1948 – ANTICLIMAX

Readers will remember that the ghost barge appeared again, in 1948, just before Goldsmith's of Grays sold most of their remaining sailing barges. The appearance was off Grays and this time the apparition was seen by several people – bargemen, lightermen and even the crew of a PLA Harbour Patrol launch, who would have made the best witnesses.

However, when I traced some of these observers, they became vague, saying things like 'It must have been a real barge,' or 'I'm not sure,' and so forth. Since no dramatic events ensued and in the absence of any positive witness, this incident is best dismissed as rumour.

The reader may be wondering why this particular barge should take to haunting. My own theory is that hers was a promising career, cut short by the incompetence of her owner and crew. If, as a ghost ship, she had some form of consciousness, she resolved to warn of danger to other barges and their crews.

Let's see how this theory stands up in individual sightings. The first one to the Upshore fishermen is not typical. It was round about the actual time of Letchworth's suicide, as far as can be ascertained. No particular danger here, the appearance was more an act of bravado as if 'Look I'm still here!' The 1936 incident is a bit odd. Yes, the Great Gale of 1936, as it came to be known, was on the way and certainly represented a time of peril to barges and crews abroad on the East Coast. But only Zeke and Matt seem to have seen it. Why not others? So was it a personal warning to Zeke of the loss of his leg?

Dunkirk, 1940, was undoubtedly a time of danger to the bargemen involved and indeed the whole of our country. But Macbeth was only seen by the crew of Hubert. They survived unscathed, despite several near misses. So this seems to be more in the nature of a general warning. It is hard to believe that Ellie Fowler's sighting was a warning to her not to have sex with Ransome. Did Ellie really see anything? She is adamant that she did, but although normally a sensible young lady and an astute businesswoman, she was rather drunk at the time.

True, if Thames and Medway had taken over Fowler and Dunn as a result of Ellie's entrapment, it would have been a retrograde step for the barge industry. But the introduction of 'Spam Cans' has also proved to be disastrous to the sailing barge. These vessels have now taken over most of the traditional sailing barge work. The 1948 appearance is uncertain and can be ignored. The reader must judge the activities of Macbeth for himself.

Normally this summing up would have ended my tale but, before it could be made public, there was another incident with the ghost barge, one in which I was personally involved.

1966 – LAST ENCOUNTER?

Daisy Maud was in London moored to a tier of lighters just off Cherry Garden Pier. Ike came in the barge's boat to collect me from the pier. These days the boat was powered by an outboard motor instead of being sculled from the stern.

"Makes life easier," Ike told me, "trouble is, we're goin' ter lose the old skills with all these motors an' such-like. An' another thing, skullin' yer could look all round, see what was goin' on. With this thing yer tends ter look forrard all the time."

We were getting close to the barge now and I could see Ruth, Ellie's daughter, laid out on the forward hatch wearing a brief bikini. It was an excellent day for sunbathing.

"Good bit o' decoration that," said Ike, referring to Ruth. He and skipper Tommy did not altogether approve of Ruth, who they seemed to consider 'flighty'. "Not many o' us aboard this trip. Just yerself, us crew an' 'er an' 'er latest boyfriend."

Since her conversion to a yacht, Daisy Maud could sleep eight passengers plus the professional crew. Normally Bill and Ellie, as the owners, would have been in residence, but it was not that long since Ellie had given birth to a baby boy. It had been difficult, particularly in view of Ellie's age, 46, so the couple were living ashore in Upshore and us three passengers were really taking advantage of Daisy Maud's presence in London to have a lift round the coast to see them.

"Good day fer it," said Tommy when I arrived on Daisy Maud's deck. "Could get foggy later on though." Ruth came aft. In deference to us older men she had put a shirt on over the bikini.

"Where's this new boyfriend, then?" I asked.

"Oh. Dave. He's just having a lie down," she answered. "Not feeling too good. Motion's upset him, he's not a good sailor."

"Motion?" I exclaimed. The Thames up this far was doing a fair imitation of a millpond.

"There was a bit of wash from tugs an' that, early on," said Tommy. Oh dear, I thought, Dave won't enjoy this trip, then. Tommy surveyed the prevailing weather conditions again.

"'Spose we'd better use the iron tawpsail ter get down river," he said. He always affected not to like using the engine unless it was essential, often muttering things like: 'Did enough bloody motorin' ter get back from soddin' Dunkirk.' And yet, immediately prior to becoming Daisy Maud's skipper and mate, he and Ike had owned a fishing boat, and all their trawling had been under power. Perhaps it just irked him to use mechanical power on what was primarily a sailing vessel.

So, with help from Ruth and myself, Ike and Tommy unmoored the barge from the lighters and we began the long motor down river. There was plenty to see on the way.

Although the London Docks were in decline, all the PLA dock systems were still open and there was plenty of river traffic. Even the 'poor sailor' Dave came up on deck and showed interest. He wasn't a bad looking lad, though his hair was a trifle long for my taste. He was sensibly dressed in jeans and a shirt.

Since our engine was not particularly powerful, several vessels overtook us. One of these was a Thames and Medway 'Spam Can' whose skipper waved cheerily enough from his wheelhouse.

"Probably used ter be sailin' barge man," observed Tommy.

46

"Now 'e's got one o' them things. Still 'e's got ter earn a livin', 'spose."

The ebb tide was running strongly and an assortment of shipping was dropping down river. There were plenty of tugs towing dumb lighters. Tommy remarked that a lighterman was never seen rowing a barge these days.

"They all 'as ter learn 'ow ter do it," he went on. "Part o' their apprenticeship. There was a bit o' fun a few years back when all the tugs went on strike. All the lighterage companies was 'untin' for old oars so as they could keep things movin'."

Several small ships, mainly Dutch coasters, were on the move, but we were in the oddly named Bugsby's Reach before we were overtaken by the first really sizeable one, a Ben liner out of West India Dock with a tug still towing her from ahead.

"She'll be off to Antwerp or one o' them," said Tommy, "drop the rest of 'er cargo there, then back to the Royal Docks ter load."

It was a sign of the declining docks that she was the only large ship that we saw. We passed into Woolwich Reach, where Macbeth had set the river on fire. Here, at the buoys once known as 'Starvation Buoys' where sailing barges once waited for cargo, was a small group of motor barges. Tommy and Ike studied these with interest. Only one, Hydrogen, was a former sailing barge.

It was agreed that we would spend that night on a buoy at Greenhithe since evening was approaching and there was not much more run in the tide. Tommy expressed the hope that there would be more breeze in the morning and that we could sail the rest of the way to Upshore.

After we had secured to our buoy at Greenhithe, we began to think in terms of an evening meal. Ruth volunteered to cook it, which was just as well since she, like her mother, was an extremely good cook. Dave, now apparently fully recovered, offered to help her and the two of them disappeared below. Tommy, Ike and I sat on the end of the main hatch and yarned until a ring on the ship's bell in the saloon announced that

47

supper was ready.

And Ruth had certainly done well for us on Daisy Maud's Aga. We started with tomato soup, moved on to steak, onions and chips and finished with jam roly-poly. There was also a bottle of wine which Ruth, Dave and I shared since Tommy and Ike preferred to split a quart bottle of beer.

After the meal Tommy let out his belt a couple of inches.

"That was real good, Miss Ruth," he said. The rest of us signified our agreement. Then Tommy turned to me: "You finished that story, Mr Jack?" he asked.

"Which one? I've got several on the go."

"Yer know which one. The ghost barge."

"Oh, yes. I've just finished it. Let you have a look next time I'm aboard."

"You saw it didn't you, Uncle Tommy?" asked Ruth. She had always considered Tommy and Ike honorary uncles.

"Oh. Yus so did Ike. Just as we were runnin' inter Dunkirk fer the evacuation."

The quiet Dave spoke for the first time: "Was that in daylight or dark?" he asked.

"Daylight or as near to as yer could get, what with all the fires an' that, ashore."

"Isn't it unusual for a ghost to appear in daylight?" persisted Dave.

"Not this one, it ain't. Zeke an' 'is mate seen it in daylight an' all."

"Mother saw it in the dark," Ruth remarked. I found myself hoping that she didn't know the full details of this event.

"I don't believe it. You must have imagined it."

"We didn't imagine Dunkirk," snorted Ike. "Bloody awful that were. An' the ghost warned us."

Tommy decided to diffuse the situation. "Why don't you tell these young 'uns 'ow it began, Mister Jack," he said. "Me an' Ike'll wash up." They had heard the story of Macbeth's demise before.

So I told Ruth and Dave the story of Macbeth's bright

beginning and fiery end but, not wishing to slander anyone, omitted names. Tommy finished the washing up and, leaving Ike to finish drying and stowing the utensils, made for the deck.

"Jus' goin' ter check the ridin' light," he said. A few minutes later he was back.

"Cor! I was right about the fog. 'Ardly see yer 'and in front of yer face up there." This was, no doubt, an exaggeration, but if Tommy said that it was a thick fog then it certainly was one. Shortly after this we decided to turn in. It was quite early for bed, but we were likely to have a long sail the next day.

I had a job getting off to sleep. I read for a while, but was then kept awake by giggles and fumblings from the cabin next door occupied by Ruth and Dave. I reflected that Ruth probably took after her mother in matters sexual and with this thought dozed off.

I was abruptly awakened in the small hours by a shout from above: "On deck! Quick!" I hastily pulled on trousers and shoes and rushed up the companionway almost knocking over Ruth in the darkened saloon. As I arrived on deck I was aware of something winking out in the fog. Tommy and Ruth, but not Ike also arrived. Dave was clinging on to the shrouds pointing in the direction of my 'something'.

"The ghost barge. I saw it!"

"Nah! Couldn't 'ave been," said Tommy. "Hasn't been seen since 1948."

"I tell you I saw it. Plain as anything, with smoke and flames coming out of her."

"You was dreamin'. What yer come on deck fer?"

"I couldn't sleep. Thought I'd get some air."

"What's all the fuss about?" Ike had arrived.

"Lad 'ere reckons 'e saw the ghost barge. Come up on deck arf awake. Reckon 'e was dreamin' 'bout 'er. We spent enuff time talkin' 'bout 'er last evenin'."

Ike was about to say something when Ruth, who was shivering in a dressing gown and not much else, said: "Listen, I

49

can hear something."

We stopped talking, kept still and listened. A rhythmic thrumming was coming out of the fog.

"Ship's engines," said Tommy. We listened some more.

"Gettin' closer," Ike added.

"Could be comin' real close. Ike, up forrard! Ring the bell," Tommy ordered. He muttered to himself: "What's a ship doin' right in 'ere? 'E'll go aground if 'e ain't careful." Our buoy was not far from the mudflats. The noise drew ever closer. Tommy sounded the engine klaxon to supplement Ike's frantic ringing of the barge's bell forward.

"There she is!" squealed Ruth. A bow wave topped by what seemed to be a huge bow came out of the fog astern.

"'E's goin' ter wallop us!" shouted Tommy. But, at the last minute, there was a slight deviation in the ship's course. She surged alongside Daisy Maud, missing by inches. We stared as rust and rivets rushed past. There came a twang from aloft as some protrusion from the ship caught our rigging. Water from her engine room out-takes poured onto the barge's sidedecks wetting our feet. As the vessel disappeared back into the fog we could hear Middle Eastern voices raised in excitement.

"Bloody Ay-rabs!" raged Tommy. "What do they think they're a-doin' of? Couldn't even see a name fer the insurance."

"We damaged, skipper?" asked Ike.

"Yus. Look up there."

We all looked up the mast. Despite the fog we could see one of the spreaders was badly bent upwards. This must have been the twang that I had heard.

"T'ain't no good," said Tommy, "We'll 'ave ter drop back ter Norton's yard at Greenwich in the mornin' an' get that sorted out. If you wants ter get ter Upshore you'll 'ave ter go by car or train. Sorry one an' all."

We all went back to bed, but I doubt whether anyone slept much.

Next morning we motored gingerly back up river to the yard at Greenwich. By the time we had moored up there, Ruth and Dave were ready to go ashore. Dave went first with their bags, negotiating the several lighters between the shore and us. I said good-bye to Ruth.

"Tell Bill and your mother I'll be along later," I said. "I'll stay and give Tommy and Ike a hand for a while. I like the new boyfriend, but what did you say his surname was?"

"I didn't," she replied, casually, "but it's Letchworth, Dave Letchworth."

Letchworth! The same name as Macbeth's owner. Could he be a descendant? Some reporter I was, I hadn't even enquired whether Nathan Letchworth had been married. I absently gave Ruth a peck on the cheek and she walked down our gangplank onto the lighters. But my mind was elsewhere. This Letchworth had seen the ghost barge and alerted the rest of us to danger. No doubt our subsequent sounding of bell and klaxon had caused the Arab ship to alter course enough to miss us. Could this be the last sighting? Had saving a relative of her owner now exorcised the ghost? It might not be, perhaps the name was a coincidence, but it was not a common name and if Dave knew anything of his family's history or of Macbeth's reputation he had certainly kept quiet about it. I must do more research before my findings were complete.

And what of the future? If the ghost was still around, I could think of further opportunities for it. Bob Roberts' Cambria was now the last sailing barge trading under sail alone and when she went... Then there were the former sailormen trading under power, like Hydrogen... And increasing numbers of barges were returning to sail as yachts and charter barges, like Daisy Maud...

Only time would tell.

THE END

THE WIMP ON THE FORT

It was all Ron Glaze's idea and it evolved in the Smack Inn in the Old Town.

The public bar was packed with successful fishermen, or, according to some purists, non-fishermen, for these were the men who trawled for white-weed during the boom year of 1953. This was not traditional fishing with a net for the white-weed was wrenched from the seabed with metal rakes towed behind each boat. During that year it was commanding a very high price, five shillings a pound being the current minimum and a boat could easily average ninety pounds a day. The weather had been benign recently so most days had been worked.

Hence the successful and affluent fishermen quenching their thirsts in the Smack. The crews of Reminder, Grey Goose and Margaret Edith occupied one table. Ron Glaze, skipper of Grey Goose, was the accepted leader of this group, who all had service in the Army in common. Perhaps this was because he was the only one of them who had been an officer or perhaps because most of his time had been in the RASC's fleet of landing craft. Anyway they gave his proposal their undivided attention.

"We deserve a holiday," he was saying. "Let's take a few days off and take the boats down to Margate."

Why Margate? Someone asked. Ron explained that there

would be plenty of girls there on holiday and that it was a reasonable run for the boats. If they left on Friday, they could spend Saturday and Sunday in Margate and return on the Monday. Everybody thought this was an excellent idea.

Preparations then commenced in earnest. It had been decided that there was no need to delay the drinking side of this venture, so supplies were obtained to drink underway. The crew of Reminder supplied a copious amount of beer, Margaret Edith's men brought along several bottles of gin while Grey Goose provided scotch and glasses. The whole lot was then 'kittied' so that each boat had a quantity of each drink. In truth that was the major preparation, only a token of food was produced since it was felt that most eating would be done ashore.

It was on the Wednesday that Bob Hutchens of the Margaret Edith dropped his bombshell.

"Gordon wants to come," he said to Ron Glaze. Now Gordon was Bob's brother and a very different type to the fishermen. An employee of the local council in some mundane desk job, his interests were primarily bird watching and angling. He was also near enough teetotal.

"What's he want to come for?" grumbled Ron. "We shan't be spotting many engine numbers."

"No, not all the way to Margate," Bob replied. "Just down to the Shivering Sand forts. Wants to do some fishing, he says. We can drop him on the way and pick him up as we come back."

"Oh! That's all right. For a minute I thought he was going to mess up our weekend. You can have him on Margaret Edith though."

The boats worked on the Friday, returning to the Old Town on the flood tide about midday. After the catch had been sold and the money pocketed the fishermen loaded their 'supplies'. While this was going on Gordon arrived in a taxi. He had brought a mountain of equipment with him. A meticulous man, he had already researched the forts and decided that he

53

would have to be entirely self-sufficient. As a former Boy Scout he had 'come prepared'.

In addition to fishing tackle he brought enough food and drink for two days, a Primus stove for cooking, a portable radio for company, a sleeping bag and a powerful torch since there was no electricity on the forts. All this was quickly stowed aboard Margaret Edith.

"He's your brother. You see to him," Ron had told Bob.

So the three boats set sail. They made a motley fleet. Margaret Edith had started life as a local bawley, fishing for whitebait under sail but now cut down to power for her white weeding role; Grey Goose was an RNLI lifeboat, converted to a yacht in the 1930s and now converted again to a fully powered fishing vessel but still able to set a mizzen as a steadying sail; Reminder was originally a Scottish Zulu, also fishing under sail, but now a motor vessel with a box-like wheelhouse.

The weather was benign and the three boats made good progress to the Shivering Sand forts. These were one of three clusters of forts set up during the Second World War in the Thames Estuary to defend the approaches to London from enemy aircraft and E-Boats. There were seven units within each group joined by walkways. The Army had only recently abandoned them and they remained in good condition, only occasionally visited by sightseers and fishermen such as Gordon. There were no amenities aboard them and that was why Gordon had brought everything that he might need.

At the forts Margaret Edith peeled off from the other two boats and found a convenient ladder hanging down from one of the units by which Gordon could board. Once Gordon was up inside the fort a rope was used to haul up his equipment. Margaret Edith, after wishing him luck and good fishing, rejoined the other two vessels.

"Rather him than me," said Bob to his mate. "Time we had a drink."

The three boats resumed their journey to Ramsgate.

The following Tuesday the weather was still good. Lucky Lady, one of the smaller white-weeding vessels was trawling in the vicinity of the Shivering Sands forts.

"Someone's flashing us from the forts!" Felicity, the mate, shouted above the noise of the engine.

Lucky Lady, a former excursion boat, had the distinction, that day, of being the only whiteweeder with an all female crew. This was a temporary measure since her normal skipper, Angus Charles, was laid up with a broken bone in his foot. Heidi, his normal mate and girl friend, not wishing to lose a lucrative catch in the fine weather, had promoted herself skipper and recruited a friend, Felicity, as mate. This was not a terribly successful arrangement, for although Heidi was a strapping blonde Amazon, capable of doing anything Angus could do, Felicity was definitely not up to the rigours of fishing boat life, even in those conditions. She proved unable to manipulate the heavy weeding rakes, so Heidi had to deal with these herself, while Felicity hung on to the wheel. As a result their catch was not good and Heidi was thinking of heading for home on the first of the flood tide.

Now, however she was studying the flashes from the fort.

"SOS" she announced. "We'd better see what this is about." She opened up Lucky Lady's engine and steered for the fort. The signaller was standing on one of the walkways, torch in hand.

"Can you take me off?" shouted Gordon, for it was he, as soon as Lucky Lady was within earshot, "I'll explain later."

So Gordon and his equipment were transferred by a reversal of the method used on his arrival.

"What's all this about?" asked Heidi once they were clear of the fort. Gordon explained how Margaret Edith had dropped him on the fort and how the three boats had gone to Margate for a party. But they hadn't returned and he had been stranded on the fort. Heidi listened with interest but Felicity hung on

Gordon's every word. He went on to say that he had caught a few fish from the fort but he had cooked them on his Primus and eaten them. When Lucky Lady had sighted him he had run out of fuel for the stove and only had a few biscuits left. He couldn't imagine what had happened to his brother and the others. It was very annoying; he should have been at work today.

"Oh, Ron Glaze's Navy," said Heidi, who knew them of old. "By now, they'll have had so much to drink they won't even know their own names, let alone what day of the week it is. They'll be back when they've got rid of their hangovers. You shouldn't have trusted them, though. Fliss, make us all a nice cuppa tea."

Felicity went into Lucky Lady's tiny cabin, forward of the wheelhouse where Heidi was steering. Gordon followed her, ostensibly to stow some of his gear, but really because he felt attracted to this girl who seemed to think that he had important things to say.

"I think you're ever so brave," said Felicity as she filled the kettle from a water container. "All on your own on that fort, not knowing whether anyone would come back for you."

Brave? No one had ever called Gordon that before. Dull, wimpish, boring, these were the epithets usually applied by his brother and his cronies. He was liking this girl more and more.

While they waited for the kettle to boil, Gordon and Felicity found that they had a lot in common. She told him that she was only aboard Lucky Lady to help Heidi while Angus was injured. Normally, if it had been term time she would have been at college and she was hoping to take up a career in local government. Gordon told her of his hobbies of angling and bird watching. She too was interested in nature, mainly butterflies, but she would like to know more about birds and she couldn't imagine anything more peaceful than sitting on a river bank fishing. But not from a fort, that didn't sound at all nice. Gordon replied that it wasn't nice and he didn't intend doing it again, riverbank angling only from now on. Felicity said that she had had enough of commercial fishing. At this point the tea was ready. Gordon absently handed a mug of it out to Heidi without realising that he had done so and certainly without noticing her knowing grin.

Conversation continued while the tea was drunk. Felicity had been a Girl Guide and the two were soon talking about Scouting – the badges they had taken, camps they had attended and anecdotes about fellow Scouts and Guides.

Heidi suddenly interrupted them: "I don't want to worry you but we're in the creek now and I wouldn't mind a hand mooring up when we reach the wharf."

There followed a brief burst of activity while mooring lines and fenders were prepared. Then, scraping the bottom on the first of the tide, they were alongside. Mooring up completed, Heidi went ashore to sell the catch. Although it was small, she expected a good price since they were virtually the first boat to arrive from the weeding grounds. Since Gordon was showing no signs of departing, she took her time haggling with the buyers who lurked round the wharf, hoping to drive quick bargains.

Gordon was, of course, still talking to Felicity in the cabin. He had slipped an arm round her, which she seemed to like. Heidi jumped back aboard.

"There's a group of three boats coming in the creek entrance like bats out of hell," she announced. "Probably Ron Glaze's Navy."

Gordon had an idea. "You haven't seen me," he said. Heidi grasped his idea immediately. "Don't worry. You two stay in the cabin. I'll deal with them."

Sure enough, it was the Navy: Grey Goose, Reminder and Margaret Edith, the crews bleary and unshaven. As they prepared to moor to the wharf, Heidi, standing in Lucky Lady's cockpit shouted at Grey Goose, the nearest of the three: "Had a good time?" Glaze's white face appeared at the wheelhouse window. "Dunno. 'Spect so. Don't remember much about it."

I thought so, Heidi reflected, nearly four days on the booze, only came back because their money ran out. Probably didn't pick any girls either in their state.

"Haven't you forgotten something?" she asked.

Glaze stared blankly back, his mind working overtime.

"Oh, my God! We've forgotten the wimp." He shouted to his mate: "Back to the Shivering Sands!" He shoved Grey Goose into gear and took off down the creek. Reminder and Margaret Edith, always loyal, followed. Heidi saw the look of concern on Gordon's brother's face. She stood and watched the three boats head towards the horizon. They'll get an even bigger shock when they get to the fort, she mused, and there'll be no Gordon. Still a bit of worry won't hurt them.

In the cabin the wimp and Felicity were sharing their first kiss.

BAR WARS

Percy Gittens was addressing 'Naval Corner' in the Old Town Yacht Club. "The trouble with this club," he opined, "is the people at the top. We've got a Commodore who's on a different planet to the rest of us, a Vice-Commodore with delusions of grandeur and a Rear-Commodore who's good at the social side but bugger-all else. The Secretary's senile and the Sailing Secretary thinks he's Napoleon Bonaparte. The Bar Chairman's too fond of his own wares and the rest of the Committee are nonentities."

"Including me?" asked Phil Lucas, who ran the club safety boat.

"No, of course not," said Percy with irritation, but no one took any notice of that; Percy was irritable most of the time. Naval Corner considered Percy's statement. They had heard it all before, with variations, and, although conceding that it contained an element of truth, took little notice.

Naval Corner was the left-hand corner of the bar with a view of the water. It took its name from the fact that its regular occupants had all spent some time in the Royal Navy. Phil Lucas had been a Seaman Petty Officer and therefore was a good choice to run the safety boat, John Silver had been a National Service AB and Fred Larkin, the club steward, who often leaned over the bar to join in, had been a Leading Steward. The group was presided over by Gittens who glossed over the fact that he had been a Stores Assistant, spending most of his service on Naval Air Stations, with very little sea time. There were others who occasionally joined this forum but Gittens, Lucas, Silver and Larkin, as much as his duties permitted, were the normal inhabitants.

Women were not tolerated in Naval Corner and, in any case, had no desire to join it. In this respect it was a throwback to the club's former men-only bar, discontinued some years previously to the chagrin of Gittens and his cronies. If Gittens had his way, the ladies would not even have been allowed within earshot of his corner, but that was obviously not feasible. And that was how Nancy Cartwright, the Sailing Secretary's girlfriend, overheard Gittens' outburst. She duly reported it to her boyfriend.

"He said you were like Napoleon," she said.

"That makes a change," replied the Sailing Secretary, Rodney Temple. "Last time it was Genghis Khan."

His job, an honorary one, entailed running the club's sailing activities in their entirety. They included devising a sailing programme, encouraging the club's sailors to support it, organising the personnel to man the starting line and support boat, allocating spaces for dinghy storage and maintenance of racing marks and other equipment. He had to deal with all manner of people and at the same time 'make things happen'. He felt vaguely flattered by Gittens' description. Perhaps the job needed a Napoleon type.

"He said the most awful things about the Committee," Nancy persisted. "Something's got to be done about him."

"You tell me what, then," said Rodney. "He's been a member of this club nearly forty years, he's been a Committee member and he spends a load of money over the bar. He's an institution. He ll never be shifted."

* * *

Nancy was not discouraged. She made up her mind to topple

Gittens, by whatever means at her disposal. Realising that Temple wouldn't be much help, with his preoccupation with sailing matters, she consulted Caroline Newbiggin, the Rear Commodore's wife, who she knew was no admirer of Gittens. Caroline had a suggestion.

"Why don't we," she said, "occupy Naval Corner?"

"That would be difficult," said Nancy. "Gittens and his friends are always there."

"So we arrive before they do," replied Caroline, "as soon as Fred Larkin opens up. It would be worth the effort."

"But what would it achieve?"

"Well it would wrong foot Gittens for a start and if it provoked an outburst, the Committee might censure him."

In the end, Nancy agreed to give it a try, so they recruited two other attractive lady members and, next evening, as a surprised Larkin raised the bar shutters, the four of them perched themselves on the bar stools in Naval Corner.

Within minutes Gittens, Lucas and Silver arrived. Their reaction was surprisingly low-key. Gittens glared at the four girls and Silver muttered something about breaking club traditions. But Gittens and his friends merely took up a position further along the bar. The four girls, eventually joined by husbands and boyfriends, had an enjoyable evening but achieved virtually nothing.

"They must have been tipped off," said Nancy later.

"Possibly," said Caroline, "and, anyhow we can't keep it up. It would mean being at the club at opening time every evening. We'll have to think again."

* * *

They did think again at a meeting at Caroline's house the following Saturday, while her husband was safely out with the children. Various schemes involving whoopi cushions and similar tricks were discussed but discarded on the grounds that they had either been tried before by various of Gitten's enemies or would not be sufficiently effective.

"How about some sort of sexual advance?" asked Nancy.

"What do you mean?" Caroline wanted to know.

"Well, suppose, for example, that Gittens was caught in a compromising position with the Rear Commodore's wife?"

"You must be joking," Caroline exploded. "No way. The man is repulsive. I think, if anything, he's the other way inclined."

After some fairly ribald suggestions, it was agreed to treat any form of sexual approach as very much the last resort. In the meantime the four ladies would keep their eyes and ears open for any useful leads.

* * *

Had they but known it, that very evening Gittens took a step that, at least partially, furthered their cause. He upset Larkin the steward. At the time they were the only two occupants of the bar. Larkin, as usual, on seeing Gittens enter, poured him out a pint while he hung his coat up. Gittens lowered himself onto his usual bar stool and picked up the pint.

"I'm not drinking that," he stated and put it down again. Larkin picked up the offending glass and held it up to the light.

"A bit cloudy like," he said.

"Then what the hell did you serve it to me for?"

"All right! All right! I'll change the barrel and give you a new one." The bad pint went down the sink.

Larkin was not one for showing his feelings to the customers. No good steward should be, but he seethed as he changed the barrel. No one should speak to him like that and no one ever had, not even the officers that he had served in the Navy, not even the snottiest sub-lieutenant and this, after the way he had looked after Mr Gittens! Perhaps the members he had inevitably heard criticising Gittens were right, he was a nasty bit of work.

I'll get my chance, he consoled himself, and there'll be a way of getting my own back.

* * *

The following weekend was the club's Annual Open Meeting, a series of races devised to attract visiting dinghy sailors. On the Thursday evening Nancy was helping Rodney Temple and his assistant Paul Griffiths, usually known as Griff, sort out the paperwork for this event. Nancy and Rodney were drawing up a points chart and result forms while Griff recorded the entries received so far. Griff opened an envelope that come through the post and studied the contents.

"The Animal's coming this year," he remarked to Rodney.

"Is he?" said Rodney, with interest. "I haven't seen the old bugger for years. I wonder whether he's still up to his old tricks."

"You mean the contests. 'I'll drink any man under the table' and all that?"

"Yeh. Liven the place up a bit. Push Gittens and that crowd into the background."

"They'll walk out."

"Good riddance."

But during this exchange Nancy's mind had been working overtime and she couldn't help voicing her main idea. "How about the Animal versus Gittens?"

Rodney and Griff stared at her in amazement.

"Now that," Rodney said slowly, "would be a clash of the Titans."

"But suppose Gittens refuses the challenge?" Griff wanted to know.

"Then he'll be dead embarrassed," said Nancy. "We can orchestrate the visitors, they'll expect some entertainment and there's enough of our own members who dislike Gittens to back them up."

"Leave it with me," said Rodney. "I'll have a word with the

Animal. I'm one of the people he'll listen to. Meanwhile spread the word but don't say anything near Gittens' cronies."

* * *

On the Saturday night of the Open Meeting, the Animal leant on the bar adjacent to Naval Corner. The clubhouse, especially the bar area, was packed. The Open Meeting was well attended, probably due to the splendid weather. Both visitors and club members were supporting the Saturday night social in large numbers, particularly in view of the rumours that something spectacular was due to happen. Curiosity about these rumours had also ensured that Naval Corner was full of its regular population, including Gittens.

The Animal's name came not just from his drinking habits, but also from his mode of dress. This consisted of a pair of shorts of ancient origin, held up by a leather belt from which dangled knives, marlin spikes and other nautical items, which might be of assistance to him in his sailing activities. To the shorts were added, according to conditions, a shirt, a jersey or an anorak, all of which had seen better days. This outfit was worn for both sailing and social events. In fact, there were even rumours that he wore it for work.

Nevertheless he was a splendid dinghy helmsman and was well pleased with his results that day, a second in one race and third in the other, leaving him every chance of an overall win. The Animal was at peace with the world. It only needed one thing to complete his day.

"Old Town Yacht Club!" he thundered. "I need a challenge! I need a man who can drink me under the table! It can be done, but it's hard! Come on! Not you, Rodney, I beat you three years ago!" There was complete silence.

"No one? Then I will ask this pretty young lady to choose someone!" He took the hand of Nancy who, as arranged, was standing close by. Now's my big moment, she thought.

"I nominate Percy Gittens!" she cried.

Speculation broke out all over the bar. Percy Gittens went a nasty shade of red.

"You'd better do it," Phil Lucas whispered to him. "You'll never live it down else." He, too, had had a good day on the water and was beginning to tire of Gitten's carping.

The victim waved feebly in the Animal's direction. It was not certain whether this was meant to be assent but the Animal took it as such.

"Percy Gittens it is! Name your poison, Percy!"

Gittens said something inaudible. Several voices, including Lucas, said that his normal drink was a pint of bitter.

"Pints of bitter, it is!" announced the Animal. "Keep them coming, landlord," he told Larkin, who promptly gave a pint to each of the contestants. While they were drinking them, he went to the spirit optics and filled a half-pint glass with vodka. This will be my revenge for the cloudy beer episode, he thought. One of his two temporary barmaids gave him a funny look but he winked at her and she grinned and turned away. Probably thinks a steward's perks, he guessed.

So the contest proceeded, watched by a large interested crowd. Pint followed pint, but to each of Gitten's Larkin added a quantity of vodka. Revenge is sweet, thought the steward.

After several pints the Animal paused. "I know! This needs livening up!" he announced. "Someone fetch me a dinghy paddle!"

Griff Griffiths, knowing the Animal's habits from other Open Meetings, already had one available.

"Now the idea is," roared the Animal, "to demonstrate that the beer has had little effect, we take it in turns, my challenger and I, to balance this paddle with one finger and see how many times we can run round it without falling over! I will go first!"

He ran round the paddle ten times with little apparent effect.

"Percy! See whether you can beat that!"

An unsteady Gittens was pushed forward.

"Do I have to?" he complained.

"Yes! Or I'll think of something much worse!"

Gittens made a noble attempt. But, handicapped by the vodka mixed with his beer, he fell over during the fifth circuit to cheers of derision. He regained his feet with difficulty.

"You bastard!" he screamed at the Animal. "This is a put-up job!" He took a wild swing at the Animal, which his opponent easily ducked, and made contact with the cheek of the unfortunate Larkin, who was taking advantage of the lull in bar orders to collect empty glasses. The Commodore, as head of the Club, intervened.

"That's enough," he said to both contestants.

"You're in it, too." cried Gittens. "'S plot to do me down."

"Calm down, Mr Gittens," said the Commodore evenly. "I suggest your friends put you in a taxi home. You're drunk. And when you are sober the Committee will want to discuss your behaviour with you."

Lucas and Silver each took one of Gitten's arms and began to propel him towards the door.

"You're all against me!" shouted Gittens as he went out into the night. Conversation renewed apace. The Commodore walked back to join his party. As he passed Nancy, he muttered "Well done", and winked at her.

CRICKET – NAVAL STYLE

Her Majesty's Cruiser Barsetshire's two comedians, Able Seamen Elkin and Davies, were chipping rust from her after gun turret. To amuse themselves they were singing a protest song which began, appropriately enough, 'If I had a hammer'. They had just reached the bit about 'I'd ring out a warning' when Davies nudged Elkin. Watching from below was Chief Petty Officer Stone, Chief Boatswain's Mate or 'Buffer' of Barsetshire and their archenemy.

"I wondered what you two skate was up to," began Stone. "Now I know, singing silly bloody songs."

"We was chippin' rust an' all, Chief," said Elkin, laying his chipping hammer on the staging.

"Yus, I can see. Don't get carried away an' chip right through. Now, cricket match termorrer, Ship's Company versus the Orficers. You're both playin'."

"I know nothing of cricket, Chief," said Davies, stressing his sing-song Welsh accent. "Rugby's my game."

"Soccer's mine," Elkin alleged, "West 'Am United."

"Ses 'ere," Stone consulted a clip-board, "list what clubs was kind enough ter give me, that yer both cricketers an' 'e should know. Muster termorrer, 1300 hours, with yer tropical whites ter play in."

Brooking no more argument, he marched off. He had, indeed, a list, squeezed out of the ship's very unwilling physical training instructor who, out of action with a torn hamstring, knew he would not be playing. It was entirely possible that the list contained inaccuracies.

* * *

"'Oo's bloody silly idea was this bleedin' cricket match?" demanded the Chief Cook, stirring something indescribable in a saucepan.

"Not mine, Chef," said Stone, "Twas the Jaunty. Cunnin old sod's got out of playin', ses 'e'll be an umpire instead. So I'm lumbered with team captain."

"More fool you. Must need yer 'ead read."

Stone took the plunge. "So you're playin'. As wicket keeper."

"I'm doin' what?" roared the Chief Cook ominously. His assistants, sensing some entertainment, all looked up.

"Wicket keeper. You're the biggest man on the ship. Nothin' 'll get past you."

The Chief Cook raised his ladle. "Get out of my galley! Bloody sauce, I was a batsman not a wicket keeper when I was a nipper. Go on, sling yer 'ook." He advanced on Stone who beat a hasty retreat. But the Chief Cook wasn t finished.

"Just ter show yer," he bawled after Stone, "I'll be yer wicket keeper, show yer some proper cricket."

* * *

Stone's next call was the quarterdeck where Corporal Binns of the Royal Marines was on duty as Corporal of the Gangway. Binns, he knew was a cricketer of some repute but would need some persuasion since he had always played for Royal Marine teams.

So he talked to Binns of the honour of the Marines and how, as a matter of honour they must have a representative, and a good one at that, in the Ship's Company team. After about quarter of an hour of this type of talk, Binns agreed to play. And that was Stone's team complete.

The Navigating Officer, who was to be captain of the Officers' eleven was on duty as Officer of the Day. He summoned Stone into his office.

"Full team, Buffer?" he asked.

"Yes, sir. Got some good 'uns."

"Splendid. So have we. Did you know that Sub-Lieutenant Page-Warner could have played for Hampshire?"

Stone hated Page-Warner. He considered him the most obnoxious sub-lieutenant he had ever met and that was saying something.

But he merely said: "Should be a close game then, sir."

"Let's hope so," said the Navigating Officer.

* * *

Back in the Chief Petty Officers' Mess, Stone contemplated his team. He himself would open the batting with Elkin and Davies would come in at first wicket down.

He had put his two 'bete-noirs' early in the batting order partly so that he could keep an eye on them and partly because he felt that they would not last long at the wicket. But a real expert, Ordinary Seaman Parker, a National Serviceman who had played well at school, scoring a century on more than one occasion, would follow them.

Corporal Binns, another mean batsman, would follow him and then Stoker Ferris, chosen by the Chief Stoker to represent the engineering department for much the same reasons that Davies and Elkin had been chosen by Stone. Then the Chief Cook and wicket keeper who, Stone hoped, was as good a batsman as he had indicated. Then there were the bowlers. For fast bowlers he had Leading Signalman Martin, who he had seen in action and who was quite good and Chief Shipwright Watkins, the ship's blacksmith who, he gathered, operated rather in the manner of the legendary blacksmith in village teams.

The team was completed by Petty Officer Nairn, the Captain of the Foc'sle, who had been a drinking companion of Stone's on many foreign commissions, but who was, nevertheless, a reasonable medium pace bowler and Mechanician Sturgeon who claimed to be a spin bowler.

Sturgeon was suspect as far as Stone was concerned. By far the scruffiest man on the ship, he was happiest when up to his neck in oil and grease repairing an item of machinery. He was hard to imagine in cricketing whites and Stone only had the word of the disaffected PTI that Sturgeon was a spin bowler.

Still cricket was a 'funny old game' and only time would tell.

* * *

At ten to two the next afternoon the two umpires, the Master at Arms and the ship's Chaplain, witnessed the toss. The Officers won and the Navigating Officer opted to bat.

A large interested crowd had gathered at the sports ground to watch this event. The Captain had given permission for the Lower Deck to be cleared, so, with the exception of essential staff led by the First Lieutenant, who was not the slightest bit interested in cricket, the whole ship's company was there. They had automatically divided into their divisions – all seamen together, all stokers, all Marines and so on.

The officers formed a small knot in front of the pavilion. A scoreboard had been set up and the Chief Writer, not without difficulty, had persuaded his staff to man it.

Stone selected his first bowler with care. He decided that it would be Nairn as his conventional medium pace would give a good idea of the capabilities of the Officers' opening pair, the Navigating Officer and the ship's Dental Officer.

The first ball was a disaster. Missed by the batsman it went over the Chief Cook's shoulder and on to the boundary for four byes. It was evident that the Chief Cook's bulk was matched by a lack of agility. Stone gestured to a fielder to stand behind the Chief Cook. The rest of Nairn's over was unremarkable and produced two runs.

Leading Signalman Martin then bowled a maiden over from the other end. Nairn's next over claimed the Officers' first wicket – that of the Dentist, who moved out of his ground to hit a short ball and was stumped by the Chief Cook. The Dentist was replaced by the dreaded Page-Warner who thumped the remaining two balls of the over for four runs apiece prompting Stone to decide he would try a new bowler against Page-Warner. Another maiden from Martin followed and then Stone called upon the Chief Shipwright to bowl.

Watkins indeed had all the attributes of the traditional village blacksmith. He took an enormous run up to the bowling crease down which he pounded like a steam engine, the ground trembling beneath him. He was a sight that would have terrified many batsmen, but not Page-Warner who, despite his other shortcomings, was no coward. The first ball was short and Page-Warner despatched it for six to the polite applause from the group of watching officers. The second ball, however, completely demolished the sub-lieutenant's wicket's. And that, Stone reflected, was the best way of getting rid of that nasty bit of work; he would have argued about anything else. Twenty runs for two wickets.

The Officers' innings the proceeded conventionally, runs being scored, Nairn and the Chief Shipwright taking wickets here and there and Martin bowling his maidens. Stone decided, despite Martin's economy, to replace him with Sturgeon.

The Mechanician, who claimed to be a spin bowler, had managed to look as untidy in tropical whites as he did in his more normal overalls and boots and it was quickly evident that he was not a spin bowler. In fact it was hard to define his bowling at all. Each ball was a surprise. It was either unplayable or asking to be sent to the boundary. But, unlike Martin, he took wickets, due more to the element of surprise than skill. And as teatime, which would mark the end of the Officers' innings, approached, their last pair was at the wicket.

71

And they were proving difficult to dislodge. The Navigating Officer was still there and his last partner was Midshipman Lucas. Elkin, who had played little active part in the game, was studying an interesting cloud formation, when he was startled by a cry of 'catch it!' The cricket ball, hit high in the air by Lucas, came into his field of vision. It was coming down straight at him. Knowing roughly what to do, Elkin made a cup of his hands and closed his eyes in concentration. To his surprise the ball landed in his hands. He clasped it to him. The Officers were all out for 140, a modest total by cricketing standards but Stone doubted whether his ragbag team could match it. Tea was taken.

* * *

Tea was a ham salad prepared by the officers' wives, with a bottle of beer for each player or official. Conversation over the meal was not solely about cricket.

"What's for supper, Chef?" the ever-hungry Davies asked the Chief Cook.

"Me favourite, corned dog fritters. But we'll be here still, o' course. So I just 'opes that PO Rowland don't mess 'em up." Davies suppressed a smile. Nothing Petty Officer Cook Rowland could do to the corn beef fritters could be anything but an improvement. Normally they were horrible.

"I was once shipmates with Stripey Wilson," Elkin was telling the Chaplain, "Cor! 'E was a card an' no mistake... You don't want that bottle o' beer, do yer, Padre? Ta. 'E was walkin' down this street in Valetta, Malta, see, an' this blowsy old tart calls down to 'im from a balcony: 'You come up 'ere, Jack, I give you something you never 'ave before.' Stripey looks at 'er curious like an' says 'What's that? Leprosy?'"

"Fascinating," said the Chaplain.

"And what do you do in the engine room?" the Dentist asked Sturgeon.

"I fixes things."

"I see. And that would be generators, compressors and so on, I expect?"

"I fixes 'un."

The Senior Engineer, Sturgeon's boss, lent over to the Dentist and said: "Give up, Fred. That's all he tells anyone."

* * *

Play recommenced at four-thirty with the start of the Ship's Company innings. A certain amount of illicit rum and beer had circulated among the audience during the tea interval and the ship's company element was now ready to give their team very noisy support. To this end they had formed three main cheering parties – seamen, led by the Chief Gunnery Instructor, stokers under the Chief Stoker and marines commanded by Colour Sergeant Macintosh. Stone and Elkin strode out to open the batting amid thunderous applause.

Stone faced Midshipman Lucas for the first over. He found the youngster's bowling fairly innocuous and hit two runs. Elkin then played and missed all six balls of the Senior Engineer's first over. Between overs Stone had a word with him.

"Hit the bloody thing for Gawd's sake," he hissed, "Watch me. Next over."

Stone proceeded to hit the 'bloody thing'. The first ball went straight to a fielder and there was no run, the second went for two runs and the third went plumb into the hands of the Dentist, fielding at first slip.

"Like that, Buffer?" Elkin asked cheerily as Stone stumped past him on his way back to the pavilion.

His friend Davies then joined Elkin. They fiddled around for a while, scoring a few runs, until Elkin stepped in front of his wicket and was given out leg before wicket by the Master at Arms as umpire. Twelve for two.

Ordinary Seaman Parker, the Ship's Company's star was next and came out to enthusiastic cheering. The run rate now

73

took off, although Davies did little but take the odd single to ensure the Parker got the lion's share of the bowling. He was at the non-striker's end when he espied a particularly pretty girl in the officers' enclave. Now was that an officer's wife or was it that nice Wren he had chatted up in the NAAFI the other night? Thus distracted, he failed to hear Parker's call for a run. The Ordinary Seaman was most of the way down the pitch before he realised that Davies was not paying attention. He tried to get back but was easily run out. He had contributed twenty-three to the total of forty-five for three.

Next in was Corporal Binns. Macintosh and the Marines went ecstatic as he walked out. Binns took a long time before he was ready. He took guard fussily, then discovered an irregularity in the pitch near his feet, which he treated with the blade of his bat. Then he took guard all over again. Finally he pronounced himself ready and was promptly clean bowled by Sub-Lieutenant Page-Warner's first ball to the chagrin of the Marine contingent. Forty-five for four. Now we're in trouble, thought Stone.

Stoker Ferris was next out to bat. He was not happy. He considered playing cricket, probably correctly in his case, to be a form of punishment. He had played no part in the proceedings so far and had no intention of doing so now. During the tea interval he had hardly spoken and concentrated on eating as much 'free' food as possible. So he made no attempt to hit Page-Warner's next ball and was also clean bowled. Forty-five for five and Page-Warner was on a hat trick.

The Chief Cook arrived at the crease and steered Page-Warner's next ball away with great care, denying him his desired hat trick. The Sub-Lieutenant's next ball was a bad one, which the Cook hit for four. It soon became evident that the Chief Cook was only interested in boundaries. His bulk was a handicap in running between the wickets, and this was evident when he responded to Davies' carefully timed singles designed so that Davies spent a minimum of time facing balls. Eventually, after another four boundaries, the Cook failed to make it to the far wicket and was, like Parker, run out. Seventy-one for six.

The next batsman was Petty Officer Nairn. A Scotsman, he had secreted a flask of his national spirit in the pavilion and now, if not exactly drunk, was at least merry. He had not a care in the world and treated the Officers' bowling with contempt. And this was his undoing for, after a promising start, he lobbed a catch straight to the Gunnery Officer, fielding in the gully. Eighty-seven for seven.

Sturgeon shambled out to bat next and had to face Page-Warner. He achieved a typically untidy mess at the very first ball and Page-Warner, supported by others, appealed for leg before wicket.

"Not out," said the umpire, the Master at Arms.

"That was definitely leg before wicket, Master at Arms," said Page-Warner, sternly.

"Not out," the Master at Arms repeated.

"You're biased..." began Page-Warner.

"And I say it was not out, my son," said the Chaplain, unusually, in cricket, coming to the aid of his fellow umpire, "And I do the will of God."

There was no answer to that and play resumed, which was just as well, since Sturgeon had looked as though he was going to hit Page-Warner with his bat. But the incident had had an effect on both bowler and batsman. Page-Warner was now sulking and bowled badly. On the other hand Sturgeon's fighting spirit was aroused and he laid about all the bowling with aplomb. The score swiftly accumulated until, at ninety-nine runs Sturgeon lost Davies who had gone for a single too many and was also run out. Ninety-nine for eight. Forty-two runs needed with the tailenders batting. Stone doubted that they could do it.

Leading Signalman Martin joined Sturgeon. Now, the Leading Signalman had a secret, his eyesight was failing. This was bad for a member of the Communications Branch. Martin was very worried, for he could foresee either discharge from the Navy or transfer to a mundane desk job. His eyesight may have caused his lack of wickets as a bowler and certainly he was now having a job sighting the ball as a batsman. Nevertheless he supported Sturgeon for a while, like Davies only scoring an occasional single. Eventually the Dentist sent him a ball that he just didn't see and he was bowled. One twenty-five for nine.

The last man in was the Chief Shipwright whose batting was as flamboyant as his bowling. He either failed to make contact with the ball or sent it a vast distance. Thus he scored a six off the last ball of the over. Ten runs needed for a win.

The next over was the penultimate one and was to be bowled by Sturgeon's pet hate Page-Warner, who, having been bowled extensively, could now add tiredness to bad temper. Sturgeon took two twos off the over.

The last over. The Shipwright would face the Dentist. Stone prayed that he would not do anything too stupid. He played and missed at the first ball. The second was definitely a catch but was dropped by the flagging Page-Warner. Three and four were also missed. Number five was going somewhere but was brilliantly stopped by the Gunnery Officer in the gully.

The last ball. The atmosphere was electric. The Navigating Officer made a few nervous adjustments to his fielders. The Dentist ran in and bowled a full toss. This time the Shipwright made firm contact. The ball flew over the heads of the spectators for a six, never to be seen again. But it didn't matter. The Ship's Company, against all odds, had won. Pandemonium broke out.

Amidst the hubbub, Able Seaman Elkin summed up their feelings: "Good. Now let's go an' get some beer down our throats."

SALVAGE

The guard held the Brightlingsea train until the last-minute passenger was able to scramble aboard. For a few minutes the latecomer could do nothing but wheeze and mop his perspiring brow and was thus unaware that he was being studied with amused interest by the compartment's only other occupant.

"You've put on weight since our barging days, Sam," said the passenger. "Too much good living ashore, I'll be bound."

"Phew! I have an' all," gasped Sam. "It's Bill, ain't it? Used to be mate of the Rose and Sarah?"

"That's right," agreed Bill, "and you were with Fred Harkness in the Maldon Belle. What are you doing now?"

"Family butcher's business. Doing quite well. Half-day closing today. Thought I'd go down to Brightlingsea for a look round." He took in his former colleague's business suit and generally well-manicured appearance. "And you?"

"Oh, a bit of this and a bit of that. Shipbroking mainly. I couldn't stay in the barges after I got these," he touched his horn-rimmed spectacles, "but I still have to do with barges. I do the odd job for the Colchester Barge Owners Insurance Club. That's why I'm going to Brightlingsea now. A tug's going to run me out to the Eva Mary sunk on the Buxey sand."

"Eva Mary," said Sam, "Josh Whiting's little ol' barge? Her with the checkerboard cabin-top? Nice pretty little thing, her. Fast, too. I'd 'ave liked a berth on 'er."

"You haven't forgotten much," said Bill, "but Josh came ashore two years back. His son Fred's got her now."

"No, I ain't forgotten," said Sam, "them was the days. I often think of 'em, even when I'm dishin' up meat." He sighed. There was a lengthy pause, while both men struggled with their thoughts.

"Of course," Bill said slowly, "if I could persuade the tug skipper and you made it worth his while, there's no reason why you shouldn't come on this trip this afternoon. You could buy something to eat in Brightlingsea and we wouldn't be too long. I've only got to find out how she sank and that will have to be done over the low-tide period."

"Come? Just try an' stop me."

And so it was arranged. At Brightlingsea the tug skipper, richer by five pounds, raised no objection to taking an extra passenger on what, in the idyllic summer weather, promised to be a holiday cruise.

During the trip out to the Buxey, Bill described what he knew of the wreck of the Eva Mary. She had left London River over a week ago laden with rape seed in bags for Colchester. A bad squall had caught her off the Buxey. The crew had taken in sail and anchored, but as the anchor did not appear to be holding too well, they had, rather too hastily, burnt flares and been taken off by the Clacton lifeboat. Shortly afterwards the wind dropped and the barge could be seen riding serenely to her anchor off the sands. However before the crew could rejoin fog clamped down and, when it lifted, Eva Mary was on top of the sands and sank when they were covered by the tide.

By the time that this yarn was finished the Buxey sand was clearly in sight. On this glorious summer day the sand had lost its normal menace and appeared as a darker version of the holiday beaches at Clacton shimmering in the heat haze to port. To seaward the sails of sailing barges and yachts showed where the deep water lay. Only the tug, belching oily fumes, was out of place in these halcyon surroundings.

The Eva Mary could plainly be seen, standing aloof on the

highest point of the sand, seemingly untouched without even an item of rigging out of place, as though she was merely waiting for the tide to return. The tug slowed down and her boat was lowered to convey the two investigators to the sand, the skipper promising faithfully to pick them up in two hour's time.

On arrival at the edge of the sand Bill donned a pair of waders to paddle ashore. Sam, not so well equipped, rolled up the trousers of his check suit and hung his two-tone shoes around his neck by the laces.

"It's funny," wheezed Sam, as they tramped over the firm sand, "I remember when the old Star of India went on here. Within a week the sands had buried 'er to the hatch comings. This one ain't like that."

"It was probably a lot worse weather when the Star went on," said Bill.

"Strange though," muttered Sam, and lapsed into silence while he concentrated on plodding over the sand.

When they reached the wreck the two men circled it looking for clues to the cause of her sinking.

"There you are," said Bill, "she sat on her anchor." He pointed to a gash, adjacent to where the anchor lay.

"Tain't a very big hole," said Sam. "We could patch that."

"What with?" asked Bill. "We haven't got any tools."

"There'll be some on the tug."

"But by the time she gets back there'll be water round here. We won't have time to do it."

"Must be sommat we can do," said Sam.

"What's got into you all of a sudden?" asked Bill. "She's had it. She's either a write-off or a job for a salvage company."

"Ah," said Sam slowly and deliberately, "but you didn't notice that vang-tackle aft. She's a-sittin' on it. Now no barge crew would 'ave left that trailin' overside. So that must've washed off after she came on 'ere an' she's on top of it. Therefore I reckon she's floated a bit since. That's why she's not gone like the Star of India." Both men digested this theory for a while.

"I know," Sam exclaimed suddenly, "give me a leg up on deck."

After considerable exertion, especially on Sam's part, he gained the deck, puffing and blowing, and promptly disappeared into the forecastle scuttle.

"Got it!" Bill heard him yell triumphantly and a few seconds later he reappeared brandishing a crowbar. "Kept in the normal place just inside the foc'sle."

"What happens now?" asked Bill, with a note of exasperation.

"Why, you said the cargo was rape seed in bags. So we take off an 'atch-cover, break open a few bags an' use 'em to plug the 'ole."

"Well, we can try," said Bill resignedly.

The crowbar proved, of necessity, to be a multi-purpose tool. First it was used as a hammer to knock out the wedges and bars securing the tarpaulin over the main hatch. Then as a lever to prize off first the heavy canvas tarpaulin and then the hatch cover. That was the relatively clean part of the task, for then one man had to stand among the sodden bags in the hold levering them to the hatch coaming where his companion could roll them over the rail to land with a soggy thump on the sand.

Then it was down to the sand again to use the crowbar as a knife to slice open the sodden bags. Their contents were then emptied and the bags driven tightly into the hole by the faithful crowbar. During these operations the tide had started to rise. It trickled remorselessly over the sand and joined one pool of sea water left by the ebb to another until the barge stood marooned on an ever-decreasing island of sand.

Evening now approached with the sun a golden ball as it began its descent towards the western land. There was however a hint of fog in the air, with the horizon purple and indistinct.

It became apparent to the two men that their labours were not over with the plugging of the hole. To give the barge every chance of floating the cargo would have to be lightened by the jettisoning of as many bags as possible. They gained an advantage by finding a suitable block and tackle to help with the raising of cargo from the hold.

This, however, did not help with the filthy conditions in the hold, for the bags of rape seed were covered with a penetrating slime. The pervading stench of wet rape seed had the man down in the hold gagging after a few minutes and both men were quickly soaked by the pockets of sour smelling water that had formed in every available space. The condition of their clothing, soon reduced to soaking, dirty and smelly rags was ignored. So, too, were the many minor scratches and abrasions they suffered as the grinding toil continued.

Bill, as the expert in such matters, estimated that approximately one hundred bags would need to go over the side to help with the refloating. Only ten bags had gone when frantic hooting announced the return of the tug. By a primitive form of semaphore Bill managed to convey that she should wait and stand by.

"Don't want them in on the act," he said with a wink at Sam, "now, do we?" He was toying with an idea that he did not wish to voice at the moment. No point raising Sam's expectations, he thought.

After this interruption work continued steadily. At twenty bags the water reached the barge, at forty it had risen halfway up the hull and at seventy it was within six inches of the iron band which marked the safe deep loading limit. At this point Bill collapsed.

"I can't do any more," he gasped, "we'll just have to chance it. Seventy bags may be enough." Sam surprisingly seemed to have thrived on the unaccustomed labour.

"That's made me hungry," he said, "We'll 'ave a blow an' eat."

Their sandwiches from Brightlingsea had been left on deck and were in better condition than their owners.

"You know," Sam mused from behind a huge mouthful of

sausage sandwich, "if she floats this l'il ole breeze is set fair for Brightlingsea. Happen we set her tawpsail we could blow in there lovely without any 'elp from the tug." Bill reflected that he was beginning to sound more and more like the Essex bargeman of a few years back.

"You thinking of the salvage money?" he demanded. He certainly had been, as part of his idea, but still did not wish to admit it.

"No, but I'd like to try it. I never did get to be skipper of a barge, y'know."

"There could be a fog."

"Nah. The breeze'll keep it down for a bit..."

"You'd have to be the eyes of both of us," said Bill, for his glasses now resided somewhere among the sodden bags in the hold. And still the water rose. Three inches from the iron band, two, one, and then the band went under as water began to flood on deck amidships.

"I'd better call up the tug," sighed Bill. Thirty bags of rape seed had defeated them.

"'Old on a minute," said Sam, "The tug's movin' – no she ain't – it's us. We're afloat! Set the tawpsail!"

Slowly and painfully, powered by the one sail, the barge crept away from what had seemed to be her last resting-place in the gathering night. As she reached deeper water, the tug took station behind her, her crew, like marine predators, prepared to follow her every move, thoughts of salvage uppermost in their minds. Her lights, brilliant in the afterglow, were a comfort to the two grimy scarecrows that manned the wallowing wreck.

One wave, larger than its fellows, could surge on deck and pour into the open hold, for they were too weary to replace the hatch cover, and then they could only hope for a speedy rescue. The evening breeze, which had temporarily banished the fog, bit through their wet clothing. But such discomforts were forgotten as they concentrated on reaching the beckoning lights of Brightlingsea.

Sam, at the wheel, brought back past skills as he eased the barge through the merry little popple of sea. Bill, unable to relieve the wheel through his poor eye-sight, laboured at the pump in a vain attempt to reduce the floodwaters below. Although his efforts were ineffective, they at least kept him warm.

And as he pumped, Bill mentally enlarged on his earlier idea. Ship owning was a natural progression from ship-broking. If they could get Eva Mary to safety, it was possible they could claim salvage on the vessel and at least part of her cargo. His share, combined with other savings should be enough to finance the purchase of a barge or similar vessel, perhaps even this one. Sam, he was now sure, would be a ready made skipper, if he could be persuaded to either sell the butcher's business or find someone to manage it. Perhaps Sam might even be prepared to invest in the project. But, at the moment, this was all a dream. First they had to reach a safe haven.

After an age the weary barge was abreast the lights of Brightlingsea.

"Down tawps'l," Sam ordered. Bill looked at him in surprise.

"Not going to round up into the tide?" he queried.

"I dursn't," Sam explained, "she'll be ashore quicker'n that in this state. We'll let go the anchor on the run an' 'ope for the best."

Bill, with forgotten dexterity, downed the topsail, then the anchor with a rush. There came a heart-stopping moment as the flood waters in the hold ran forward under their momentum. The vessel lurched sickeningly and snubbed her anchor chain. Water poured on deck as she spun round while Sam heaved on the wheel to ease the spin. Then, suddenly, she rode peacefully to the tide. The butcher and the insurance man had brought their barge home.

"Well done," said Bill extending his hand to Sam, "well done, skipper."

THE MAIDEN VOYAGE

She was launched on a Friday, the 27th February 1897. Just an ordinary sailing barge, destined for the Ipswich grain trade, but she should never have been launched on a Friday, the old longshoremen said, no good ever came of vessels launched on a Friday. Why, this one had already had a go at one of the shipwright who built her. Nearly took his arm off.

Jack Nelson, the ambitious young skipper who was to be her master would have none of this. He had no time for superstition and anyway, he said, the shipwright should have been more careful when using a two-handed saw on his own. Jack had been born on his father's barge and had sailed out of Ipswich ever since he was tall enough to reach a steering wheel. No barge would ever get the better of him, he maintained.

During the weeks of fitting out, while the barge acquired her masts, sails and fittings, her reputation gathered strength. It was embellished in countless public houses, shipyards and shipping offices and was the topic of conversation whenever several sailing barges were anchored together.

Eventually, when Jack sought a crew, several competent young barge mates, who, in the past, had pestered him for a berth, turned him down. Nothing personal, they said, but they didn't like his new barge. Ideally, Jack would have liked to have his former mate, Tommy Simmonds, a cheerful character who would have had no truck with this silly superstition business either. But Tom had been promoted to command Jack's former barge Rosemary, a position that he thoroughly deserved and one that Jack had no desire to disturb.

Eventually the owners took a hand in the crew problem and looked outside Ipswich. They produced, as mate, a dour individual from Colchester. Because of her size the barge warranted the luxury of a third hand, largely as cook and general menial. Normal practice was for the skipper to appoint a third hand, but on this occasion the owners insisted on engaging an uncertain youth, who was vaguely related to one of the partners. Since the position required no particular expertise, Jack accepted their decision.

With his crew now complete and the barge ready for sea, Jack took orders for a cargo of grain from the Royal Docks in London for Ipswich. First, of course, the barge had to sail, without cargo, from Ipswich to London. This proved difficult as the voyage was bedevilled with light and contrary winds from the south-west. The crew fretted, for in those days they were paid a share of the freight and on that system an empty barge earned no money.

After a frustrating three-day trip, they reached the Thames and it was there that the accidents began to happen. First a block fell from aloft, narrowly missing Jack's head as he stood at the wheel. Then a pan of boiling water overturned on the cabin stove, nearly scalding the young third hand. The mate's turn was reserved till last.

They moored for the night at Erith, handy to fetch up to the Royal Docks the next morning. The night was quiet with no further accidents. But, as they hove up the anchor in the morning, one of the windlass handles became unshipped throwing the mate over backwards. Fortunately he landed on the furled foresail and injured only his dignity. He completed the short voyage to the Royal Docks in a resentful silence.

Jack had expected an outburst from the mate, but this was postponed until the barge was safely moored in the docks and all three crew had repaired to the nearest hostelry.

"I ain't stayin' in that barge anuther minnut," the mate stormed, "an' neither are you 'appen you got any sense," he added to the third hand.

"Yes, you are," said Jack calmly. "You're both coming back to Ipswich. It's old wives tales. Plenty of blocks fall an' plenty of windlass handles come adrift. No-one's been hurt an' no-one's goin' to get hurt, you'll see."

In the end the mate grudgingly agreed to stay. Whether this was due to the skipper's reassurances, the inconvenience of making his own way home or the several pints of old and mild that he was apt to consume whenever the opportunity arose was not known.

Trouble continued in the docks. The stevedores were more than usually uncooperative and a careering steel lighter damaged the barge's boat and davits. When loading was eventually completed, they had the pleasure of a gentle sail down river as far as Southend.

But there they remained for several days plagued by a succession of fickle easterly breezes, which on two occasions freshened sufficiently for them to run back upriver to the Lower Hope for shelter.

"Ain't nuffin' ever goes right in this barge," said the mate, gloomily.

Then one morning Jack arose at 5am to find the wind from the south-west set fair for Ipswich. His former command Rosemary, fresh out of Surrey Docks, swept past, a grinning Tommy Simmonds at the wheel.

"See you in Ipswich," he hailed delightedly.

Jack stamped on the cabin roof with a sea-booted foot.

"Come on, we're goin'," he shouted to his recumbent crew. But as they made sail it appeared that several other barges were remaining resolutely at anchor. An old skipper was studying the leaden clouds that were now sweeping up from the south-west.

"We're a-stayin' here," he called as Jack's craft passed him, "That's a-goin' ter blow out there an' it's a Friday. Bad luck to sail on Friday."

"Old woman," Jack muttered to himself.

But, within the hour, the old man was proved right. By this time the barge was racing down the Swin towards Ipswich, under reduced canvas. The third hand had retired to the cabin, overcome by seasickness, while the mate gloomily paced the deck, expecting the worst. The weather had closed in, with the lowering clouds oozing sheets of rain to meet the wild sea. The navigation buoys swept past – South and East Shoebury, Blacktail Spit and Southeast Maplin.

"She goes well in a blow," Jack thought.

At this time he did consider anchoring but there was no sign of Rosemary which was somewhere ahead of them and Jack felt that what his former mate could do, he too could do. Tommy must, by now, be at the Spitway, the narrow and dangerous short cut to the north for sailing barges. Once through there he would be partially sheltered by the sands as he sailed up the Wallet channel which ran a good way towards Harwich harbour and there he would be nearly home, with only a river sail to Ipswich. Anchoring here would be hazardous in this sea, and in any case the chances were that this wind would moderate as quickly as it had arisen. At no time did the 'unlucky ship' theory enter into Jack's calculations.

And so they raced on to the Spitway. Here there was an awesome sight. The sands either side of the slim channel were a maelstrom of boiling surf while a confused cross-sea whipped up by the wind ran in the passage itself.

"You're not goin' thro' there!" cried the mate, aghast.

"Yer, I am," Jack shouted above the wind, "an' you're goin' to help me. It'll need both of us on the wheel. You take the leeward side."

They shot towards the opening with both men grappling with the wheel. As they passed between the sands an enormous sea picked the barge up, flooding the decks and submerging both men to their thighs. And yet it was this monster wave that was their salvation, for it swept the barge through the channel and into the deeper, calmer waters on the other side. Jack gave a silent prayer for the strength of the mate on the other side of the wheel.

It was indeed better in the Wallet and the wind appeared to be moderating. To the amazement of both men the cabin hatch suddenly opened and a ghostly third hand appeared, bearing two mugs of hot soup. How he had prepared them, alone and weakened by sickness, in the tumbling hell of the cabin, defied the imagination.

"He's alright, that lad," Jack said to the mate, as they gulped the welcome liquid. "He'll be a good 'un."

Off Clacton they passed Rosemary, her sails in rags and the Walton lifeboat standing by.

"Bad luck, Tommy," thought Jack and then realised the implication.

Harwich harbour was in sight when the wind suddenly regained its old force. But the harbour entrance, although difficult, did not present the same dangers as the Spitway. Until, that was, a packet steamer, belching smoke as she picked up speed, appeared round the harbour wall on a collision course with the barge.

A change of course was too dangerous for Jack, as it would have whipped the mast out of the barge. All he and the mesmerised mate could do was to cling to the wheel and hope that the steamer would draw clear. It was no good, they were going to hit. Jack's only thought was that the pessimists were right after all ñ this was an unlucky ship.

Then the unexpected happened. There was a sharp crack from aloft as something broke and then the topsail split asunder, the barge slowed slightly and the steamship surged past, her bow-wave pouring over the barge's quarter. A row of passengers' white faces topped by the gold braid on the bridge and she was gone.

The sailing barge Nemesis and her crew, winners of the 1898, 1899 and 1902 Upshore Barge Matches were safely home from their maiden voyage and a would-be myth was destroyed.

THE COURTESY VISIT

HMS Barsetshire steamed proudly into Hambrook Bay to pay a three day courtesy visit to the seaside resort of Homerton-on-Sea. Once she was anchored to the Captain's satisfaction, the cable party and the men manning her sides were dismissed for tea. In Number 4 mess Able Seaman Elkin was addressing his 'oppo' Taffy Davies and anyone else who cared to listen.

"Seaside resort?" he snorted. "Did you get a whiff of that factory ashore? What's it making? Shit? I 'aven't smelt anything that bad since I followed Stripey Wilson inter the heads."

"Still there might be some decent girls ashore," Davies consoled him. Leading Seaman Porteous, the leading hand of the mess, banged on a mess-deck table for attention.

"I just thought that I'd clarify the programme for the next three days," he announced.

Porteous was, for the Navy, a studious and well-spoken type, generally known as 'The Professor'. "Tomorrow night, Friday, there's a visit to Homerton Working Men's Club," he paused for effect, "for which free beer vouchers will be handed out, but only to those attending."

"Cor! We'll 'ave some o' that," whispered Elkin.

"There'll also be a dance for the ship's company at the Ajax 'om..."

" that'll do for afters," said Elkin.

" Saturday there will be a football match against the

factory team. And we can do what we like on Saturday evening..."

"We'll think o' something."

"... Sunday from 1200 the ship will be open to the public." This caused a hubbub of speculation.

"Bags ladder sentry," said Elkin. This was a most popular task. It was customary for a rating to be allocated to each gangway or ladder on the public's route, ostensibly to help the civilians to negotiate them. As far as the ratings were concerned this duty provided an ideal opportunity to look up the skirts of the prettier girls visiting the ship.

Porteous continued, "And finally, in the evening, the Captain and his Officers will return the hospitality of the Mayor and Corporation with a cocktail party on the quarterdeck."

* * *

In the Chief Petty Officers mess, the Chief Writer, who was also Mess President had just finished a similar announcement. The Chiefs were less interested than the junior ratings, since they were mostly married men. In fact those of them who lived in the vicinity and could be spared had been granted local leave.

"What are you goin' ter do," the Chief Boatswains Mate, CPO Stone, asked the Torpedo Instructor, CPO Ryan, one of the few bachelors in the mess. Ryan was a native of Cork in the Irish Republic and a quiet well-spoken man with a soft Irish brogue.

"Sure, and I've got weekend leave."

"How did yer swing that?"

"A favour repaid," said Ryan mysteriously, "Still, I'll enjoy meself me usual way. Book into a decent hotel, a bath, change into civvies, a few glasses of wine and, hopefully, the company of a fair lady."

"So that's 'ow yer do it," said Stone, impressed. Stories of Ryan's female conquests were legendary.

90

"You'd call it Irish blarney," said Ryan.

* * *

Meanwhile, in the ship s Regulating Office, the Master at Arms, who was responsible for discipline, had called a meeting of his staff.

"We'll 'ave patrols ashore all the time," he announced, "especially in the evenings. You'll be in charge of one each. Me, I'll 'ave a rovin' commission. Ship's company will supply your staff, mainly seamen as usual."

"Any chance of pickings, Master?" asked Regulating Petty Officer Griffin.

"Not 'arf. The dance is good for a start. 'Arf of 'em will 'ave got pissed at the Working Men's Club. We'll keep a good eye on the Dance 'All. Don't forget there's some nasty little bleeders on this ship 'oo's 'eadin' for a fall." He consulted a list. "Stoker Ferris, Able Seaman Elkin an' Able Seaman Davies for a start. As for Saturday night, the Skipper ses they can do what they like – an' we all know what that is, don't we – pissin' up an' bangin' off. Yus. There'll be rich pickin's, all right."

* * *

Before any of these pleasures could take place, there was a small trial for several of Barsetshire's crew. Friday was a normal working day and the ship's company was relaxing over a mug of tea during 'stand easy' when the ship s broadcast sprang into life.

"Port Watch of the cable party muster on the foc'sle."

In Number 4 mess no one took any notice. Stand easy was sacrosanct and was not to be interrupted. Anyway none of them was in Port Watch of the cable party. A little while later the Starboard Watch was summoned.

Now this was different as it included both Porteous and Davies.

91

"'Spose we'd better go," said Porteous, stretching.

"Anyone from the cable party muster on the foc'sle at the rush."

"Sounds desperate," said Porteous as he and Davies headed for the focísle.

"Probably the skipper's not got sunshine in his cabin," said Davies cynically, "so he wants the ship moved."

He was almost right. The Captain was not happy about the way the anchors were holding and wished to change the shipís berth. There followed an arduous morning for the cable party as the anchors were hove up and re-laid several times until the Captain was satisfied.

* * *

Despite these exertions, Davies and Porteous were there with Elkin and the rest when the party due to attend the Working Men's Club fell in. Before boarding the liberty boat each man was given two vouchers worth one pint of beer each.

"Cor! We ain't goin' ter get very drunk on these," grumbled Elkin.

"You can always buy yourself more," said 'Professor' Porteous.

The liberty boat landed them at a quay where a double-decker bus waited to take them to the club. It was on the far side of the town where the smell of the factory was not so noticeable, but unfortunately the normal clientele consisted of very old men, most of whom claimed to be former sailors. Their one idea was to obtain by fair means or foul the free beer vouchers or, failing this, to cadge beer from the sailors. In their pursuit of these aims, all had stories to tell and, after about an hour, Elkin began to feel that if he heard another yarn beginning something like 'Now when I was on the Iron Duke at Jutland,' he would go mad.

At this point the cabaret was announced. A large and brightly painted woman stepped on to the small stage and began to sing very loudly and very badly.

"That does it," thought Elkin, "I definitely need a change of scene." All evening he had been hearing, in between Jutland stories, rumours that most of the younger female population of Homerton would be attending the Ship's Company dance and there should be roughly four girls to each sailor.

He suggested to those around him that it was time to make a move to the Ajax Ballroom. The bus that had brought them to the club was round the corner and he was sure that the driver could be persuaded to take them to the dance. They agreed and the idea spread rapidly. Soon only 'Professor' Porteous, who was making notes of the Jutland-type stories for a book he might write someday, and a handful of others were left in the club.

The rest assembled by the bus, whose driver was soon bribed with cigarettes, bottles of beer, small sums of money and worthless beer vouchers to take them to the dance.

The bus took off at speed as the driver considered the sooner this journey was over the better. As it was some of the brighter spirits had imbibed rather too well at the club and performed acrobatics on the bus's platform. As the bus hurtled through the streets of Homerton-on-Sea it was spotted by one of the Master at Arm's' patrols which set off in hot pursuit. Unfortunately the patrol was on foot and by the time it arrived at the ballroom, the bus had decanted its passengers and disappeared.

* * *

CPO Ryan was having a very different type of evening. He had duly booked into Homerton s one presentable hotel, the Royal, had a bath and changed into civilian clothes – a blazer and flannels with a neutral tie – nothing to connect him with the Navy. He had just completed a reasonable meal, during which he had made eye contact with a petite blonde at the next table. He noticed that she wore an engagement ring, but he hadn't let such things put him off in the past. He took his coffee over to her table.

"Do you mind if I join you? No point in us both sitting on our own."

"Not at all. Please do."

And after that things went swimmingly. She quickly discovered that he was Irish and wondered what he was doing in Homerton. Ryan used his first-line cover story that he was visiting an aunt and uncle in the town but unfortunately there was no room for him in their small house and he was forced to stay in an hotel. In return he discovered that her name was Cynthia and she was a commercial traveller calling on clients in the town. Ryan told her that he ran a chain of garages back in Ireland. At that point they moved into the hotel bar where they discovered a mutual liking for red wine. Ryan's evening was going very well and he had high hopes for the night as well.

* * *

"Cor! They weren't jokin'. I've never seen so much clacker!" exclaimed Elkin in the Ajax Ballroom. There was indeed about four girls to each sailor. They stood about in chattering groups, they danced together but few, as yet, were dancing with sailors.

Davies looked at his watch. "We've got one and a half hours till the last boat back."

"That's plenty. Let's get stuck in."

They did much dancing with a different partner each time, but seemed unable to progress beyond this. Whether this was because their dancing was fairly rudimentary or because the Homerton girls wished to stay within their groups, believing there was safety in numbers, they didn't know. But all this changed for Elkin with about twenty minutes dancing left.

"I'm goin' ter ask that redhead," he said to Davies.

"Good luck," replied his 'oppo' who was becoming despondent.

"She's probably like the rest."

But she wasn't. She was slightly taller than Elkin, which he found a little disconcerting, but she compensated by dancing close. She was also far more talkative than Elkin's earlier partners. He learnt that her name was Doreen and she was a sales assistant in the local department store. She lived at home with her Mum and Dad, her Grandma and a sister. He told her how he had saved the ship when she was in danger of being cast ashore that morning. When the dance ended, Elkin decided to stay on the floor with her. He indicated this by holding on to her hand.

They did several more dances, with Doreen dancing even closer and resting her cheek against Elkin's. Cor! This ones askin' for it, he thought. Suddenly Elkin noticed a complete absence of sailors. He looked at the Ballroom clock. Five minutes to the last boat. He quickly asked Doreen for her address, gave her a cursory peck on the cheek and dashed out of the Ballroom, minus his cap, which he had left with Davies and straight into the arms of a patrol.

"Where's your cap?" a voice asked. It was Able Seaman Anderson, who owed Elkin a favour.

"You're lucky, mate," Anderson went on. "RPO Griffin's gone for a slash. Here's your cap, your mate gave it to me, an' a bus is waiting round the corner to get everyone down for the last boat."

* * *

Ryan had enjoyed his evening but it was now time for its climax. He hoped, but wasn't sure that he had Cynthia in a responsive mood.

He stretched and said: "Time for bed." Cynthia said nothing.

"Would you be fancying a night-cap up in my room?" he asked unabashed.

"Oh! No, thanks for the offer but I've got people to see early tomorrow."

95

She leant over and kissed him on the cheek.

"See you at breakfast."

* * *

As the last liberty boat disgorged its contents, the Master at Arms was on deck. He noted that the boat contained Elkin and Davies, but they seemed subdued and comparatively sober. They had evidently eluded his patrols as well. Bloody pity, they were both duty watch tomorrow. He'd probably lost his opportunity of putting them 'in the rattle'.

* * *

A lonely Ryan returned to his hotel room. Shame, he thought, it usually works, engagement ring or not. He slowly undressed and, thinking that he would read for a while, slipped on a dressing gown.

He had just picked up his book when there was a tap on his door. He opened it and was surprised to see Cynthia there also wearing a dressing gown.

"Oh, good. I've got the right room," she said brightly, "I thought that I'd take you up on that offer, after all."

And, as Ryan was soon to discover, she was wearing nothing under her dressing gown.

* * *

As the Master at Arms thought, Elkin and Davies were duty watch next day. But Elkin had already had a 'sub' to take his place and soon obtained one for Davies as well.

"That s ten bob yer owes me," he told the Welshman, "an we're off ashore as soon as leave starts at 1200."

"What's so important about going ashore, man?" asked Davies.

"I'm goin' ter find that bird. You know, the redhead."

"Then you won't want me to hold your hand, boyo."

"But she's got a sister."

Davies showed more interest. "How do we find her then?"

"I know her address. At least, I think I can remember it."

* * *

On the 1200 boat, Elkin said that he recalled the address as 47 Acacia Drive. Needless to say, he and Davies went into the first pub they came to for directions. The staff didn't know Acacia Drive so they had a pint anyway and moved on to the next pub. Here they were luckier and received the precise location of Acacia Drive. They decided to have a pint to celebrate and then one thing led to another and they didn't leave until half-past two, which was closing time anyway.

The friendly barmaid in the second pub had drawn Elkin a map. Somewhat befuddled they studied it and set off in what, they hoped, was roughly the direction of Acacia Drive. On the way they passed the backdoor of a third pub. As they drew level the door flew open and the Chief Gunnery Instructor of HMS Barsetshire, another enemy, landed at their feet.

"An' don't come back!" shouted the irate landlord.

The Chief GI got hazily to his feet, groped inside his trousers and proceeded to urinate against the pub's back wall. Elkin and Davies moved on.

"Disgusting! A disgrace to the Navy!" said Elkin in apparent outrage. Davies sniggered, remembering the many similar incidents when they had been the chief offenders.

* * *

Despite the map, they had several false attempts before they finally found Acacia Drive. By then it was four o'clock and the effects of the beer had worn off. They knocked at No. 47 and were told by a rather nervous old lady that Doreen and family lived at 49. They tried again and this time the door was opened by a middle-aged lady whose red hair was flecked with grey, obviously Doreen's mum. Elkin asked for Doreen.

"Oh, yes. You must be the boys from the dance last night. Come in."

She explained that Doreen wouldn't be home from work for a while yet but they could wait and have a nice cup of tea. An ancient lady who was grandmother was introduced. They gathered from Doreen's mum, who talked incessantly while she made the tea, that her husband had been in the Army during the war and was watching a football match at the moment. Her youngest daughter was playing netball. Davies brightened at this. She made them a cup of tea and chattered on, telling them she had a soft spot for the Navy as her brother had been on the Malta convoys during the war.

After about an hour, Doreen arrived home and seemed pleased to see the two sailors, Elkin in particular. Her father and sister quickly followed her. To Davies' dismay, the sister, although a miniature version of Doreen, was just twelve years old. Pandemonium ensued, with everybody talking at once about football, netball, work and the Navy. During all this, the mother managed to convey that the two sailors must stay to tea. This proved to be a veritable feast. There was ham, egg and chips, jelly and cream and all sorts of cakes.

"Can't beat a bit of 'Up-homers'," Elkin muttered to Davies, "Feet under the table an' all that."

Davies, disappointed about the age of the sister, needed cheering up. After the meal Elkin suggested to Doreen that they go out for the evening.

"Oh! No, sorry," the girl answered, "Mum, Dad and Grandma are goin' to the pub, so I've got to look after Lizzie. But you two can stay. We can play cards."

The older people eventually departed for the pub. Davies wished he were going too. Cards were produced and a debate started about what to play. The girls merely giggled at Elkin's suggestion of strip poker. They played blackjack for about an hour until Davies suggested that it was time that he and Elkin went. Doreen said that she didn't mind since she was tired after the dance and a full day's work and Mum and Dad would be home soon.

"What did yer want ter do that for?" Elkin demanded as they walked away, "I was makin' progress there."

"No you weren't, boyo. Not with her family around. Anyway the pubs close in an hour. And thanks for fixing me up with a twelve year old."

"I didn't know, 'onest," said Elkin, lamely. But Davies wasn't finished.

"You're all talk, look you," he went on. "Even if you got somewhere with that bird, I bet you couldn't even find out the colour of her fanny fluff."

"Yes, I could. You're on. That bird or the next one. Ten quid on it."

"All right," said Davies evenly. "I know when my money's safe."

During this argument they had become lost again. By the time they had sorted their route out and arrived at the quayside pub, there was only half an hour's drinking time left.

* * *

On board Barsetshire, the Assistant Officer of the Watch, Sub-Lieutenant Page-Warner, was fed up. Most of his evening had been taken up with the supervision of the embarkation of boatloads of sailors in varying degrees of intoxication. And he could do without the Master at Arms and RPO Griffin at the head of the gangway minutely examining each arrival. But now, at last, the final boat was due.

The Master at Arms, too, was depressed. Elkin and Davies had arrived back earlier and try as he might, he could find nothing wrong with their sobriety or dress. What was going on? He suspected a woman was involved.

But, to his delight the last boat contained Stoker Ferris, accompanied by a large, potted Yucca plant that Ferris insisted was his friend. Page-Warner told him to drop the plant over the side and get turned in. Ferris suggested that Page-Warner take a running fuck at a rolling doughnut and was promptly put on a charge. In the ensuing confusion the Yucca plant was forgotten and remained standing at the head of the gangway.

* * *

As second-in-command of Barsetshire, the Commander was in overall charge of the arrangements for the Captain's cocktail party on the Sunday evening on the Quarterdeck. Early the next morning, the Commander held a meeting there of his principal assistants – the Chief Steward, responsible for food and drink, the Sailmaker who would rig awnings over the Quarterdeck and CPO Stone, the Chief Boatswain's Mate, responsible for general cleanliness. The Commander suddenly broke off from what he was saying to the Sailmaker: "What's that Yucca plant doing here?" Stone thought quickly.

"It's a decoration, sir. Should brighten the cocktail party up. Not too nautical."

The Commander beamed. "Excellent idea, Buffer. Make sure it is prominent."

Just then the ship's broadcast sprang to life.

"'Awa the noo, the second moty cutter's crew."

"Who is using that thing?" the Commander wanted to know. This is getting bad for my nerves, thought Stone, I wish the Commander would go away. Again he had the answer.

"Able Seaman Macleod, sir. Boatswain's Mate, a Scotsman. That's the way he talks, he can't help it, sir."

"I'll get him elocution lessons," said the Commander grimly.

* * *

From midday, Barsetshire, or at least part of her, was open to the general public. They arrived in their hordes, conveyed out to the ship by a shuttle service of excursion boats normally employed to take visitors 'round the lighthouse'. Once aboard they found their access limited to the main deck, less the area set aside for the cocktail party, plus the gun turrets, the bridge and a few compartments of interest below decks, such as the Main Signal Office.

Despite strict shepherding by the officers and men of Barsetshire there was always the danger that they might stray elsewhere. Various precautions were taken about this. The Senior Engineer had the engine room and boiler rooms barricaded off and the Chief Cook, brandishing his largest carving knife, declared that he would murder any civilian who came near his galley where he was trying to prepare snacks for the evening's cocktail party. This so alarmed his assistant, Petty Officer Cook Rowland, that he posted two of the burliest cooks at either end of the galley flat to repel any invaders. A squad of Marines was assigned one of the Corps traditional functions – that of guarding the officers' quarters – this time against marauding visitors not mutinous sailors.

Most of the ship's company was employed in supervising the visit, either as guides, demonstrators of equipment or as gangway sentries. Elkin had, of course, landed one of the prime jobs – sentry on the gangway leading to the Main Signal Office. His duties largely consisted of helping the elderly and the young off the gangway. To these he added pretty young ladies whose arrival he often observed from under the gangway where he had a good view. Allowing for all possible contingencies he had armed himself with the keys to the focs'le locker. As he was doing a stint as Focs'le Lockerman, he had been entrusted with the keys by the Captain of the Focs'le, Petty Officer Nairn, who was on weekend leave. The locker was a tiny compartment used for the storage of equipment for the Focs'le Party – drums of paint, coils of wire, etc. Elkin had tidied it up a bit, laid some canvas on the small piece of floor revealed and considered that it would do for the possible emergency he had in mind.

The clack of high heels on the gangway grabbed his attention. Automatically he looked up. 'Cor! This one ain't wearin' much under her frock, I can see 'er stockin' tops,' he thought and moved smartly to receive the young lady at the foot of the gangway. To his surprise it was Doreen.

"What are you doin' here?" they both asked and then laughed.

"Family with you?" Elkin enquired.

"No, I'm on my own."

"'Old on 'ere a minute," Elkin darted into the Main Signal Office, where several signalmen and telegraphists were lurking. He pressed some money into the palm of the nearest one, "Take over from me, Sparks. Got some urgent business."

He returned to Doreen, jangling the keys to the Focs'le Locker.

"Would you like to see where I work?"

* * *

At five o'clock the last of the general public left Barsetshire, well pleased with what they had seen and done, especially Doreen, who Elkin had just got on to the last boat.

Now most of Barsetshire's ship's company could relax. This did not include the cooks and stewards putting the finishing touches to food and drink for the cocktail party. The Chief Cook had sworn so much that he had now lost his voice to the great relief of his staff. Neither did it include an Ordinance Artificer who was trying to extract the remains of a lollipop from the breech of one of the guns, or the two seamen swabbing up a pool of sick left by a little girl in a corner of the bridge or a Leading Telegraphist attempting to repair a typewriter that had been well played on in the Main Signal Office.

But, all in all, it had been a successful day.

* * *

Chief Petty Officer Ryan had returned to Barsetshire. He had had an interesting, if energetic, two nights and one day in the hotel with Cynthia, spent mainly in one or the other of their bedrooms. But on the Sunday she said she had things to do, so they said a fond farewell. Ryan liked children so he had rejoined the ship and spent the afternoon showing off his torpedoes and explaining to audiences largely comprised of small boys how they were fired.

Now he was catching up with the newspapers in the Chiefs' mess when the ship's broadcast summoned him to the quartermaster's lobby. Why should this be? He mused as he walked aft, the lobby was within feet of the cocktail party, which was now in full swing, and, whatever it was must be urgent for the quartermaster to send for him.

The Duty Quartermaster was Leading Seaman Porteous, assisted by Macleod as Boatswain's Mate. As soon as he saw Ryan, Porteous said: "Young lady to see you, Chief," To Ryan's amazement Cynthia, dressed in a little black cocktail dress emerged from the lobby.

"What are you doing here?" he asked, echoing Elkin.

"Attending the cocktail party," she said, with a smile, "at the invitation of my fiancè, Sub-Lieutenant Page-Warner." Ryan moved her out of earshot of Porteous and Macleod.

"How did you know I was on the ship?"

"That was easy. I saw your uniform in the wardrobe at the hotel. There's only one ship here, and she's only got one Chief from Southern Ireland. That nice Quartermaster knew you straight away."

"So you're not a commercial traveller," Ryan was beginning to get angry, "I wondered why you didn't go to see your so-called clients on Saturday."

"Oh yes, I am," she retorted. "I merely adjusted my schedule so that I could be here during the ship's visit. And you didn't go to see your mythical relatives, either." She softened, "But it's not as you think. I came here to break the engagement off, but I got cold feet and then – well, distracted." She slipped her arm through his, "Now I've met you I'm definitely going to do it, tonight."

Ryan digested this information – the future looked rosy. She pressed a piece of paper into his hand.

"My London address and phone number," she whispered. "Look me up, when you can."

"Why are you talking to that Chief, Cynthia?" a voice demanded. It was Page-Warner.

"I lost my handkerchief," said Cynthia glibly. "He was kind enough to return it."

"I see," said Page-Warner, with disbelief. "Time you came back to the party."

As Page-Warner led her away, Cynthia mouthed silently at Ryan: "I'm going to do it." At the last moment Page-Warner turned round and gave Ryan a venomous glare.

The sub-lieutenant would make a bad enemy, Ryan thought. He resolved to leave Barsetshire at the next opportunity.

* * *

Monday morning. HMS Barsetshire was back at sea. In the Regulating Office, the Master at Arms stubbed out a cigarette in the tub of the Yucca plant that he had 'liberated' from the remains of the cocktail party. Not a bad haul, he reflected. Stoker Ferris was in the cells, various other miscreants were undergoing punishment and the Chief Gunnery Instructor was facing charges relating to indecent exposure and, unless he could wriggle out of them, was likely to be demoted.

Strange, though, about Elkin and Davies. Normally they were at the heart of any drunken debauchery and the mischief resulting therefrom. This time, however, they had been quiet and relatively sober although, he understood, there had been a near miss with Elkin after the dance. But he thought he had a clue. The previous afternoon he had glimpsed Elkin leading a particularly pretty redhead in the direction of the focísle lock-

er. Good luck to him, he thought in a rare moment of benevo-
lence.

* * *

Elkin was stirring paint in the foc'sle locker. This was where it
all happened he mused. Good job I got rid of the johnny before
PO Nairn noticed it. Good girl, that Doreen, didn't mind
rolling around in the locker in the altogether at all.

He remembered his bet with Davies. No difficulty there!
She was a natural redhead all right! But he doubted whether
Davies would ever pay up for there were no witnesses and the
Welshman was unlikely to take his word for it. In any case, he
felt that, just for once, he would keep that item of information
to himself. He thought he would stay in touch with Doreen.

THE MATCHMAKER

An unusual sight. Not one, but two sailing barges moored at the mill at Nether Rushbrook. Given the normal dilatory nature of the miller, Barney Thornton, in unloading arrivals, they were likely to be there a long time, especially the last to arrive, Gardenia. And this presented an ideal opportunity for her skipper, Maurice Norman, known to all as 'Morrie.'

For some time now, Morrie had been concerned that his mate, Johnny Read, was still single at the age of twenty-five. By that age, Morrie considered, a barge mate should be settling down, raising a family and looking for a skipper's job. Indeed many became wed much earlier and, despite the hardship of supporting others on their often-meagre earnings, appeared content with their lot.

So, recently Morrie had embarked on a campaign to find a suitable partner for his mate. In Ipswich it had been the barmaid at the Rose and Crown, in Whitstable the fishmonger's daughter and, back home in Upshore, any eligible relations of his fellow barge skippers. Here in Nether Rushbrook, he had high hopes of Barney's two daughters, April and May, and failing them several of the local farmers must have single females in their families.

However Morrie appreciated that his task was not going to be easy. Barney, despite his many business interests, kept a very good eye on his daughters. Not that they had much of a social life, largely being employed as barmaids at the Miller's Arms, of which Barney was the licensee. The miller also used his pub as his 'office'. Moreover the miller was very generous to visiting bargemen, perhaps to compensate for the time that he took to unload their vessels, not just with food and drink but also with permission to hunt on his land.

This opportunity was of particular interest to the crew of the other barge, Voracious, who spent most of their time out with their dog and guns, making occasional trips to Upshore to dispose of their catches. Morrie found himself spending more and more time supervising the discharge of Voracious, which largely meant trying to chase Barney into actually doing something, and less on his main preoccupation of attempting to find Johnny a soul-mate. But although this was the situation during the day, he still had his evenings free to promote his mate's cause.

And Johnny himself was a problem. Unusually for a barge mate, he was a studious lad, spending much of his spare time reading. He even preferred this activity to visiting the Miller's Arms, which, of course, contained the delightful April and May.

"Why don't you leave the poor lad alone?" advised Captain Brewster of the Voracious. Bad weather had put a stop to his hunting activities and he and Morrie had met in the Miller's Arms.

"What's your suggestion then?" countered Morrie.

"'E'll find the right girl in 'is own time."

"'E'll never do that while 'e's sittin' in the foc'sle readin'".

Barney appeared from somewhere and commenced tacking a poster on to the wall nearest the door.

"What's that all about?" demanded Brewster.

"Village fete. Next Saturday," replied the miller. "Or rather it's us an' the village next door, wouldn't be enough people else. Still won't concern you, you'll be finished an' gone by then."

"What sort o' thing's involved?" asked Morrie, who

thought that there was every chance that Gardenia would still be there, and so probably would Voracious.

"Usual nonsense. Judgin' o' vegetables. Pony rides for the kids, dance in the evenin' and so on."

"So you're not in favour of it?"

"Oh! Yus I am. I'll run the beer tent an' the bar fer the dance. Trouble is, 'that ol' bastard up at the 'All's involved. 'Is idea as it 'appens. So 'e'll want ter present all the prizes an' make speeches an' that."

Although Barney seemed to control most local enterprises – the mill, the pub, the village store and many of the surrounding farms, he had absolutely no time for the 'local squire' who inevitably referred to as ìthat old bastard up at the 'All'. This, Morrie assumed, must be rooted in some form of business rivalry that Barney did not care to reveal.

"So we're welcome to join in?" Morrie asked Barney.

"Not 'arf. We got just the thing fer yew bargemen. Tug 'o war." Morry wished he hadn't asked. Hope of the two barges being finished had now probably disappeared.

"Yus. With yew four off the barges plus some lads I'll find fer yer, yew could make up a team. Give yew an appetite fer yer beer." Barney now seemed to assume that Voracious and therefore Gardenia would be staying for the fete. And, thought Morrie, Johnny would not be able to stay with his books; he would be needed for the bargemen's team. Moreover, either side of that event, there would be many opportunities to involve him with April or May, for their father would be dashing around organising. And, in any case, there was certain to be other young ladies at the fete.

But when Morrie explained what was going to happen to Johnny, the mate didn't seen terribly interested.

"Oh! I don't know," he said. "I might come along. I don't know about a tug o' war. Never done one o' them before."

"It's easy," Morrie encouraged him. "All you gotta do is lay back an' pull. If old boys like me an' Brewster can do it, so can you." He had an inspiration. "An' there might be a bookstall in the fete."

"Ah, well, that could be worth a look."

"An' the tug o' war?"

"Yeah, all right, can't let the side down."

Got you, thought Morrie, I just hope that April and May aren't too busy in the beer tent and, even if they are, there's a few village girls about.

* * *

For the rest of the week there was intense activity in the village of Nether Rushbrook. Tents were erected on the village green and bunting strung between prominent points.

Tables and chairs appeared and were distributed among the tents. Barney became increasingly busy both directing this work and often disappeared on undisclosed missions. All work on the discharge of Voracious's cargo ceased, much to the chagrin of Brewster who, although interested in the fete, still wished to be clear of Nether Rushbrook as soon as possible. Barney's absences, however, left April and May in charge of the Miller's Arms, thus giving Morrie the chance to advance his mate's cause with them.

"An' 'e's goin' ter be on this tug o' war?" asked April, nudging her sister, "That we'll 'ave ter see. Close the beer tent fer a few minutes."

"All that pullin' an' 'eavin' on yer barge," said May, "'e must 'ave muscles. Why don't 'e come in 'ere more often?"

"Oh! 'E likes his books," said Morrie, "Never was a readin' man meself. I can't see it. I 'as a job ter get 'im off the barge. But Friday we'll be practisin' our tug o' war".

"'E'll be around then all right."

* * *

On Friday the bargemen's team tried out their tug of war technique by fastening the actual rope that they would use for the competition to a sturdy tree alongside the green and pulling on it. A small crowd which included April, May and Barney watched. To the delight of the girls the younger men stripped to the waist.

"'E 'as got muscles an' all," April whispered to May and received an admonishing glance from her father.

Two strangers – a neatly turned out man in plus fours and a rather plain young lady, who carried a notebook, joined the crowd.

"Who's that?" Morrie asked Barney in a pause between pulls.

"The old bastard hisself from the "All', said Barney, not too loudly.

"An' the girl?"

"'Is daughter. Dunno much abaht 'er. Probably a chip off the old block, though."

"This is the practice for the tug oí war?" asked the Old Bastard after a while.

"Yes, sir. Bargemen's team," replied Barney, with a smirk at Morrie, "'Spec the other teams is practisin' elsewhere."

"Jolly good. Nice to see them taking it seriously. Make a note of this, Frances."

Frances, the daughter started. She had been gazing at Johnny. But she made the required note and the couple moved on.

"Come on, lads," Barney exhorted. "One more pull an' I'll buy you a pint up at the pub."

* * *

The fete was blessed with good weather and it was certainly a splendid event. It was well supported for, in addition to the population of the two main villages, visitors had come from many outlying hamlets and farms. There were even people from Colchester, the nearest big town.

There was plenty to entertain them. Inside the tents they

could admire the flowers and vegetables awaiting judgement. Or they could slake their thirsts in the beer tent or sit down to tea and cakes. Outside there were many stalls selling everything from vegetables to books. A Punch and Judy man amused the children and adults could try their hands at games of skill, such as 'Trap the Rat' and the 'Wheel of Fortune'.

There were performances by Morris Men and sheep dog competitions. And, of course there was the tug of war.

There were sufficient entries for this for heats to be held, until two undefeated teams would face each other in the final during the afternoon. Morrie's team survived, although struggling at times, and was due to face a team from the next village in the final. Their last pull had been particularly difficult and Morrie sought the beer tent, with Brewster for company.

"Where's that mate o' yours?" April asked Morrie as she served him.

"Dunno. Thought 'e was right behind us."

"Strange lad," Brewster added, "You'd 'ave thought 'e'd need a pint after that last pull. Rest o' the teams all in 'ere."

May returned from collecting glasses from outside the tent. "That mate o' yours is in his seventh heaven," she reported. "Found a stall sellin' books. That girl Frances is runnin' it."

"'E oughta be in 'ere chattin' ter you an' yer sister," said Morrie.

"Garn! Leave the lad alone," exclaimed Brewster, "'E's 'appy out there. An' 'e's off the beer. Someone's got ter keep their 'ead for this afternoon's final."

By the time that Morrie found an excuse to leave the beer tent, Johnny was deep in animated conversation with the plain Frances.

"She knows a wunnerful amount about books, skipper," he confided in Morrie as the teams assembled for the tug of war final. He placed a small pile of books on the grass. "She gave me these off her stall." Morrie merely grunted.

The bargemen's team, after a hard struggle, was the tug of war victor. They were warmly congratulated and Morrie was nearly bowled over as April and May rushed into the crowd that surrounded the team. But it was Brewster's mate that they were heading for. And a young female, Frances, was already embracing Johnny.

"Come on, you two, get the beer tent a-goin'", Barney shouted to his daughters. A dejected Morrie followed them into the tent.

"What's up wiv you?" asked Barney after they had secured a pint each. "Won the cup, didn't you?"

"After all I done fer 'im," said Morrie bitterly, "tryin' ter fix 'im up with a girl, that lad 'as ter make 'is own arrangements."

"Oh, yus. Tryin' ter fix 'im up wiv me daughters, weren't yer? Well that wasn't on, I'm savin' them fer someone special. Not any ould barge mate."

So Barney had worked that one out. Morrie wondered vaguely whether he had engineered the Frances situation. No, not possible, not the way Barney detested her father, or was it?

Johnny arrived hand-in-hand with Frances, books tucked under his arm.

"Shan't be around this evening, skipper," he said. "Dining up at the Hall."

Morrie suddenly felt a bit better.

"Good luck ter you, lad," he said.

THE SKIPPER OF THE SCORPION

It was the worst fog to smother the River Thames that winter. John Prentice had just paid off as Third Engineer of the motor vessel London Queen in Tilbury Docks. To his dismay he found on arrival at Tilbury Town station, that there was considerable delay on the railway service to London. Not liking to leave the station for a café or public house, in case a train suddenly appeared, he bought a local paper to while away the time. The train was just approaching the platform when he noticed a small paragraph on the back page.

NIGHTWATCHMAN DIES

'The body of an elderly man, found on board a hulk at Hewitt's yard, Grays, yesterday has now been identified as that of Arthur Graves, former night-watchman at the yard. Police do not suspect foul play.'

Arthur Graves. So that was his real name. John had, like his fellow apprentices and, indeed, everybody else at Hewitt's yard known him only as the 'Skipper of the Scorpion'. The Scorpion was the derelict sailing barge hulk that was the old man's only home. No one could remember him admitting to any other abode and it was generally accepted that the two had been together for a very long time.

Night watchman was a rather grand title for the old man.

Perhaps Hewitt's assumed that he did guard the yard at night, but normally he would be cadging drinks in the nearest pub or snoring in his bunk aboard the hulk. During the day he would shamble round the yard with his odd, crab-like gait, looking for entertainment, which would generally consist of yarning to the apprentices or starting an argument with the barge crews. Now and again the yard foreman would persuade him to do a little light work, like carrying a message or conducting a search of the piles of junk that littered the decks of the Scorpion in the hope of finding a wanted fitting or a length of wood of a particular size.

John had observed all this while he had served part of his apprenticeship preparing landing craft for the Normandy invasion. Part of Hewitt's yard had been requisitioned for this purpose while the remainder continued to service their fleet of sailing barges, reduced in number by the war, for many had been taken for mine-watching duties. John was one of several engineering apprentices recruited from Thames-side shipyards to help with the installation of the landing crafts' engines.

It had been an exhausting period with work going on from dawn until late at night and on more than one occasion John had been almost too weary to travel back to his lodgings. Indeed once he had missed the last bus back. At a loss to know what to do next and with very little money in his pocket, he called at the local pub, which was nearing closing time. Here he met the skipper of the Scorpion, somewhat the worse for drink.

"You're late, boy," said the old man. John explained his problem.

"Why, stay on the lil ol' Scorpion with me, lad. Won't be a minnut." The skipper produced a pint of beer from a hiding place under the table. A few seconds later it had disappeared and John decided that it was worth escorting a somewhat befuddled old man back to the yard in return for a bed for the night.

Once aboard the Scorpion, John found the interior as chaotic as the decks. The old man rummaged around in the junk that filled the cabin and eventually produced a dark green bottle and two disreputable tin mugs. He poured two considerable tots from the bottle.

"Get that down 'ee, lad. Do yer good." He downed his own with one gulp and vanished up forward. By the time John's eyes had ceased to water from the effects of the raw spirit, he had returned towing a brassbound chest behind him.

"There's a lot'd like ter know what's in this 'ere chest," he said, "but they won't. Not till I'm dead an' gorn. Then us'll see what they think oí their ol' skipper then."

Just as suddenly, he trundled the chest back to its hiding place and, without a word, returned with two greasy blankets. One of these he tossed to John, rolled himself in the other and was instantly asleep. Not so John, who lay awake for a long time, uncomfortable in his cluttered surroundings and disturbed by the unaccustomed spirit that he had consumed. When he did fall into a fitful sleep, he dreamed of the skipper, complete with halo and wings, exhorting him to do something that he could not remember.

When he awoke next morning, the old man had gone, no doubt on his morning potter round the yard. And that was virtually the last that John had seen of him, for shortly afterwards he moved on to another yard and further landing craft.

"Grays! This is Grays! All stations to Fenchurch Street!" The porter's shout woke John from his reverie. While he had been remembering the past, he had boarded the train and had been conveyed, albeit slowly, up the line to the scene of the events that he had relived. On impulse he leapt from the train, spurred on by a vague feeling that he was needed. Inevitably, he found himself retracing the well-remembered route to Hewitt's yard.

John was not sure how he would gain access to the yard and the Scorpion, and was therefore pleased to see a light glowing through the fog from the yard foremanís office.

Inside he found the same foreman from his apprenticeship

days, Mike O'Reilly, known along the river as the Kilkenny foreman, for reasons that his brogue made obvious. Mike was a little balder, but otherwise seemed the same jovial despot that John remembered.

"Why hello, me bhoy," said Mike in greeting. "Indeed a strange night to come visiting."

John explained, briefly, about the skipper of the Scorpion, his box and his compulsion to revisit the yard.

"Sure, and didn't the old fella tell me the same yarn?" said Mike. "I thought it was a bit of ould blarney. But we'll take a look." He took a bunch of keys from his desk. "The old Scorpion's bin locked up for the first time in her life."

"The yard's a lot smaller now," he explained as they made their way round to the Scorpion's berth. "Most of our sailing barges are gone now, and the guv'nors are turning over to motor coasters. Shame I t'ink."

On board the Scorpion nothing had changed. The two men carefully picked their way over the deck-load of junk to the cabin hatch which O'Reilly unlocked with a key from his bunch. Once below the same blackened oil-lamps had to be lit to reveal the chaotic muddle of the interior.

"If I remember correctly his box is up forward somewhere," said John. A brief turnover of the rubbish in the fore-cabin revealed the brassbound chest under a heap of mouldering tarpaulins.

"It's not locked," John observed. "Here goes." He pushed the lid open. Surprisingly, it opened easily on well-oiled hinges. Both men bent over for a first sight of the contents.

"Well, oi'll go to the foot of our stairs," said Mike, the Cockney expression sounding strange in his brogue. He reached in and lifted aloft a glittering silver rosebowl. He read the inscription: "Seamanship Cup, 1915 Thames Barge Match."

"'Tis real silver, I t'ink. Worth a fair sum these days. Sure, an' the ould feller didn't win that, did he? No, we'd have heard. He must have pinched it."

John was looking into the chest again. "There's some letters in here. This one's pretty old." He took the yellowing document from its envelope.

"Listen to this," he said when he had finished reading it.

Dear Captain Graves,
May I convey the best wishes of my board and myself for your speedy recovery from your injuries. Since it was your actions alone that enabled our sailing barge Hyacinth to survive the violent weather that beset the recent Thames Barge Match, it is the unanimous wish of the Match Committee that the Seamanship Cup awarded for this feat should be presented to you in perpetuity. This view is heartily endorsed by both the barge's crew and my Board of Directors.

Furthermore, when you have recovered, a position awaits you in command of our river barge Scorpion.

Yours sincerely, James Hewitt, Chairman.

"The founder of the firm," said Mike, impressed. "What's in the other letter?"

"Well, it's not sealed," John replied, "and it's written on the back of an old fag packet, unsigned. 'Don't forget yer ole skipper an' yer sailin' barges.' The envelope is addressed to 'the guv'nors'."

Mike stared at the guttering oil-lamp. "Oi reckon they might not, for a while, anyway."

PANIC

Unusually the cruiser fleet was racing home from the River Medway. Normally racing was from home to a destination at some distance, but this time an eccentric Class Captain had suggested a race back.

This was not, originally, a popular move, since it was felt that after a probably energetic race on the Saturday, followed by the normal evening celebrations, a Sunday race home would be too taxing. However, when the Sunday dawned bright and sunny, with a light westerly wind, a number of helmsmen changed their minds, making face-saving remarks like: 'Well, we were going that way anyway.'

Curlew was the last boat to clear Garrison Point on the way out of the Medway. By this time the wind had dropped to virtually nothing so the owner decided to put George on the helm. This was a good idea since George could stand for hours at the helm in light weather, unlit pipe clenched between his teeth, concentrating on any indication of a breeze, however slight, and probably trying to forget his hangover from the previous evening ashore.

On this occasion the change of helm certainly paid off, for Curlew soon began to overhaul the other boats in the race. George, as usual, ignored all repartee including: 'Where are you getting your wind from?' as they gradually went past one boat after another.

The rest of the crew found other amusement, as there was not much to do in the sailing line. The owner pottered about the deck, tidying up the odd rope end here, oiling a block there and keeping a rough eye on the spinnaker, which occasionally lifted to a faint air. John decided to wash-up the breakfast things and placed the crockery to dry in the cockpit, which was empty, apart from George, as Rosemary was laid out sun-bathing on the cabin-top.

After a while, the Grain Spit buoy, which they had to round as a mark in the course, was near enough to be passed in the next half-hour. George, who had been sailing an inshore course, now began to angle over to the buoy, taking advantage of the ebb tide.

This gave him a gain on the other boats, which had to fight the ebb to make up to the buoy. Provided the tide did not change early and there was no change in wind direction, they were ideally placed to take the lead.

"I'll take her now," said the owner suddenly as he came aft.

Somewhat reluctantly George gave up the helm and settled back in the cockpit to light his pipe. This entailed much puffing and blowing. Unsatisfied, he produced a knife and scraped the pipe bowl thoroughly. This apparently was not the answer, for he disappeared below and emerged with a pipe cleaner. Not an easy task, for he had to clamber over John and the washing-up on both journeys.

He then cleared the stem of the pipe, gave a few experimental puffs on it, threw the pipe cleaner overboard and filled and lit the pipe with obvious satisfaction. He looked round, through clouds of noxious smoke to see how the race was going

Three changes had occurred. The owner, evidently mesmerised by the other boats, had changed their own course to match their rivals and was now heading upstream of the buoy. Telltale bubbles and scraps of seaweed were now drifting from east to west, indicating that the tide had turned, and was assisting to push the boat further upstream. Thirdly, and most importantly, a dark line was spreading rapidly across the estuary to the east, announcing that a smart breeze was about to come from that direction, again not in their favour and likely to reach the other yachts first.

"Wind's going round," yelled the owner and George in unison.

"Get the spinnaker down," added the owner.

George was already leaping to obey. But his path was directly over the washing-up laid out to dry by John. One large foot caught the rim of the frying pan and a shower of crockery descended to the cockpit floor. At the same time, the red-hot dottle flew out of George's pipe and set fire to the tea towel, which had been drying over the cabin doors. George, off balance, landed, as he had intended, on the cabin top, but also on top of Rosemary, who had dozed off while sunbathing.

By the time that George had extricated himself, the wind had arrived and, perversely, set the spinnaker aback round the crosstrees. Although George could normally have managed the spinnaker on his own, this entanglement changed a simple one-man task into one requiring two or more people. His shipmates were otherwise engaged – the owner struggled amidst spilt crockery to trim the other sails, John fought the fire in the cabin entrance, while Rosemary lay winded on the cabin top. Meanwhile the yacht drifted helplessly up-wind and up-tide, while her rivals rounded the buoy and set course for home and the end of the race.

Somehow George, at first on his own, and later with Rosemary's assistance, managed to disentangle and lower the errant sail. But it was too late, especially by the time they had beaten back against the wind to round the buoy. The other boats were all well away with a good lead and they were last again. George went below and spent the rest of the trip noisily making cups of tea in the cabin, which still smelt of burnt tea-towel.

TED – A TRIBUTE

Although I first started to sail with my cousin on a small non-descript dinghy that was his pride and joy, it was not until I joined the Old Town Sailing Club that I first experienced the joys and thrills of yacht racing.

The ideal was to be selected to crew on one of the club's One Designs, but despite considerable effort in helping the owners in tasks such as scrubbing marine growth off the bottoms of the boats at low tide, this was not always possible. But, failing this delight one could always crew for Ted.

And, in retrospect, us youngsters probably learnt more from Ted than anyone else. Critics would, no doubt, say we gained an insight into 'how not to do it', for if anyone was accident-prone it was Ted. Unfortunately he was handicapped with very poor eyesight and his time-keeping suffered from the fact that he lived in East London, with a lengthy journey by train to reach the club. But there was no denying his keenness, and every weekend he would appear to take up his lodging with an elderly widow and indulge, hopefully in plenty of sailing and beer drinking.

In those early days, Ted owned a ramshackle One Design, whose origins were the south coast, not the local Essex estuaries with their notoriously shallow waters.

This vessel had a fixed rudder that could not be adjusted and consequently added a good two feet to the boat's normal draught. Owing to Ted's often-late arrival for the start of a race and his determination to finish once he had started, he frequently ended up still racing a long time after high water with the fixed rudder finding every mud bank in the vicinity.

The early sailing days of many of the Club's Cadet members, myself included largely consisted of heaving his boat off the mud. Perhaps this was what was meant by how not to do it, but we certainly knew where the banks were after a few crewing sessions with Ted.

Another important factor in sailing with Ted was improvisation. All the boats he owned were run on a shoestring. He was by profession a self-employed printer and a very good one, providing, of course, that his customers would tolerate receiving their work, not in accordance with any timetable, but when Ted considered it to be as perfect as he could make it. Therefore shortage of funds meant that Ted's boats only received rudimentary fitting out and that a supply of odds and ends of rope, twine, bits of wire, etc. was kept in the after locker ready for emergency repairs, which were frequent.

Rarely were the correct materials available and a form of 'jury-rigging' always took place using whatever was to hand. Still, the pundits say that improvisation is the height of good seamanship and on this basis, us youngsters learnt a lot from Ted.

Slightly later on, when we came of drinking age, we realised Ted's considerable capacity for beer and, according to him, women. The first was no problem; it was there for all to see in the club's hallowed men-only bar, but the second was problematical.

Ted was not an imposing figure. His poor eyesight meant that he wore glasses – a particularly battered pair of the cheapest National Health ones. He also had false teeth, probably from the same source, which did not fit at all well. Since he was a pipe smoker, he had considerable difficulty manipulating both pipe and teeth.

On one notable occasion I visited a neighbouring yacht club

which had its headquarters on a former Trinity House light-ship. Ted was among those present and when my party came to leave, we were surprised to find a group of people fishing about for something in the mud alongside. We asked what was going on and were informed that Ted had been sick over the side and had lost his teeth overboard. We couldn't help wondering whether his pipe was still clamped between them.

None of this was calculated to make Ted attractive to women and neither was his style of dress. For sailing, and very often for social activities, this consisted of an extremely old shirt, shorts and knee-boots. To this ensemble would be added, according to conditions, a moth-eaten jersey, an ancient oilskin or a disreputable pair of corduroy trousers. It was not exactly an outfit likely to appeal to the fairer sex.

Nevertheless, if Ted was to be believed, when not sailing during the week, he lived with a succession of 'housekeepers' in East London. There were also rumours about his landlady in the Old Town.

After a few years Ted parted with the boat with the fixed rudder. Great things were expected of its replacement, a vessel with a lifting rudder, much more suitable for the shallows of the Thames Estuary. There was little improvement, however, for the new boat possessed a centre-plate of uncertain reliability. It was apt to descend without warning and resist all attempts to raise it. Alternatively it would refuse to budge from its raised position, thus preventing any sailing taking place at all and, if a race was involved, making Ted and crew late for the start. Crewing for Ted continued to be hard work.

By this time, however, I was in the fortunate position of being a boat owner myself and therefore observed these events from afar. A new breed of Club Cadets had taken over crewing for Ted. My involvement with Ted was by now mostly social and I began to appreciate his good-natured humour. Often the butt of alcohol-inspired pranks by the younger members of the club, he was never unduly upset, but would merely bide his time until he could inflict revenge on the perpetuators.

He certainly had an eye for the ladies and was a very good dancer. At club dances he was seldom off the floor, dancing with all the ladies in turn, be they wives, fiancèes or single.

Eventually Ted progressed from dinghy sailing into cruising. His ownership of a cabin cruiser was, unfortunately, short-lived. His newly acquired cabin cruiser, more suitable for the Norfolk Broads than the Thames Estuary, did not survive the first autumn gale. No doubt normal Ted 'improvisation' had been applied to the mooring arrangements for the vessel and these did not cope with such a strong wind. Ted's cruiser ended up in the open-air swimming pool, damaged beyond repair.

Undaunted, Ted gave up the idea of ownership and started crewing on cruisers. One of his former young crews had graduated to this type of sailing and was pleased to offer Ted a berth. Clive, Ted's new skipper, was competitive and they took part in most of the club's cruiser races with some success, on one occasion achieving something that had eluded Ted in his dinghy sailing days – a first place.

As usual it was in the social graces that Ted was a liability. On one occasion the race was to a rather prestigious yacht club where an evening meal could be obtained, provided one came ashore correctly dressed, i.e. blazer and flannels with tie. One crew decided to dine at the club and came ashore in the right attire. As they went to enter the club, they had to pass the club's changing rooms. Here they encountered Ted, clad in dirty singlet, shorts and knee-boots, scrubbing his false teeth under an exterior tap.

"Coming up a treat, ain't they?" he cried, holding the 'gnashers' aloft for all to see.

On another occasion, one Percy Gittens, a particularly unpopular member of our own club, had been invited to spend the weekend on a Thames barge moored up a remote creek on the River Medway. The Sunday morning was a pleasant one and Gittens was relaxing on the deck of the barge, savouring the aroma of eggs and bacon being cooked below for breakfast. Up the creek, on the high water came Clive's vessel, with Ted sitting on the foredeck. As they drew level with the barge Ted hailed Gittens: "Good session ashore last night, Percy! I spewed up. Bright yellow it was..."

Gittens did not want his breakfast after that. But such was his unpopularity that the rest of us suspected that this had been a deliberately put-up job by Ted and Clive.

Eventually Ted ran out of 'landladies' and started spending weekends with my family and myself. He invariably turned up with a copious supply of meat as a contribution towards meals and very often with presents for the children. His only other requirement apart from accommodation and meals was that I should accompany him on drunken forays to either the club or to a pub. Clive, in the meantime, had moved away and was keeping his boat elsewhere. Ted was now finding it hard to find crewing jobs within the club and his activities were largely social.

All this changed when Ted retired. He sold the printing business as a going concern, which was surprising given the antique equipment and the prevailing muddle. With the proceeds he bought a house near the club which he occupied with a young lady at least thirty years his junior. He had apparently met her in an East End pub. He was now able to regale those club members who were interested with tales of the 'hanky-panky' that went on at their abode. They lived there in splendid squalor until Ted suffered a severe stroke, which he only survived for a few days in hospital.

But Ted was not finished with us yet. About three weeks later I heard rumours that the hospital was a bit disturbed that it was still holding Ted's body in its morgue. I consulted Ted's somewhat scatty girlfriend only to find Clive on the same mission. We asked her whether Ted wished to be buried or cremated. Neither, she said, Ted had indicated to her that he wished to be buried at sea.

"You mean a coffin sliding over a ship's side?" I asked.

"Yes," she agreed, that was exactly what he meant. Clive looked at me.

"That's your department," he said. "You work for the Port Authority."

Not liking to point out that I was an accountant with little or no dealings with the marine side, I agreed to look into the problem. At work I made enquiries and was referred to a Senior Harbourmaster, who, I was told, knew about such things. He heard me out and then said: "Oh, yes. One of our launches can do that for you. But normally it's the RNLI that does it."

I was immediately suspicious.

"You're thinking of the scattering of ashes," I said, "what he wanted was actual burial at sea. You know coffin sliding from under an ensign, weighted with firebars and all that."

The Harbourmaster said he'd not come across this before but he was now intrigued and would find out what he could. After a couple of hours he rang me back. He told me that burial at sea actually came under the Ministry of Agriculture and Fisheries. He had spoken to them and they had explained that there were only certain areas where it could take place. The nearest one was off Lowestoft, many miles out at sea. I would have to charter a trawler from Lowestoft, transport the body and all mourners up there and then convey the lot to the burial area. This would, of course, be inordinately expensive.

I thanked him for his trouble, reported back to Clive and then we arranged a simple cremation to be followed, at a later date, by the scattering of the ashes on the sea in the area where Ted used to sail. We felt that Ted's wishes had been misinterpreted. The cremation went off without a hitch with a wake at Clive's home afterwards. But Ted still wasn't finished.

Some weeks later there was still no sign of the ash scattering being arranged, so Clive and I sprang into action again. We contacted the RNLI but, although their padre was available, they had no lifeboat available. We then contacted the local Sea Scouts, who were happy to oblige with their launch.

On the due date the mourners and launch crew gathered in a local pub prior to the ceremony. We boarded the launch from the wharf outside and set off for the buoy that marked the entrance to the Creek.

When we arrived there we felt the full weight of wind and sea, for it was a fairly windy day. It had already been decided that Ted's girlfriend should actually scatter the ashes after the Padre had said a few words. She did so all right, but over the windward side of the launch.

We all received a liberal helping of Ted in hair, eyes and mouths.

THE FILM STARS

Harry Norris, skipper of the London lighterage tug Vincent leant on the tug's steering wheel as he guided her towards the sunset. He was at peace with the world. It had been a good day, nothing had gone wrong and he hadn't had strong words with anyone. Now, after dropping six empty lighters at the basin entrance of the Royal Docks, he was headed home, which, on this occasion meant his firm's roads off Rotherhithe.

All was well with the tug and her crew. The mate, Alf, was yarning aft with a handful of lightermen who had begged a lift to Rotherhithe, which was near their homes. Dennis, the engineer, was probably singing as he watched over the powerful diesel engines, not that he could be heard over the roar of the machinery.

But Harry's peace was shattered when the radio next to him in the wheelhouse sprang to life. He recognised the distinctive voice of Arthur Crabb, the firm's Labour Master.

"Where are you, Harry?"

"About half-a-mile below the roads. Be there in a few minutes."

"Got any lightermen with you?"

"About half a dozen."

"Right. Guv'nor wants to see all of yer in the office. Tug crew and lightermen."

They're not going to like this, thought Harry; they want to get off home.

"What's it about?" he asked.

"Dunno. Special job o' some sort."

When the tug had moored up, Harry broke the bad news. There was much moaning, diluted by some speculation. Nevertheless, all concerned made their way to the office that consisted of two shops knocked together a few hundred yards from the foreshore adjacent to the roads. There, owing to lack of space, the men had to perch themselves where they could. Knowing the habits of management, they settled in for a long wait.

Out came the cigarettes and newspapers and even a pack of cards.

After about ten minutes the 'Guv'nor', Lavinia Talbot-Russell, strode out of her office to address them. With her tall angular frame and her accessories, a monocle and a long cigarette holder, she was an impressive figure. Although her husband owned the firm, she had, for many years, controlled its day to day running. Known to her own employees as 'Miss Lavinia' and to other users of the Thames as 'The Lady' or 'The Duchess' and several other, less repeatable nicknames, she knew all the answers and could be a deadly opponent if aroused. Now she addressed the group of employees distributed around the main office.

"You men," she said, "have been especially selected for an unusual task.'

Hardly the case thought Harry, the lightermen had just happened to scrounge a lift.

Lavinia continued: "The firm has been asked to provide a tug and lighters to assist in the making of a film." A murmur of anticipation went round the room. "Film people like early starts, therefore you will all report to the roads at 5a.m. tomorrow. Vincent will then acquire six empty lighters..." Harry thought with regret of the six he had left at the Royal Docks earlier. If he had known about this, he would have kept them, they weren't needed urgently. "...and report to the film company at Waterloo Bridge. You are at their disposal as long as

129

they need you. Normal rates of overtime will apply." She obviously considered the matter closed, for she turned on her heel and strode back into her office.

However there were mutterings among the men about 'unfair' and 'bloody early start.' Harry even heard the words 'union' and 'shop steward'. But he knew that, as usual these would come to nothing. And, anyway, it was not worth arguing with Miss Lavinia; you wouldn't win, in the end.

In the circumstances, Vincent's crew did not go straight home, but adjourned to a nearby pub to discuss the new development.

Alf, the mate, was highly excited.

"We're goin' ter be film stars", he said, "Everyone 'll see us at the flicks."

Harry was more cynical: "Tug an' lighters, mebbe, but not us. Crikey! The film company would 'ave been in touch if we'd got proper parts. We'd make a few bob that way."

In the end they decided that all would be revealed in the morning.

* * *

The next morning two of the lightermen failed to turn up. Harry had been expecting some thing of the sort and considered four lightermen to be more than enough for the little bit work involved, so he didn't wait for them and began collecting empty lighters. There were two available from the roads and he 'borrowed' the rest from wharves where the firm delivered cargo. He considered that he was only doing his normal job as he would probably been told to pick them up during a normal day's work anyway. With the required tow of six behind, Vincent set off for Waterloo Bridge.

When they arrived there was no sign of life. Not wishing to cause disruption to river traffic by dawdling in the middle of the river, Harry moored tug and lighters to a nearby tier and awaited developments

They were on their second mug of tea when Alf reported someone waving from the bridge.

"Let's hope it's for us," said Harry.

Leaving the lighters where they were, he took Vincent within hailing distance of the bridge.

"Is that our tug?" asked the long haired young man on the bridge. Harry replied that it was, if he was anything to do with the film.

"Yes. Assistant Director. Where's your barges?"

"Over there."

"OK. Can you pick them up and go up and down between this bridge and Westminster Bridge until we tell you to stop? We'll be filming from the shore."

"Film stars, my arse," Harry said graphically as he steered over to pick up the lighters.

"Still they might get some good shots of the tug and lighters," said the ever-hopeful Alf. "Might even be able to see ourselves."

They proceeded to Westminster Bridge. If there was any filming going on from the shore, they could detect no signs of it. At the bridge they turned around and went back to Waterloo Bridge. Again no evidence of film making.

"Better do it again," said Harry. "He's goin' to tell us when to stop."

Back they went to Westminster. And so it went on. After about an hour or so, Harry became heartily sick of the sight of the two bridges. More importantly, he felt he was becoming a menace to navigation. It was not easy to turn the tug with its tow of six barges, two abreast, in such confined waters and he was interfering with normal river traffic. Several of his fellow tugmasters had enquired what the hell was he doing and one motor barge had had to go full astern to avoid Vincent and her tow just by Waterloo Bridge. But there was no sign of any respite.

Alf came up to the bridge of the tug.

"Surely they've finished filming by now, skipper?" he said.

Harry shook his head. "Better do as we're told," he said, "Else we'll have Miss Lavinia to contend with, as well as the film people."

"Try radioing the office," suggested the mate.

Harry did so and raised the Labour Master who knew nothing. Harry asked to speak to Miss Lavinia but was told that she was in a business meeting. (Business lunch, more like, Harry thought cynically.) He did, however, speak to Lavinia's husband, who merely told him to obey instructions. So off they went to Westminster again.

They steamed up and down forever, or so it seemed to Harry. True, there had been a brief respite over high water, when traffic had eased off and he managed to snatch a cup of tea and a cheese sandwich, while Alf steered, but now the ebb had set in and the river was busy again. The strain was beginning to tell. The constant helm alterations and whistle signals to indicate Vincent's intentions were wearing him down, as were the frequent telegraph rings to the engine room when speed was changed. Harry felt that it must be almost as bad for his engineer, Dennis, having to make frequent throttle and gear changes and all the time subjected to the roar of the diesels. Normally on a long haul, say from one of the riverside wharves to Tilbury Docks, the engineer could come on deck for spells away from his engines. But this lark needed constant attention and Dennis must be feeling as worn out as himself. The four lightermen had a softer option but were making themselves useful as lookouts. However their continual demands for mugs of tea were keeping Alf busy in the tiny galley.

"I thought film companies did their filmin' early in the day," said the mate on one of his visits to the bridge.

"So did I," replied Harry ruefully. "Me arms are aching from pullin' that bloody siren lanyard."

"I'll do it for a while. They're drinkin' too much tea down there."

And so they continued Waterloo – Westminster – Waterloo and so on.

In the end Harry took an executive decision.

"Bugger this. It'll be dark soon. I'm packin' it in."

So they returned to their moorings, dropping the surplus lighters on the way.

Harry swore that this would be the first and last time he worked with a film company, a sentiment the others echoed.

* * *

A few days later Lavinia summoned Harry and told him that the filmmakers had apologised for not telling him that filming had finished. That had been about ten o'clock in the morning. Lavinia was annoyed as the episode had tied up a tug, six lighters and seven men for the whole day. But she made no mention of the monetary side of the day. Sensing that she was in a receptive mood, Harry obtained the name of the film from her. Despite the experiences of himself and his crew, there was still plenty of interest in the film not just from those immediately involved but from the whole of the firm's workforce and especially their wives and girlfriends. Indeed word had spread round the whole of the London lighterage industry. Attitudes varied from the 'film star' theory to 'Let's go an' see 'Arry makin' a fool of 'imself.'

The film was awaited with anticipation, although it was largely appreciated that it would be some time before it reached local cinemas.

In the meantime, Harry established from the firm's accounts clerk that Lavinia had been paid for a whole day's use of equipment and personnel anyway and that there had been a generous lump sum on top. He swore that he would find some way to get even with his employer. She had done very nicely out of the film company and only paid the employees involved the absolute minimum that she could get away with. She had not been available when he needed advice and had left no instructions with anyone else. He started to study film reviews in the papers, hoping to find something about 'his' film. He also had the germ of an idea and began to drop hints among important personages within the firm, such as the Labour Master and the shop steward.

Eventually the film was released. It was a romance and classified as a 'B' picture that meant that it would be subsidiary to some other film that was considered to be more important. The critic in Harry's paper gave it a very bad review. To make quite sure, Harry bought several other papers and, to his satisfaction, found that all the critics hated it. He was well aware that critics were sometimes proved wrong but this was all he had to go on.

With the film about to be distributed, it was time to activate his plan. He applied pressure to the shop steward who had several meetings with Miss Lavinia. Soon the film arrived at the nearest cinema. Enthusiasm had not abated for, as Harry had guessed, no one else had bothered to read the film reviews. To a man, Miss Lavinia's employees decided to attend the opening night with their partners. The great event was almost upon them when the shop steward announced that, after a long battle, Miss Lavinia had agreed to pay for the cinema trip, which was exactly what Harry wanted.

On the night the manager of the local cinema was extremely pleased with the audience. He had never known so many people turn out to watch such a mediocre programme. Not only were Miss Lavinia's employees and their partners there but many other rivermen as well. Discreetly tucked away at the back was Miss Lavinia herself, puffing away at her cigarette holder and accompanied by the firm's senior employees

The 'A' film, a rather obvious Western, was shown first. It was remarkable only for the amount of audience participation, with the cavalry being cheered as they rode to the rescue and the villain booed. Then, to the delight of the lightermen the latest 'Tom and Jerry' followed the news. And, finally, the 'B' picture that they had all come to see. The critics were right, it was awful. So bad that it didn't hold the audience. There was much fidgeting, and rustling of paper bags. At one point a wag cried out: 'Come on, get on with it!' And still no tug and lighters. But, suddenly, there was a love scene on a riverbank, obviously the Thames to those that knew it. And, for a few seconds, over the heroine's left shoulder a tiny Vincent and her tow of lighters could be seen for a few seconds. There were groans of disappointment. But Harry relaxed in his seat. At least there's one good thing, he thought, thanks to my efforts Lavinia's paying for this rubbish!

THE GOLD RUSH

The telegram from Geordie Smart merely read: 'Come at once. Good money to be made. M.v. Island Girl. Old Town, Essex.' But it was enough. Life with Geordie, I had found during our past in the Navy, was never dull and, given a reasonable slice of luck, could be profitable, if a trifle illegal.

Obviously, since a boat was mentioned, some kind of maritime adventure was intended and so, after packing some suitable clothing and other bits and pieces, I was soon at Fenchurch Street Station to entrain for the Old Town. There was nothing to detain me in London, just a few minor gambling debts that were probably best forgotten and a temporary liaison with a young lady who was busily trying to spend money that I did not possess. Geordie would make a refreshing change.

It was only when I alighted at the Old Town station that I realised that I had no idea where to find Geordie or the Island Girl that could be anything from a yacht to a small coaster. An enquiry at a nearby public house was not very helpful.

"Probably one oí they layabouts as is cashin' in on the white-weed," the landlord said. "They don't come in 'ere. I want to keep my licence."

Further up the High Street, a shop front proclaimed the legend: 'Barvis Brothers, White Weed Merchants'. It seemed likely that Geordie was involved with this 'white-weed' so, in hope, I tried the door, but it was locked. Heavy hammering from the rear of the building drew me through a wicket gate into a sizeable yard at the back. This space was a scrap dealer's paradise. Several discarded marine engines and other assorted metal junk occupied the centre of it, but it was the peculiar structures leaning on the surrounding fence that caught me eye. Roughly triangular in shape, they had a metal loop at their apex and a row of metal teeth along their base.

It was one of these objects that an obviously female figure was attacking with a sledgehammer.

"Can you tell me where I can find Geordie Smart, please?" I asked during a pause in the assault. The girl flicked a strand of blonde hair out of her eyes. She was not unattractive and had a good figure underneath her overalls.

"Don't mention that name around here," she said. I became slightly alarmed, as I had no wish to antagonise a girl armed with a sledgehammer.

"He worked for us for a while," she added, lowering her weapon to the ground, "but things didn't work out. Now he's keeping out of Roy Barvis' way." It sounded as if typical Geordie complications had arisen.

"That's a white weed rake," she went on, noticing my curious glance at her recent opponent, "And I'm Sue Morris, secretary, mechanic, shop assistant, accountant, office cleaner, cook and anything else you care to mention to the Barvis Brothers."

"Anything?" I speculated to myself. She wiped her hands on her not over clean overalls and offered me one. "You wouldn't be Geordie's new mate, would you?"

"It seems quite likely." I admitted.

"Island Girl is down at the wharf. Tell him to watch his step. If he keeps stirring up trouble, Roy Barvis'll have him."

"What trouble?" I asked, but she had disappeared into the building.

Still at least I now knew where to find Geordie. But I didn't have to, for as I went past the doors of the next pub, Geordie emerged, stern first.

"I'm right, I tell you," he bellowed at the remaining occupants of the bar. "They mean to take us all over."

"What are you up to, Geordie?" I asked quietly.

"Awa' man, Bill!" he exclaimed with obvious pleasure. "Glad ye could make it. Come an' have a beer. No, we won't go back in there, the atmosphere's hostile. I've got a bottle onboard."

After much probing and the best part of a bottle of scotch, I managed to get a more or less coherent story out of Geordie.

He had bought Island Girl, a sturdy local fishing vessel and joined the current boom of white weed fishing. This fern-like creature, for it was not a plant, was dragged from the sea bottom by rakes similar to those that I had seen in Barvis' yard. Geordie had, like many others, contracted to sell his catch to Barvis Brothers. However profits were better if the catch was sold to one of the smaller independent buyers. This, naturally, did not appeal to Barvis', who were now conducting a campaign to coerce the white weed fishermen to sell to them.

Things had become somewhat heated between the 'independent' men and Barvis' own employees who crewed the dozen or so boats that they owned outright. There had been a confrontation, no doubt fuelled by alcohol, during which Geordie's mate had sustained a broken arm. Geordie suspected that the fight had been engineered by the Barvis brothers and had immediately withdrawn as one of their suppliers. This action was purely nominal, as he couldn't fish without a crew anyway. He had merely sent for me and embarked on an anti-Barvis campaign around the local pubs.

"Tide's right tomorrow," Geordie said in conclusion, "an' the forecast's good. Fancy havin' a go?" I replied that I had nowhere to sleep.

"No problem. We sleep here," he gestured round Island Girl's foc'sle. The accommodation, although rudimentary, was no worse than others that we had shared in the past.

* * *

So the next day was my first experience of white weeding. We were away from the wharf at 6a.m. just before the ebb started running, Island Girl's diesel pushing us downstream at a steady seven knots. This made us faster than some of the boats that had left earlier and we were soon amongst them. I was surprised at the motley fleet. Some, like us, were local fishing vessels that had only substituted white weeding gear for the nets that would have normally caught shrimps or whitebait. Indeed Geordie told me that many of them were apt to revert to their original trades if trading conditions demanded it.

There were also many fishing vessels from further afield. There were Zulus and Fifies from Scotland that had probably started their careers under sail. There was a Rye beach boat that appeared very old indeed. And there were others less identifiable whose registrations gave away their ports of origin: Maldon, Colchester, Faversham and Rochester. All of these must have been redundant in their callings and, according to Geordie, bought up cheaply to harvest the white weed of the Thames Estuary.

There was also a third group. These were the non-fishing boats: converted yachts and motor cruisers, old lifeboats which had once hung in davits aboard liners and cargo ships and the beach boats that took trippers on sixpenny rides. Even an ex-RNLI lifeboat, almost unaltered and a wartime tank landing craft.

Geordie told me that many out of these three groups would not be going as far as us. His chosen trawling ground was the Ouse, which was quite a way out and only frequented by the bigger, faster boats. Sure enough, when we arrived there we had the area virtually to ourselves, although we were gradually joined by about a dozen other craft. The method of fishing was to trawl down with the tide and then dash back at full speed to fit in another run. At the end of each trawl the rakes would be hauled in with the aid of a lorry axle converted into a winch and balanced on the boat's quarters while the catch

139

was removed from the teeth along the bottom edge.

It was quite odd to watch the procession of boats trawling down slowly and then racing back in the opposite direction. But, suddenly, the pattern was disrupted. One of the former Scottish boats, running back for another trawl, veered towards a vessel coming the other way. The two just missed each other and we could hear the resulting invective over the water.

"What happened then?" I asked Geordie.

"Barvis boat intimidating the opposition," said Geordie. "Always at it. Goes on all the time. Been one or two collisions but nothing serious."

Soon after that, he decided it was time to head back to the Old Town. There was plenty to do on the way back. The catch had been put to one side as it accumulated. Now it had to be 'culled', which basically meant removing anything that was not white weed – crabs, starfish, bits of shell, other weeds and so forth. This was a long job and normally fell to the mate, but Geordie had discovered, by past experiment, that if he hung the starting handle on a certain spoke of the wheel Island Girl would virtually steer herself, so he was able to help me. This was just as well, as this being my first attempt, I was a bit slow.

This gave us time for conversation as we worked and I took the opportunity to ask about Sue Morris, the girl in Barvis' yard. Geordie thought for a moment before replying.

In the end he said: "She's a strange lass, that one. Don't know where she came from but she started out as crew on one of Barvis' boats. Didn't suit her, though. I guess the dirty ol' man that was skipper tried to get her down the cabin. Anyway she greases round the Barvis brothers an' gets that job in the yard. Funny though, she don't seem to like the brothers much." I told him that I had the same impression.

While we had been talking the pile of culled white weed had built up. Free of the rubbish from the seabed, it had assumed a golden tint. Gold, I thought, that was what this whole situation reminded me of a gold rush like the Yukon or the Klondike with men rushing to become rich, although in this instance they were afloat to do it.

Geordie gave me a nudge. "Won't be gold for long," he said falling in with my train of thought. "Mostly gets dyed green, then it's largely exported to the United States."

"But what's it used for?" I asked.

"Decoration mainly. Shop windows and so on. The Yanks are very keen on it at the moment. There's some big election or sommat goin' on out there."

He went back to the immediate future. "We'll likely sell this lot to old Abie if he can still take it. Pathetic old sod, he even wades out into the creek to catch the first boats in. Barvis is doin' him no good at all, so he'll probably be glad to see us." He surveyed the now nearly complete piles of weed. "There's a lot here. Should get a tidy old sum for it."

And we did. By the time I had added, on Geordie's instructions, a quantity of sea water to each sack of weed to 'help the weight along' we achieved ninety-four pounds of weed at ten shillings a pound. Forty-seven pounds for one day's work in 1953! My share was twelve pounds, more money than I had ever earned in one day!

As we walked away from Abie's van, after catch and money had changed hands, Geordie said: "Don't look now but we're bein' watched." But I couldn't resist a glance. A Rolls Royce was parked among the dealers' vans on the wharf. Its occupant was watching us walk back to the boat.

"Alfred Barvis," Geordie muttered. "Always down here at tide time, watching what goes on. Harmless, though, it's his brother Roy you've got to watch out for. Him and that so-called Chief Skipper of his. It's them what causes the trouble."

* * *

Geordie had, just like when we were in the Navy, exhorted me not to spend it all at once . Not a policy that he ever observed himself. So, that night we were out on the town in the pub that he had been in the previous day. This was the acknowledged haunt of the white weeding crews, at least those of them that were intent on spending their earnings rapidly. Unusually for a waterside inn, this establishment was known as the Fox and Hounds. Perhaps, in days gone by, a hunt did meet there, but now it was definitely maritime in its outlook. The clientele, at least in the public bar, were almost entirely white weeders, with a sprinkling of other watermen. I noticed that they were split into two main groups and, correctly, worked this out to be Barvis employees and the rest.

Geordie introduced to some of his cronies. There was Ron Glaze, an ex-Army officer, Heidi, a strapping blonde Amazon and her boyfriend Angus, who had been a deep-sea diver. There was also Nobby, a little wizened man who ran an engineering business in addition to operating one of the largest weeding boats, the former excursion vessel, Estuary Queen.

"Good lad, Nobby," Geordie told me while the little man was away at the bar. "Does all our engineerin' work. Dunno how he finds the time to run his own boat. That's right Nobby lad?" The engineer was resuming his seat.

"Aye," said Nobby evidently a man of few words.

"See the man himself is here," said Angus, "with his cronies."

Heidi thought I was due an explanation: "See the tall man with the hook nose? That's Roy Barvis. The small man next to him with very few teeth is his so-called Chief Skipper, Frank Marks. Now he's bad trouble, not long out of prison. Robbery with violence, I heard. One of his fellow jailbirds is his mate, Rollo. He's the brains because Marks hasn't got any. Rollo's subtler than Marks, more of con man, I would say. But he's not here tonight, which is odd."

"And here's Barvis' tart," said Angus. Sue Morris had appeared from the back of the pub. I was amazed at the change in her. She was wearing a dress that showed off her sun-tanned arms and shoulders and she had let her blonde hair loose so that it hung to her shoulders. She certainly didn't look like a tart.

"Now that's unfair," Geordie was saying. "She just works for them."

"No smoke without fire," Angus persisted.

"Why don't you ask her?" said Heidi, "she's coming over."

She stopped at our table. "Hello there," she said, smiling at me. "You found him all right, then?" I explained that I had indeed and that I was Geordie's new mate with one white weeding voyage to my credit.

"How are you getting on with Barvis'?" asked Angus pointedly.

"Hard work," said Sue enigmatically and walked back the way she had come. I wasn't sure whether she said something as she went past Roy Barvis' group but Barvis, Marks and a couple of others picked up their drinks and came over.

Roy Barvis stared at me. "You're new," he said. "A word of advice. It doesn't pay to talk to this crowd or Miss Morris, either. Not unless you work for me, which I hope you will, when you've learnt the error of your ways."

This sounded distinctly like a threat to me. But Geordie intervened.

"Give the lad a chance," he said. "He's only just got here. Crewed for me on one trip."

"And that's another mistake, crewing for a has-been like you." Geordie tried to get to his feet but Heidi placed a restraining hand on his arm.

"And where's your mate Rollo, tonight?" Glaze said to Marks, conversationally.

"Important bus'ness," said Marks. His teeth certainly were bad. Barvis gave his Chief Skipper a sharp glance, as though he had said too much.

"Make the most of it," he said and he and his retinue moved on.

"What's he mean, 'has-been'?" Geordie fumed.

"Take no notice," Heidi advised. "They're only trying to rile you. If you took a swing at one of them it would be just what

143

they want.

This struck me as good advice and I said so. But I, personally, wondered what little Miss Morris was up to.

* * *

There was no further confrontation that night, or any further sign of Sue Morris. We had a good drink and, nevertheless were away early next morning to take advantage of the prevailing good weather. Our catch wasn't as quite as big as that of the previous day, but still a good one.

As we headed home, Geordie said: "Funny, we haven't seen Nobby or Ron Glaze today."

"Probably working somewhere else," I suggested.

"Yeah. That's likely it."

But when we reached the wharf both Estuary Queen and Glaze's vessel were aground alongside it.

"They've not been anywhere today" Geordie commented.

We sold our catch to Abie, who seemed even more nervous than usual and, once again, were observed by Alfred Barvis. Nobby appeared on the deck of Estuary Queen. From his appearance he had been working on her engine.

"What's up?" asked Geordie.

"Sugar in petrol tank," replied the little engineer. "Same as Ron an' a couple o' others. Reckon that's what that bastard Rollo was up to last night."

"Can you fix it?"

"Be a long job. Others to do as well."

We went back aboard and had a cup of tea. Geordie was obviously fuming.

"He's really steppin' it up, that Roy Barvis," he said to me. "Near collisions, tryin' to pick fights, now this. An' I wouldn't mind bettin' he's frightenin' poor old Abie. Did you see the state he was in?"

"Still we didn't get the sugar."

"No. But we were the furthest boat. Reckon Rollo ran out

before he got to us. Barvis'll have something else in mind for us. Or rather brother Alfred will. I'm sure he's the one that calls the shots. He's the real brains. And a businessman, only interested in what money they can make." He lapsed into thought for a while and then said: "We've got to have some answers, then we'll know what to do about it. That girl, Sue, she must know more than most. She works for them. We'll have to get hold of her and ask her a few questions."

"So you're proposing the easy way out. Scare the information out of a girl. Why not Rollo? Or Marks? Why not take it all to the police?"

"Police would be a waste of time. We've nothing concrete to go on. What the coppers would like is an excuse to put the lot of us inside. They reckon we're all bad 'uns."

"And I'm not talking about scarin' anyone, that's Barvis' department. No, that's where you come in."

"What do you mean?" I asked in some alarm.

"I reckon she's got a soft spot for you. Ask her out, see what you can worm out of her."

I made to pour myself another mug of tea.

"Now," said Geordie, "before something else happens. You should still be able to catch her before she leaves the yard."

* * *

Somewhat resentfully I made my way to the Barvis establishment. Why didn't Geordie do his own dirty work? I thought. I found the prospect of making a date with a girl I had only spoken to twice highly embarrassing, let alone trying to squeeze information out of her. She might not know anything of value anyway. But I need not have worried.

Sue was just leaving the yard, wheeling a bicycle. She looked very upset about something, almost on the verge of tears.

"Hello," I said. "What's the matter?"

"I've just been sacked," she said in a small voice.

145

"Why?"

"I think Roy Barvis has worked out what I'm up to. Look, I'm going for a swim. That always cheers me up. Why don't you come with me?"

"No swimming costume."

It was a brilliant late afternoon and I was wearing shorts.

"They'll do," she said, "They'll soon dry off in this sun and I'll tell you more while they dry."

An offer not to be refused. We went to a beach some distance from the Old Town as Sue evidently felt the need for privacy, her wheeling her bicycle and me walking alongside. She avoided the subject of her dismissal and we talked about the white weeding industry in general.

She had a swimming costume on under her clothes and we were soon ready for the water. I was pleased to note that she had a very good figure. She was also an extremely good swimmer, far better than I was. By the time we came out of the water, I was pleased to lay back on the sand and dry off. She settled beside me and then I broached the subject: "Now what's this all about?"

"Roy Barvis killed my husband," she said bluntly, her eyes filling with tears.

Now this was a surprise. I had guessed her age as twenty-three or four and in the absence of any rings assumed her to be unmarried.

But then the whole story came gushing out. She had married very young to a man quite a bit older than herself who was an officer in the Merchant Navy. In order to be near his young bride, he had come ashore and taken command of a small salvage tug based in Cornwall and they had settled there. Although Sue never met him, Roy Barvis had been in the area, searching for alleged treasure from a Spanish galleon.

Somehow Sue's husband and his tug had become involved in this enterprise. Sue did not tell me the details, but Barvis had ordered the tug to sea in the face of very bad weather. The tug had gone down and although the rest of the crew had been saved, Sue's husband had been lost. She had been too upset to attend the inquest where a verdict of 'misadventure' had been returned.

Two years later she had discovered that Barvis was involved in the white weeding business in Essex, so she followed him there in the hopes of achieving some form of retribution. The job at Barvis' yard had cropped up and she had obtained it, hoping that she might have access to something that might bring about his downfall. But she hadn't found out much, although she had overheard discussions about a monopoly of the trade. Barvis certainly meant to have all the local boats under his thrall, with the exception of the original fishermen who he knew would merely revert to fishing and shrimping if threatened.

I asked how she came to be sacked. She wasn't sure but assumed that she hadn't covered her tracks properly and had left some papers disturbed or something like that. This had indicated to Barvis that she was spying on him and he had dismissed her on the spot.

"What are you going to do now?" I asked.

"Oh, I'll stay around. Things are hotting up nicely..."

She suddenly pulled me to her, wrapped her arms around my neck and planted her lips on mine. The clinch lasted for a couple of minutes.

"What was that for?" I asked when I finally came up for air.

"Marks, walking along the seafront. I didn't want him to see us together, so I made us look like any old courting couple. But you enjoyed it didn't you?"

I certainly had. With us only wearing bathing clothes I had felt her breasts pressing into my chest and my loins had stirred as a result.

"We'll have to do it again sometime," I said.

"I hope so," she said quietly and then carried on, "Before we were so rudely interrupted, I was telling you that I would stay around. There's a barmaid's job going at the Fox and Hounds, so I'm going to try for that."

I walked her back to her lodgings. In the circumstances we held hands, as best we could, while she wheeled her bicycle with her free hand. When we arrived there she said: "Why don't you come in? Have a coffee? Finish what we started on the beach?"

This struck me as an admirable suggestion, so I went in, but we didn't bother with the coffee.

* * *

Nothing much happened for a fortnight. Geordie and I had several good days weeding and I saw as much of Sue as I could. It was difficult as she was now working as a barmaid at the Fox and Hounds, while I was afloat a lot of the time.

After a week, rather to Geordie's dismay, I moved in with her. Then one day Abie disappeared, as did several of the other small buyers. Many boats, deprived of any other reasonable outlet, sold to Barvis', but Geordie, Angus and some others stuck with the remaining independents, albeit at a lower price.

About this time there was a day when the wind suddenly freshened as we were about to leave the wharf. Geordie changed his mind about putting out, so we had several cups of coffee in a local cafè and only then did I return to the lodgings. Sue was just leaving, smartly dressed in white blouse, black skirt, stockings and high heels.

"Where are you off to, all dressed up?" I asked.

"Just reporting to headquarters," she answered.

"What headquarters?"

"Never you mind." She had gone a bit pink, but I let it go, for the moment, since she was obviously in a hurry. A strange thing to say, I thought, as I made myself a cup of tea and odd, too, was her apparent ability to obtain any job that was on offer. I wouldn't have thought the Fox and Hounds, was a good place for her with almost daily contact with Barvis and his cronies. Still she seemed quite capable of parrying any snide remarks made at the bar. When she returned, she claimed to have been to the dentist and, love being blind, I accepted this.

Then came shocking news. Abie had been found drowned off the Pier. It was suicide for there were witnesses who had seen him jump. The word was that white weeding had been the last in a series of disastrous business ventures for him and, faced by imminent bankruptcy, he had taken his own life.

"Poor old lad," said Geordie, "Never did anyone any harm. I reckon Barvis is partly to blame. Time we did something about him."

But he wasn't to get the chance.

* * *

It was about midnight when Sue and I heard the bells and sirens of the emergency vehicles. Sue, still naked, went to the window and tweaked the curtain aside.

"That last one was a fire engine," she said, iheading for the waterfront. We'd better go and see what's happened."

"Put some clothes on first," I chided her. We hastily dressed and ran down to the Old Town. By the time we arrived the police had the wharf area sealed off. Firemen were dousing the flames on a converted ship's lifeboat called the Seagull and ambulance men were loading a stretcher into an ambulance.

The Seagull was one of the smaller weeding vessels crewed by a young lad called Paul, who was a bit strange to say the least of it. Sometimes Paul slept aboard Seagull and sometimes he didn't. No one knew where he went then.

Ahead of us in the crowd watching the conflagration was Nobby. Sue asked him what had happened.

"Dunno. She just suddenly took fire, they reckon. Paul was asleep down below but Geordie got him out. They're both hospital jobs though."

The ambulance went past, it's bell ringing.

"Can you take us to the hospital?" Sue asked Nobby, who

149

had a van.

"Sure," said the little man, "I was thinking of going meself."

* * *

At the hospital we had a long wait before we could see Geordie. He was sitting up in bed and quite perky under the circumstances. Most of his burns were to his hands and arms, but he was also suffering from smoke inhalation. Paul apparently was a lot worse but expected to survive.

"That's me out of weeding for a while," said Geordie.

"Don't worry about it," I consoled him.

"But listen, flower, that was arson. I know a petrol fire all right. Did enough fire fighting in the Navy. Barvis again."

He paused to get his breath.

"Don't tire yourself," said Sue.

"No, lass. I got to tell you this. Don't give in to them, they'll come unstuck in the end. Just keep Island Girl runnin'." Sue and I exchanged glances. We weren't sure whether he was talking to both of us or just me. At that point a nurse chased us away, saying that Geordie needed rest.

* * *

"What happens now?" Sue asked after Nobby had dropped us.

"We get some sleep. Then, tomorrow, I move back aboard Island Girl."

"So do I," said Sue. "You'll need a mate and I've done it before."

"You'll stay out of it. Things are getting dangerous and there's your job at the Fox and Hounds."

"I've been in this longer than you and I can work round my shifts at the pub. Anyway you won't get back inside my flat if

I don't come." She dangled her keys in front of me provocatively.

* * *

And so it was arranged. Another period of quiet arrived. Sue and I went weeding in Island Girl when we could in between her duties at the pub. We didn't do that well since we didn't make such a good team as Geordie and myself. Moreover the price paid for weed had fallen quite drastically. This had the effect of driving most of the traditional boats back to their original trades and the market adjusted itself, although not entirely back to it's previously high level.

The police and fire brigade couldn't make their minds up about the fire. It seemed like arson but there was no positive proof. True, an opened petrol can had been found, but such carelessness was quite common aboard fishing boats. Paul was known to be a heavy smoker and not averse to smoking in bed. Nevertheless, the fire seemed to have deterred Barvis and company from further mischief. That was until the night of Angus' birthday.

Sue and I had adopted a policy of not leaving Island Girl unattended for very long. At least one of us was usually aboard, in case of further trouble. But when Angus asked us to have a drink with him on his birthday, we decided that we would go but not stay too long. Sue was not on duty as a barmaid and an additional attraction was that Geordie, now partially recovered from his burns, would be there.

It turned out to be a jolly evening. Geordie was on good form, although fretting about having to stay in shore lodgings. He hoped it would not be long before he resumed weeding. The usual crowd – Heidi, Nobby, Glaze and, of course Angus were all there. For once there was no sign of the Barvis faction. However, because of our resolution about Island Girl and also as we had other activities in mind, Sue and I left well before closing time and returned to the boat.

All was quiet until about midnight, when there was a hammering on the cabin doors.

Sue rolled off me reluctantly and, after wrapping a sheet around myself, I opened the doors to see what was going on. It was Nobby, slightly the worse for drink.

"Come an' see what we caught!" he bawled, his eyes bulging at the sight of Sue's nudity. Whatever it was, the little man was highly excited so, quickly donning a few clothes; we followed him to Angus' vessel. There was a strong smell of petrol about the boat and an interesting tableau in the cockpit – Angus and Heidi were guarding a scared looking Rollo.

"It seems that we were next in line for a fire," said Angus, kicking an empty petrol can away. "Good job we invited Nobby back for a night-cap. We caught this bastard red handed."

"We thought you might like to ask him some questions," said Heidi.

"We certainly would," said Sue and then addressed Rollo. "Who told you to do this?"

Rollo kept silent.

"Come on. Answer."

Still silence.

"Let me try," said Heidi. She took a step backwards and landed a kick in Rollo's crotch. He screamed in agony.

"That's for trying to kill my friends. Now answer." Very faintly Rollo said: "Barvis."

"Good. Now we're getting somewhere," She lowered her voice, thrust her face close to Rollo's and stroked the area she had just kicked. Rollo winced and moaned as she said: "Don't forget I know a lot more tricks, particularly for these parts. Very painful, they can be."

"Keep her off me!" Rollo shouted.

"I think," said Sue, "that he ought to write a full confession and sign it. If he doesn't want to do it, the rest of us can always withdraw and leave him alone with Heidi."

"No! I'll do it!" screamed the unfortunate Rollo.

152

Angus produced paper and pen from somewhere about the boat and Rollo scribbled for fully five minutes. When had finished, he signed at the bottom. Sue took the statement from him and read through it.

"Very good," she said. "Now I suggest you leave town, if only for your own safety, as soon as possible." Rollo left immediately, with a backward glance at Heidi. Sue handed round the statement for the rest of us to read.

"What do we do with it?" asked Heidi.

"I'll take charge of it, for the moment." said Sue. I must have looked worried for she added: "Don't worry I've got a good hiding place for it."

But I was worrying about more than that. Sue now seemed to have taken charge of the situation and that, added to the headquarters incident, was making me wonder whether she hadn't been honest with me and was hiding yet another secret.

* * *

"Why did you take that confession?" I demanded yet again. "It'll only put us more at risk. If Barvis finds out we've got it, he'll come looking for it and he won't ask nicely."

"I told you it's well hidden. I'm not even telling you where."

We were approaching the wharf after the next day's trip and having what seemed to me very much like our first row.

"I don't know why you want it," I went on.

"I can't tell you that."

There was no reasoning with her and, once we had moored up, I went ashore to sell the catch. As usual Alfred Barvis was watching. But this time, as I walked back, he swung open the passenger door of his car.

"Mr Read, isn't it?" he asked. "Get in." I hesitated.

"I assure you that you will come to no harm," he said. Curiously, I believed him and climbed in. As soon as I had done so, he drove off at speed.

"We need to talk," he continued, "and I want you to do something for me."

"What's that?" I enquired.

"Just repeat what I am about to tell you to your colleagues on the boats. That's all."

He paused for a while as if marshalling his thoughts and then went on.

"As you probably know my brother looks after the operational side of Barvis Brothers while I control the financial side. That is one of my many commercial interests, most of which are far from this place. For some time now I have become increasingly worried about my brother's methods, especially the strong-arm tactics he is using to expand our scope. I abhor violence and consider that it has no part in a business venture. Far better to use stealth and financial manipulation to achieve one's ends."

Is he genuine? I was thinking. For a businessman he seemed to spend an inordinate time just watching what went on. But he continued:

"Therefore I intend to withdraw my support from my brother and concentrate on my other, more profitable interests. Do I make myself clear?"

I agreed that he did indeed. But he still hadn't finished.

"However, I have no intention of interfering in the present dispute. I have my own reputation to think of. You and your young lady and friends must settle your differences with my brother and his employees as best you can."

Nothing's changed, I thought glumly.

"Furthermore there are other considerations. As you must have heard, much of the white weed harvest goes to the USA, after treatment and dyeing. The Americans are very fussy people and they have recently received a batch of the weed which had been badly treated and shed its dye during handling. They were not pleased about this and orders from America are drying up as a result."

"I cannot see that there is sufficient demand from this country or the near continent to support the industry at its present level. That is another reason why I am withdrawing my support. My advice to any young man involved in the white weed trade would be to make the most of it while you can and bear in mind that there may not be a living in it in, say, a year's time."

We were headed back towards the wharf. I digested what Alfred had told me. I felt that it had the ring of truth about it. The white weed trade, like much fishing, must, by its nature be transitional. His advice was good, I would think about other employment, but not until this affair was finished.

"You're clear about what I said?" he asked as we arrived back at our starting point.

I said that I was and that I would pass it on. He let me out of the car and drove away. I stood on the wharf and looked around. To my horror Island Girl, and Sue, had gone.

* * *

For a moment I panicked. Then reason took over. There was no sign of Angus, Heidi or Nobby but I asked round the idlers on the wharf and found that Island Girl had been seen heading upstream and it was thought that Roy Barvis was aboard. Upstream lay the marshes and a ramshackle boatyard, largely constructed out of old Thames lighters. A good hiding place. But what did Barvis want with Island Girl?

Of course! Rollo must have told him that we held his confession and assumed that it was hidden on Island Girl and that if he couldn't find it himself he could prise it out of Sue. What better place for such activities than the marshes and especially the boatyard? No doubt he expected me to come after him, which would give him another source of information. But what the hell? I was going to rescue Sue.

Her bicycle was where she left it on the wharf and was fortunately unlocked. I mounted it and set off for the sea wall that led to the boatyard at my best speed.

As I went along the High Street, I met Geordie coming the other way. I stopped and gave him a brief summary of the situation.

"Get some help!" I shouted as I pedalled away. He had offered to come with me, but he had no bicycle and probably would not be much help with his hands still bandaged.

As I approached the marshes my mind was working overtime. Alfred, I thought, must have been genuine. He was getting out. And I didn't think he had been a decoy, otherwise why let me go? His brother's seizure of Island Girl must have been on the spur of the moment. Grabbing Sue as well was a bonus.

I reached the sea wall. Here the surface was uneven and difficult for a bicycle. I cursed, for I should have taken a different route that would have connected with the track that led to the boatyard. But I could now see Island Girl, moored to the end lighter of the boatyard. And if I could see them, they could see me, so I promptly abandoned the sea wall and took to the field behind it. I had to abandon the bike for there was no way that I could cycle through the long grass. I ran until I was abreast the path that led over the saltings to the yard and then risked a peek over the sea wall.

Island Girl was about one hundred yards away. So far as I could see Barvis and whoever was with him were concentrating on throwing everything out of the cabin.

Sue was aft, apparently lashed to the white weeding rakes that were stowed over the engine room hatch. I surveyed the terrain between Island Girl and me. The direct route would be over very soft mud and leave me extremely exposed. No, the only possible approach was along the path to the boatyard and over the lighters, which would still mean that I could be spotted from the boat, but there was some cover from a number of vessels moored either side of the path. It was beginning to get dark, which would also help. I'd better go now while the men were not on deck.

Darting from boat to boat, I made it along the path to the

foot of the gangway on to the first lighter. Now I could not be seen from Island Girl and, in fact, could not be until I was right on top of her, the bulk of her neighbouring lighter would screen me. But I must be careful on the lighters. There were probably all sorts of junk on them that could be dislodged and cause a noise and I certainly did not wish to lose my footing and end up in the mud. Fortunately there was no one else about; Barvis had almost certainly persuaded the yard's owner to make himself scarce.

Very carefully, I negotiated the three lighters between me and Island Girl, bent double and watching where I put my feet. At the last one I slid behind a pile of old tarpaulins to await my chance to board Island Girl.

After a few moments, I cautiously raised my head so that I could look down on the boat. Barvis and Marks had just come on deck and, fortunately were standing with their backs to me, looking at Sue. I ducked down again.

"So you're not going to tell us where this confession is?" Barvis asked her.

Sue said something very rude.

"Well, we can't find it," Barvis went on. "So I guess it's either on you or on your boy-friend, who should be joining us shortly." Sooner than you realise, I thought.

"Strip her," Barvis commanded Marks. There was a pause, then the sound of ripping fabric. I risked another look. Marks had untied Sue and torn her shirt off and was searching the remains. Barvis was watching still with his back towards me. Now! I thought and leapt down on Barvis, knocking him to the deck. He tried to struggle up, but I banged his head on the hatch coaming and he went still. But Marks had grabbed Sue and was holding her in front of him like a shield. He produced an evil-looking knife.

"Back off or she gets it!" he snarled. Blue flashing lights had appeared opposite the path to the yard.

"Give up, Marks," I said, holding out my hand for the knife. Then I was violently seized from behind. Barvis had not been out for long.

"Finish him!" he shouted at Marks. The skipper hesitated and that was Sue's chance.

In a trice Sue had him face down on the deck and was kneeling on his back, twisting his arm behind him. The knife had spun over the side into the surrounding mud. I drove my elbow into Barvis' midriff and he went down again.

Suddenly the boat was full of police. One of them, an inspector, went over to Sue who stood up, leaving Marks to two constables.

"Well done, constable," the inspector said to Sue. "But for God's sake put some clothes on, you'll get my men excited."

I followed her into the cabin where she was searching for a fresh shirt among the debris.

"He called you constable," I said. "You're not..."

"Detective Constable Sue Morris at your service, sir," she interrupted, giving me a mock salute.

"You lied to me ..." I began.

"No, I didn't. It was all true. About Cornwall and that. I just didn't mention that I was a policewoman down there. Then I wangled a transfer to Essex and, by a remarkable coincidence, I hadn't been here long when they were looking for someone to go undercover in the white weed trade. I think they were more interested in Alfred Barvis not Roy. But never mind we'll soon catch up with him now. So there you are, all true."

"But we were living together. We had sex, many times."

Her demeanour changed. "Even policewomen fall in love." After that neither spoke for a while, we were too busy.

When I came up for air, I said: "And where was the confession?"

She smiled. "Barvis came very close. It was taped to a certain part of the female anatomy..."

"Say no more," I interrupted her.

* * *

Sometime later Geordie suggested that Sue and I take Island

158

Girl away for a weekend before he returned to white weeding. This, I thought, was a good idea; we needed to get away for a while.

They were all there to see us off – Geordie, Heidi, Angus, Nobby, Ron Glaze and many others. I hoped for their sakes that Alfred Barvis was wrong about the decline of the white weed industry. We gave them all a good wave as we headed off down the creek.

When the Old Town had become a blur on the horizon, Sue announced that she was going below to change. I stayed at the wheel, musing on recent events. Rollo's confession had been enough to indict the Barvis gang. He had said a lot more once the police had caught up with him. Enough for Alfred to be arrested.

Sue reappeared in the cabin doors. She was wearing a policewoman's cap at a jaunty angle, our engagement ring and nothing else. I put the engine into neutral, hung the starting handle on the right spoke of the steering wheel and went to join her.

TROUBLE IN DOCK

The third lock of the day into the West India Docks comprised one Dutch motor coaster, two tugs, fourteen lighters and two sailing barges – Jessie May from Upshore in Essex and Avocet from Otterham in Kent.

Once the lock waters had risen sufficiently, the mate of Avocet scrambled ashore and walked down the lockside to chat to his opposite number on Jessie May. He was a sociable lad and always keen to gossip with other river users.

"Nice day," he remarked, "better than that rubbish we had coming up river last night."

Freddie Hemmings, the mate of the other barge agreed, it had, indeed, been a bad trip. He looked aft to his skipper for confirmation, but the old man made no response, apparently immersed in coiling a rope.

Avocet's mate asked the usual question, common whenever two sailing barges met: "Where you for?"

Freddie gave him the name of the ship that Jessie May was due to load from.

"Why, we're for 'er as well," replied the other lad, just as his skipper bawled for him to return aboard.

"What you want ter talk ter 'im for?" Freddie's skipper, Josh Oates demanded. Freddie was new to Jessie May but had already decided that Josh was a nice old boy, who really knew his trade, although he did hold some odd opinions. Perhaps this was going to be another one.

"He seemed a nice lad," he replied.

"Ah! But 'e's a Kentishman, see. Don't do ter be matey with them."

So it was another of his skipper's quirks. Freddie already disliked it, but wanted to know more.

"Why not?" he asked.

"'Cos they'll do yer down, any chance they get. There's a sayin' in Essex – 'Never give way to a Kentishman 'cos 'e'll never give way to you.'"

That so far as Josh was concerned was final and he stumped off to take the wheel as they were towed out of the lock.

Freddie, still smarting over his rebuff, would have been interested to learn that a similar conversation had just taken place aboard Avocet between skipper and mate, but this time with Essexmen cast in the role of villains.

When they arrived at the ship that they were due to load from, Josh discovered that there was little hope of their cargo being available for a while. Therefore he decided to lie alongside the vacant stretch of quay forward of the ship. To his annoyance, Avocet had decided to do the same, as had the Dutch coaster that they had locked in with.

"Ain't lyin' alongside no Kentishman," he said to Freddie. "We'll go astern of 'im."

There was just room for Jessie May to squeeze in between the ship and Avocet.

After this activity, Josh and Freddie retired below for a cup of tea.

*　*　*

Two mugs later they returned to the deck to complete some odd jobs. But, before they were properly started, Josh spied a figure on a bicycle approaching.

"Oh Gawd! It's 'Itler," he muttered to Freddie.

"Who's 'Itler?" asked Freddie.

"Well, one's a nasty little bloke what's stirrin' the Germans up, but this one thinks 'e runs this dock. Transport Foreman, 'e is. S'posed ter go round the dock visitin' ships, makin' sure their paperwork's orlright an' that. But 'e interferes with every bloody thing an' all us skippers knows 'e's on the fiddle."

'Itler' had dismounted from his bicycle and now addressed them: "You can't moor here."

"An' why not?" Josh wanted to know.

"Too close to the ship. Move alongside the other barge."

And, for the moment this was his final word. He mounted the bike and cycled imperiously away.

"I'm not goin' alongside no Kentishman," Josh grumbled. "Bloody 'Itler. 'Appen I'd given iim a pound note 'e wouldn't 'ave said nuffin. Not as if 'e said anythink to that pesky Kentishman, either. We stays 'ere."

Freddie felt the need for information. He asked Josh what had caused the enmity towards the barge crews of Kent. The skipper proved to be quite well versed on the subject and told him that it went back a fair way.

With the prevailing wind coming from the south-west the north coast of Kent was a weather shore while the south coast of Essex was a lee shore, always more difficult to sail along, as the wind tended to push boats onto the shore. Therefore the Essex men always considered themselves better sailors than their Kentish counterparts. Moreover, in recent years, it had been the Essexmen who had made the longer voyages in barges, often down to the West Country or across the Channel. Freddie did not think much of this latter reason, for he was aware that there were several Kentish owners that also sent their barges on long voyages.

He was mulling the subject over when there came a hail from ashore.

"Gawd. It's that 'Itler agen," Josh moaned as they made for the companionway.

"You still 'ere," said 'Iitler' when they emerged on deck. "If you ain't moved next time I come round, I'll get a tug to tow

162

yer an' you'll have to pay!"

"I'll fix 'im," said Josh, "We'll move up next to the Dutchman."

This proved to be easier said than done. Josh would not consider any form of assistance from Avocet and did not wish either himself or Freddie to set foot aboard the Kentish vessel. With no motive power, there was only one option – to row up to the Dutch vessel with the long handled sweeps carried for such emergencies. After some very hard work they threw their mooring lines aboard the Dutch coaster. To their surprise, the lines were caught by a middle-aged woman and a boy of about twelve years old.

A small fat man who looked very much the old sea dog with his peaked cap and reefer jacket sporting the four gold rings of a captain supervised them.

"Ah! The English bargemen!" cried this individual. "Please to come aboard when you are made fast. We have little drink. Yah?"

Intrigued, for neither had been on a foreign vessel before, Josh and Freddie jumped aboard the Dutchman a few minutes later. The little captain greeted them.

"Van Tromp," he said shaking hands vigorously, "please to come to wheelhouse."

The wheelhouse proved to be a spacious compartment and not used solely for navigation purposes. It had a homely feel. Numerous potted plants hung overhead, while a string of washing was airing down one side. A chest of children's toys was pushed under a table at the back, on which stood two bottles of schnapps and several glasses.

Captain van Tromp promptly poured large measures of schnapps into three of the glasses and handed them round.

"A toast of the English, Yah?" he announced. "Cheers!" and downed most of his glass in one gulp. Josh and Freddie tried to follow suit but found the raw spirit rather strong and ended up spluttering.

"We have party. Yah?" van Tromp went on. "My wife, who

163

is mate, make the food. My big son, who is engineer, fetch your friends from the other barge and his brother, who is deckhand, find the man you call 'Itler."

Josh and Freddie exchanged worried glances but the little Dutch captain rushed on.

"We all men of the sea, Yah? Me, I sail barge when I am young. 'Tjalk' we call them in Holland. But I save money and now me and my family, even the little ones, we sail the seas in this lovely ship."

The two from Avocet arrived and accepted glasses of schnapps, not without suspicious glances at the Essexmen, which did not go unnoticed by van Tromp.

"You are from different places. Yah? And you have the rivalry? It is like that in Holland also. The men from Volendam, they do not like the men from Hoorn. But when they are in big trouble they help each other, and when they have little drink together, all are friends. So, drink up, my friends."

At that point van Tromp's wife and two small daughters arrived with the food. It was a typical Dutch repast. There were strips of ham and pork, hard-boiled eggs, slices of various cheeses and bread and jam. 'Hitler' also arrived and was given the Captain van Tromp treatment.

"Why you call him 'Itler? Is German and Germans are..." he used a Dutch obscenity and made to spit out of one of the wheelhouse windows to the obvious annoyance of his wife.

"It's a joke," said Freddie.

"Ah! Joke, I see. The English sense of humour." For a couple of minutes the Dutchman was convulsed with laughter. When he had recovered he asked his guests to start on the food and, of course, to have some more to drink.

And so the party went on. And as it progressed, so inhibitions melted.

"Sorry I gave you an 'ard time about movin' berth," 'Hitler' said to Josh, "only my guv'nor, the Dockmaster, is gettin' very fussy about barges takin' up room in the dock. Pompous old sod, he is."

"That's all right," said Josh, who was leaning against the Dutch vessel's steering wheel, "only doin' yer job."

"Me real name's Sid," said 'Hitler'.

"I'll remember that in future," said Josh.

"If we're here a few days," Avocet's mate said to Freddie, "P'raps you and I could go to the pictures."

"I've got a better idea," replied Freddie. "What say we find a couple o' girls an' then take them to the pictures?"

Avocet's skipper had been trying to make conversation with van Tromp's two older sons, but found it difficult since they did not understand much English. He made an excuse and wandered over to Josh.

"You couldn't possibly let us 'ave some lamp oil, could you?" he asked, "we're right out of it. I'll let you 'ave it back soon as I can find a chandler what's open."

"Sure," said Josh, his dislike of Kentishmen submerged under a tide of schnapps. "Come aboard soon as we finish 'ere an' I'll find you some."

* * *

They didn't finish there until both food and drinks were exhausted. Captain van Tromp insisted.

Freddie had been ashore, to assist 'Hitler'/Sid back onto his bicycle when he fell off it for the second time. The young mate had had rather less schnapps than the others and felt himself best equipped for such tasks. As he made his way across the Dutch coaster he gave a cheery wave in the direction of the wheelhouse. It was answered by one of the sons. Captain van Tromp had evidently retired.

Aboard Jessie May he found Avocet's mate fast asleep on the main hatch. Voices attracted him to the foc'sle. There he found the two skippers poking about in search of lamp oil.

"Did you 'ear the Dutchman?" Avocet's skipper was saying to Josh, "Uses 'is family as crew. No wage bill. An' 'is boys was tellin' me that they can go where we do. Shallow draught, just

165

like us. An' that coaster is big. She'll carry more than us."

"We'll 'ave ter watch them Dutchmen," Josh agreed, "else they'll be takin' our trade."

Freddie sighed. Some people never learn.

Th_ ROADTRIP BOOK

How to Take a Great Roadtrip
Without Breaking the Bank

Jeremy Krug

Acero Publishing
Books for the 21ˢᵗ Century

The Roadtrip Book:
How to Take a Great Roadtrip Without Breaking the Bank

Copyright © 2009 by Jeremy Krug
All rights reserved.

Acero Publishing
Books for the 21ˢᵗ Century

ISBN 0-615278-38-8
EAN 978-0-615-27838-4

917.3 – dc22

The Roadtrip Book – Mayfield, Kentucky.

To obtain additional copies of *The Roadtrip Book*, visit the author's website at www.theroadtripbook.com.

CONTENTS

For my wife, Aracely, who accompanies me on my travels and gave me the best reason of all to travel.

For my parents, John and Paula, who instilled in me a love of travel and a curiosity about other places.

For Gerrit, who took me along on my first two-week, 4,000-mile roadtrip and showed me how to do the same.

 ## Preface

Back to the Road

At some point, I decided that air travel was just not worth it. When I was a little younger and the price was right, I didn't mind squashing myself into those little seats for the convenience of arriving at my destination the same day. But as time went on, airfares started to increase, service started to decrease, and the convenience simply went away.

I remember a flight from Nashville to Atlanta that should have taken 45 minutes, but due to fog, actually took five hours, counting delays. I remember another flight, a Sunday night red-eye from California to New York, where a middle-aged man sitting behind me spent five hours kicking my seat because he had had a bad weekend. On another flight, my luggage was misdirected and didn't get delivered for five days. These experiences simply wouldn't have happened had I avoided flying.

Flying in today's society often involves more hassle than it's worth. Dealing with long lines, delays, surly airport personnel, and security rules that do little to actually improve security make air travel a stressful experience. Although I still fly when I have to, I've learned that traveling by road lets me appreciate the cities, towns, and countryside I'm passing through – a luxury that air travelers simply don't have.

So I've gone back to the road. My parents took me on my first roadtrips – to Texas, to Florida, to Washington, D.C. And a good friend named Gerrit took me on a roadtrip to Mexico – four days in each direction. It was on that roadtrip where I met my wife. So traveling the highways has a special romance for me, quite literally.

This book is a compilation of the lessons I've learned from countless roadtrips, mainly from personal experience, sometimes learned the hard way. I hope that readers can avoid some of the mistakes I've made along my travels. I hope they'll enjoy their travels by being flexible and willing to discover the unexpected.

In the preparation of this book, I decided to use *roadtrip* as one word. The dictionary officially states that it should be written as two words: *road trip*. However, I've come to learn that a roadtrip is more a state of mind than a method to get from Point A to Point B, more an attitude than a drive along a strip of pavement. It's a word that deserved to be coined.

And therein lies the superiority of road travel, at least for those who want to discover what lies along the way. For those who get as excited about the journey as they do about the destination, for those who are ready to expect the unexpected, the roadtrip opens up an endless adventure. If you've ever wanted to savor the journey, then this book is for you.

CHAPTER 1

Why Take a Roadtrip?

If you're reading this book, then, at the very least, you have a passing desire to take a roadtrip. But why? Why do we have this desire to get out on the road, to wander, to take in everything that surrounds us? Although roadtrips can be taken in almost any place in the world, they seem to be a very American way to get to know this land. Ever since the early days of automobiles, buying a car has been advertised as an almost patriotic way for workers to spend their hard-earned money. Discovering America by car has always been the best and most popular way to explore big cities, small towns, and everything in between.

Some of us take roadtrips out of necessity. When families move cross-country, they load up all their possessions onto a moving van and drive to their new home. Others take roadtrips to visit family in distant places. The annual "trip to Grandma's house" may be a trek unto itself. Families get together for different reasons: weddings, graduations, funerals, reunions. You may find yourself getting into a car and driving to any of these events.

More Options than Flying

The main difference between flying and driving is the freedom to discover places along the way to your destination. When in an airplane, you may be fortunate enough to have a window seat on a sunny day and see the surrounding countryside from 30,000 feet. Still, the view of the terrain from the air cannot compare to the sheer majesty of seeing much of the same terrain from the ground. And when you find an area that you might like to discover a little more, you won't have much success convincing the pilot to land the plane so you can explore the region.

When driving, you are in much more control of the travel experience. It gives you the freedom to discover an area unplanned; when you see a place that looks interesting or a historical site that catches your eye, you're free to stop and see what it's all about – something you can't do with other modes of transportation.

Flying involves the stress of airports, standing in long lines, taking off your shoes, dealing with surly security personnel, waiting in the gate area, hoping your luggage ends up in the same place as you do, hoping your flight is not delayed; the list goes on and on. But I think you get the picture: If you strictly want to get to a specific destination, take the plane. It will usually get you there faster.

Even that last statement, though, isn't always correct. Short-haul flights often take longer than driving, especially for travelers who don't live near a major airport.

George, from southern Missouri, lives two hours from the nearest major airport, which is in St. Louis. If he wants to go to Chicago, 375 miles away, he would have to drive two hours to the airport, spend another 20 minutes finding a parking space and taking the shuttle back to the terminal. If he arrives at the airport two hours before his flight, like he should, he'll spend some time waiting in the gate area before his one hour flight to Chicago. Once George's plane lands, it will take him yet another hour to get to his actual destination in Chicago. From door to door, George has spent nearly six and a half hours getting to his destination. This journey could have easily been driven in six hours.

But isn't it cheaper to fly?

With today's high gas prices, many travelers think that a roadtrip would be prohibitively expensive. Usually, taking a roadtrip, especially those within 300 miles of your home, actually cost less than flying. Take

George's trip to Chicago, for example. This flight could easily cost $170 roundtrip, plus any long-term parking fees at his 'home' airport. Once he gets to Chicago, he will need to get to his actual destination. Cab fare or renting a car will add to his expenses significantly. Even with gas at $4.00 a gallon, he could easily make the drive with $160 in gasoline, with a vehicle averaging 20 miles per gallon.

The real benefit to a roadtrip, though, isn't the cost savings or the time savings, but the freedom and adventure of discovering your very own strip of America. When choosing to take a roadtrip, you're able to enjoy new sights, sounds, and tastes at your own pace. My favorite roadtrips are the ones where I'm not tied down to any specific schedule or destination. And that's the charm of this type of travel; you can stop for the night when and where you really want. Later in this book, I will show how it's possible to reserve an inexpensive room, even at the last minute (literally!) while on the road.

Road trips don't have to be expensive. This book will show you how to slash 50% or more from the typical lodging bill. Although eating in local restaurants is a fun way to get to know an area while passing through, it can get quite expensive, especially for a family. I'll share tips that will save money on food – and they don't involve skipping meals! We'll even discuss ways to save money on gas while on the road.

Although the typical roadtrip discussed in this book will last several days, your trip doesn't have to consume that much time, either. Roadtrips are more about the feeling you get by being free to explore and wander on your own time. It's possible to enjoy a great trip in just one day, too. Do you have a free weekend? Why not try a weekend getaway discussed in Chapter 9? It may be just enough of a getaway to get you through the next workweek. The point is that short jaunts can be just as enjoyable as a month-long excursion.

Consider Your Options

For many, a roadtrip is a relaxing way to spend a few days of vacation. When you're driving down a lonely stretch of highway surrounded by awe-inspiring scenery, it can be a mind-expanding, nearly euphoric, experience.

You're Never Alone on the Road

Every day, millions of us take to the road, traveling to places outside our normal routine. During peak holiday travel times, as many as 50 million Americans take a roadtrip of some sort. Even the most isolated of interstate highways have upwards of 5,000 vehicles traveling them each day. Whether your plans call for a short daytrip or a 10,000-mile marathon journey, you're never alone on the road!

Throughout the eastern half of the United States, you'll see much of the natural beauty in the variety of green valleys, rolling hills, rivers, lakes, and rugged mountains. Along the coast, the Atlantic Ocean and nearby beaches will grab your attention. In the Northeast, plan on discovering history scattered through nearly every city, town, and village along your route. Obviously, you could spend days in any major city in this part of the country and still not see all the sights.

But what will *you* choose to do? Will you visit museums, catch a baseball game, go to historic sites, sample the local cuisine? Really, it's your choice, because that's the luxury of a roadtrip!

If you plan to travel through the West, the scenery will be quite different. If you are one of the many Easterners that has never driven cross-country, you may be surprised by the wide-open spaces and long distances involved in driving out West.

There are places in this part of the country where major towns may have just a few thousand people, and those towns may easily be 80 to 100 miles apart from each other.

Out here, everything just seems bigger. The spaces are bigger, the mountains are bigger, and the states are definitely bigger. In many parts of the West, you can easily drive 500 miles in one direction without ever crossing a state line.

U.S. Highway 50 through northern Nevada, often called the "Loneliest Road in America", crosses nine mountain ranges over its 400-mile trek across the state. Travel this road if you want to experience what 'wide-open spaces' are really about. Ribbons of asphalt literally stretch in front of you as far as the eye can see. On a clear day, being able to see mountains 100 miles away is not out of the question.

If you've never visited the West, you may be a little surprised to see how flat much of this frontier is, with occasional mountains scattered across the distant landscape.

No matter where your journey takes you, remember to keep an open mind. I've talked to many people who seem to be mentally opposed to taking roadtrips. Somehow, they think that spending a day on the road – or multiple days – would have to be boring. The first thing I tell them is that no roadtrip has to be boring. There's so much to see on the road that even the most mundane of trips can be exciting – if you choose to search out the excitement.

Keep an Open Mind

I'll be sharing tips I've learned over the years to keep your trip exciting. Some individuals may have an unfair prejudice against driving through many Plains states, such as Kansas, Nebraska, and the Dakotas. These states, while relatively small in population, make for some enjoyable driving, especially if you're willing to get off the interstate highways and join two-lane highways. So keep an open mind about your route!

Make no mistake, though: This book is different from other roadtrip books on the market. This volume won't tell you where to go; plenty of other books give ideas of places to visit and sights to see. Although I've included a few sample roadtrips for your perusal, the book's main purpose is to show readers how to enjoy their roadtrip to the fullest and save money in the process.

As you progress through the chapters, you'll find ways to plan a route that makes sense for you and takes you past places you want to see. Later, you'll read about ways to get your vehicle ready for a long journey. Eventually, we'll discuss ways to enjoy the trip once you're on the road, as well as discussing food and lodging options. And, of course, I've included a comprehensive packing list, tailored to the needs of roadtrippers.

Are you convinced? Are you ready for that roadtrip you've always wanted to take? Whether your roadtrip takes you to your destination, or if the roadtrip *is* your destination, you're sure to discover something unexpected on the open road.

CHAPTER 2

Who Will Go Along?

If you're convinced that a roadtrip is for you, then the next step is to decide who will be traveling with you. This step is important because the people you take along will often determine what kind of trip you can take and to what extent you will enjoy your trip.

Years ago, a friend of mine took a roadtrip to Texas, and she invited two friends to join her. Their plan was to leave at about 5:30 on a Saturday morning and drive to their destination in one long day. They had planned their budget and space in the car around the fact that three people would be on this trip. The morning of the trip, though, one of her friends showed up at the door, announcing that she's invited her elderly father to come along.

Needless to say, she was shocked. Instead of a leisurely trip with three friends, the uninvited fourth passenger wanted to control where they stopped, where they ate, and the topic of conversation. The other two spent the last 700 miles (and the next two months!) discussing how they *should have had* a stronger will and refused to take an uninvited person on the trip.

Does this experience sound familiar? If it does, you probably learned a valuable lesson: be *extremely selective* of whom you invite on a roadtrip.

If every person in the car doesn't feel comfortable with every other person in the car, one or more of you will be miserable.

Just as importantly, if you're coordinating the trip, make it known to any friends accompanying you that the roadtrip invitation is *just for them*, and not for *their* friends or family. Besides, a car has limited space, and it's not exactly a block party where extra space abounds.

Allow Plenty of Space for Everyone

On most of my roadtrips, I drive a full-side sedan. For a week-long trip, three adults can fit comfortably. Four is really starting to push the limit. Although the car technically has six seatbelts, every person will have his or her own luggage, possessions, and roadtrip gear. If you take along a cooler, a camping tent, or even a couple of pillows, trunk space will fill up very fast. If you want to really enjoy yourself on this trip, you won't want to be sitting on top of your neighbor.

Remember, you're going to be living out of this car for the next several days, so you'll want to be comfortable and have enough personal space for everybody. Although I have had up to six people in my Buick on a roadtrip (four adults and two children), long trips are much more comfortable with a maximum of four people in the car.

If you drive a van or an SUV, you may be able to fit more people in your vehicle, but the same principle applies. Don't take the maximum number of passengers permitted for your vehicle; leave a couple of seats empty for personal belongings and elbow room. You'll thank me if you do.

Don't Force Anyone to Go

Lots of people, especially the younger half of the population, don't have to be convinced, cajoled, or coerced into taking a roadtrip. That's why I kept the last chapter short. If you bought this book, you probably *want* to travel. Still, many people simply abhor the idea of spending hours, days, or even weeks in a car driving around the country. They want to get *somewhere* and aren't really concerned about the *ride there*. These people – although not wholly understood by me – are fully entitled to their opinion and shouldn't be forced or convinced to go along. (Truth be told, these people probably don't understand *your* desire to wander around the country in a car for days on end.)

If you suggest the idea of a roadtrip to a friend, and he or she reacts negatively, don't try to convince him or her otherwise! Taking a 'non-roadtrip person' along with you could ruin the trip, and more importantly, impair your friendship. Stick to taking those along that really *want* to go.

Roadtripping With Friends

When you take friends along on a roadtrip, discuss expenses *ahead of time*, not as you roll out of the driveway. Later in this book, we'll cover ways to save money, but for now, make sure that everyone in the car knows that they will be expected to cover their equal share of the *group expenses.*

I consider gasoline, lodging, tolls, and parking to be group expenses. Consider this method for sharing expenses: at the beginning of the trip, everyone in the car puts $50 cash into an envelope. That envelope will be used only for group expenses. When it runs out, everybody puts in another $50. Any money left over at the end of the trip is divided equally.

This method is one of many for ensuring that everyone in the car pays their fair share. You might think of a better one. Personally, since I pay for gas and lodging with credit cards, I keep a running total of group expenses in a small notebook. Then, at the end of the trip, each person gets to pay his or her part of the bill, either by cash or check.

Not all expenses are group expenses. Each individual should pay for his or her own food, souvenirs, and admission to attractions. That being said, every person in the car should bring along enough cash or credit to cover these personal expenses.

With several people in the car, it's usually wise to rotate seats occasionally. Unless everyone in the car is satisfied with a specific seat, it may get old being in the back seat for the entire trip. Rotate drivers too, as long as the car's owner allows it. Make sure that each driver has a valid license and feels comfortable driving in unknown territory. Rotating drivers every few hours will let everyone have a better chance to enjoy the scenery and relax on the trip.

For safety's sake, it's best to let the driver control the radio and the temperature in the car. Some people may disagree with me, but the fact is that the driver, by far, is under more stress than anyone else in the vehicle. If the driver is too cold, too warm, or too grumpy, he or she could get drowsy or cause an accident. When the driver chooses a station the rest of the passengers don't like, make use of your MP3 player. Don't have one? Get one! We'll talk more about MP3 players in Chapter 4. If you're cold, make use of a sweatshirt or blanket. If you get too hot, take off a layer of clothing.

When it's time to choose a place to eat, why not let each passenger have a turn at selecting an eatery? Everybody has different tastes, and sometimes not everyone will like the restaurant. But that's part of the fun of a roadtrip – discovering new places and letting everyone have their chance to call the shots.

Letting everyone in the car have a chance to choose a place to eat also keeps the whole group from eating at the same fast food chain every meal. And seriously, if you feel you have to eat at the same fast food chain every day (or even multiple times a day!), then maybe you'd be better off taking a solo trip. More on that at the end of the chapter.

Roadtripping With the Family

Although many teens and twenty-something's dream of taking a cross-country roadtrip with a group of buddies, most roadtrips are taken with the family. Mom, Dad, and the kids pile into the car to visit some destination many hours away. Maybe they're visiting Grandma, an aunt, traveling to a wedding, graduation, or possibly even a funeral.

If it's just you and your spouse on this roadtrip, try not to irritate each other too much. Remember, sometimes people act differently when they sit in a car for many hours at a time. Converse for a while, then listen to music for a while. Even when you're driving, let your spouse stop where she (or he) wants. On our roadtrips, we always look for an outlet mall or other attraction near the interstate to walk around and spend some time. Sometimes, the best souvenirs are purchased, not in tourist traps, but in local stores, or even supermarkets.

Most families will take their children along. Since young children have a short attention span, they need to be kept occupied. Most young kids won't appreciate the scenery on the road as much as adults, so they'll enjoy their time much more if the adults break up the trip. Whereas most adults can sit in a car for several hours at a time, children need to get out and walk around – or run around – every hour or so.

Young kids like to be entertained. While license plate games and puzzle books do pass the time, many children today don't get very enthused with those kinds of activities. If your kids enjoy playing video games, a portable version and a good set of batteries would be a wise investment. A DVD player or MP3 player will also keep them entertained for relatively little money. Most of these devices have car adapters that will allow them to be used without constantly recharging batteries.

Although most small children will need to be entertained throughout the ride, older children will be able to appreciate the trip much more. They may be able to help plan your trip and even document it. Giving teenagers a camera and letting them take pictures will make them look for interesting sights along the way. Many teens are good with maps and may be able to help navigate or suggest places to stop. Whatever the case, let your teens be a part of the trip's success, and they will enjoy it much more.

Some of these tips may work for you, and others may not. You know your children's likes and dislikes better than anyone, so do what works when you take your kids on the road!

Kids like snacks, and those can get expensive if bought exclusively at fast-food restaurants along the road. Stop at a supermarket and buy snacks that you know they'll enjoy. You'll save money and time by avoiding extra fast-food stops.

One more thing: if the kids get tired and want to sleep while you drive, let them. It will give you a chance to relax for a couple hours and enjoy the scenery that much more.

Taking Along Your Pet

If you've decided to take your pet along on your roadtrip, you're not alone. Millions of people do the same thing every year as they drive across the country. Traveling with your pet need not be difficult.

Of course, some pets travel better than others on the road. Fish or other animals that live underwater don't handle long roadtrips very well and should probably be left home. Exotic animals such as snakes, monkeys, and certain birds may be more easily left at home, too; these animals may even be prohibited from entering certain states without prior authorization or documentation.

For the most part, dogs and cats are the pets most commonly taken on roadtrips; they seem to fare the best on these types of adventures.

Before you take your animal companion on the road, please remember that many public places simply do not welcome pets. Most enclosed public buildings, such as supermarkets, restaurants, and shopping centers expressly prohibit pets, and those prohibitions should be respected. Of course, seeing-eye dogs and other service animals are not pets and are to be welcomed anywhere the public is allowed to enter.

Get Your Pet Ready for the Trip

Getting a pet, especially a dog, used to being in the car for long periods of time takes time and patience. If your dog has never been on a roadtrip, you will need to work with him long beforehand to get him accustomed to the car. If you get in the habit of taking short trips to places he likes to go, he will learn to see the car as a fun place to be.

Over time, lengthen the trips somewhat until he is ready for a longer roadtrip. Very young puppies may have trouble at first, as some tend to get carsick. With puppies, you may want to avoid curvy roads and stick to main highways.

The pet needs his own place in the car. My dog feels most secure when he's riding in his carrier, and he seems to entertain himself pretty well in there. Taking a roadtrip is out of most animals' routines, and many of them act shy, scared, or just plain different when put into unfamiliar surroundings.

Bringing along some favorite toys can help make your pet feel more comfortable on the road. Animals thrive on routine, and any routines from home that you can bring on the road will help your pet immensely. Set a fixed feeding time, and stick to it religiously.

Remember that your pet will need as much exercise as when he is at home, maybe even more. After being enclosed in a carrier for a long period of time, he will want to run around and play. Interstate rest areas are perfect for this, and most of them have specified pet exercise areas, well away from the main building. Usually, your pet will have to be kept on a leash in these areas, but they give pets – and their owners – a great opportunity to move around, run, and play while on the road.

If you spend several days on the road, pets will get used to your daily travel routine. Still, you know your pet better than anyone else, and he may still need to stop very often. It's not unusual for a pet to need to stop every hour. Most can easily handle two or three hours without a stop, though.

At the end of the day, you and your pet will need a place to stay. Many hotels and motels, especially the common chains found at most interstate exits, welcome pets. It may be wise to plan ahead, though, since not all hotels do, and others charge hefty fees to let them spend the night. Many roadside hotels do charge a pet fee of $10 to $30; others charge nothing. Some ask that you pay a 'pet deposit' to ensure that the room stays in satisfactory condition while your pet is a guest. Each hotel's website can give specific information about pet policies, deposits, or fees.

Remember, too, that there are other lodging opportunities when you travel with your pet. Campgrounds tend to welcome pets more consistently than hotels, and they almost never charge extra to bring the four-legged members of the family along. Campgrounds give them a chance to exercise a little more freely than would otherwise be available in a hotel. Whatever you choose, remember that there are plenty of options when traveling with your pet, especially if you plan ahead.

Traveling Solo?

Many travelers end up driving alone by circumstance; others do so by choice. In either case, nothing is stopping you from have a wonderful time on a roadtrip by yourself. Still, it takes a special person to purposely decide to take a multi-day roadtrip alone. Most of us would rather have company on such an adventure, but solo roadtrips are actually one of my favorite type.

Think about this: When traveling alone, you get to make all the choices. You get to decide when to begin your driving day in the morning and when to retire in the evening. You'll choose where and when you eat, and the stops you'll make along the way.

Taking a roadtrip by yourself is a perfect time to reflect on life, but beware: some solo travelers also tend to isolate themselves. That's why it's especially important to make an effort to talk to people while you're on this type of roadtrip.

Whether you attend a religious service or talk to tourism guides at interstate welcome centers, try to start conversations and make friends on the road. If I'm in a local eatery on a solo roadtrip, I start a conversation by asking the server a question about the area. Tourist guides at interstate welcome centers or local chambers of commerce are usually quite friendly and are glad to share information and tips about a particular area.

Be Kind to Yourself

When traveling alone, avoid becoming your own worst enemy. Without friends or family along the route to tell you when to take a break, a solo driver can get fatigued much more easily. From experience, I've found that I tend to push myself to drive more than I should when alone.

It's easy to feel overconfident, especially in the early evening, just before sunset. Several times, I thought I had enough energy to drive through the night, only to get very drowsy around 1 to 2 a.m. By then, it's really too late to check into a hotel. Avoid this mistake by recognizing your limitations. Driving through the night when alone is not only dangerous, it also seriously reduces your ability to enjoy the following day's drive. Make plans to get a full eight hours of sleep each night, especially when driving alone.

Beforehand, decide how long you'll drive before taking a break. If you've never taken an 'independent roadtrip' before, a good rule of thumb is to stop *at least* every two hours. Set a countdown timer if you must, but force yourself to stop, walk around, and eat at regular intervals.

Sharing the Ride

If you're taking a solo roadtrip, especially during busy travel periods, it's likely that someone else in your area may be headed to the same destination. It might be possible to divide expenses by carpooling. Check out www.ride-share-directory.com for nationwide opportunities to carpool or share the ride. Not only will you save money, you'll make new friends. Many online rideshare bulletin boards offer secure posting methods, so you can safely screen potential carpool buddies.

By being kind to your body, you'll be able to relax and enjoy your time on the road. If you plan to be on the road several days (3 days or more), plan to alternate long driving days with short ones. If you make every day a long one, you will tire very quickly and stop enjoying your journey within a couple of days.

Since you won't have anyone to help drive, you may have to cover less distance each day of your solo trip. On the other hand, you may not need to make as many stops throughout the day as a family of four, so you may cover more distance. Again, the key is to plan for your own limitations. Bring along your favorite CD's or audiobooks. Satellite radio will keep your mind occupied, especially if you're a talk radio fan.

When I'm by myself on the road, I enjoy documenting my trip so I can share it with others later. Taking pictures of roadside scenery or attractions, recording videos, or writing a journal of your trip will help you remember not only what you see, but also the feeling of freedom that goes along with being an independent traveler. If you feel awkward writing on your trip, take along an audio recorder – the cheap digital kind that costs $20 will do – and record your impressions as you drive or at stops along the way. Later, you can make a roadtrip album as a memento to your solo roadtrip.

No matter whether you're taking a trip alone or with a vanload of friends and family, the circumstances and dynamic of every group will be different. So be flexible! Be willing to stop if you see something that might be memorable, wildly interesting, or simply a diversion. Try something new and out of the ordinary, and don't be afraid of the unknown!

Now that you've decided to take a roadtrip, and hopefully you know who will be along for the ride, it's time to decide on a place to go, and how to get there. The next chapter will discuss just that: how to choose your route.

CHAPTER 3

Choosing Your Route

By this point, you may be ready to jump out the door, into your car, and take off onto the road. But don't leave just yet, because planning your trip is part of the fun, too. Maybe you have an idea of where you'd like to go and the sights you want to see. This is the time to start putting your ideas onto paper, long *before* the trip begins.

Probably the best way to start planning your trip is to acquire a quality road atlas covering the entire country. Rand McNally's road atlas is my favorite; it's published every year and can usually be found for less than ten dollars.

Although Rand McNally is a little slow to include new highways and updates into their maps, their value and overall quality are good enough for most travelers. Each state is mapped separately, and most larger cities have separate, more detailed maps.

Browsing a road atlas for an hour or two can give you an idea of places and attractions you might like to visit. If you want to visit the West, you might want to browse those states and find out what locations catch your eye. You may find that some places warrant a multi-day visit, whereas you might simply pass through other areas, depending on your plans and interests.

If this will be your first trek across the country, you may be surprised at the sheer size of the United States. Especially if you plan to explore the West, expect long distances between towns and cities. Many first time roadtrippers from the East want to 'go out West' without knowing what of expect.

For example, just driving across Texas normally takes a full day – sometimes much more. It is very easy to drive 500 miles within a single state in many parts of the West. By looking at maps, you can start to plot a reasonable route, along with destinations and stops you want to make.

Other Maps You'll Need

Along with a quality print atlas, I recommend enlisting the use of computer mapping software. Many travelers recommend *Microsoft Streets and Trips* or *Delorme Street Atlas USA*. Both of these products have detailed street-level maps, as well as GPS capability. They also include information on hotels, restaurants, gas stations, museums, and other points of interest along the way. You can calculate exact mileage for a route, estimate fuel stops, and even hear turn-by-turn directions if you install the optional GPS receiver and take your laptop along. I don't use all these capabilities, but many of them are useful for planning any type of roadtrip.

Even if you don't want to purchase mapping software, anyone with an internet connection has access to free online mapping services, such as Google Maps, Mapquest, and Yahoo! Maps. Although these services don't have quite as much capability as purchased software, most simple trip planning tasks can be accomplished on these increasingly-robust websites. For example, satellite imagery can be very useful for finding a specific location in a city. Although some software programs have limited satellite image availability, Google Earth provides much more comprehensive satellite images.

Members of AAA can order custom-made maps, called TripTiks, for their roadtrips. Along with these maps, AAA offers guidebooks listing most hotels, popular restaurants, and key attractions for each state. Members receive these trip-planning services free of charge, and they do come in quite handy.

Know Your Own Limitations

When you plan a roadtrip, it's important to be reasonable in the distance you plan to cover. Answer these three questions to see how well you know your limitations on the road:

> ❑   How many hours can you drive without a break?
> ❑   How many hours do you plan to spend on the road each day?
> ❑   How many miles can you drive in one day?

These questions are posed in order of increasing difficulty, and it's important to know the answer to each one before you commit to a long, multi-day roadtrip. The first question is usually a tough one for new roadtrippers. Honestly, although each person is different, most drivers find they *really* need a stop or some sort of break after three hours behind the wheel.

To be honest, drivers that stop every three hours probably have a specific destination, and they need to be there fairly quickly. Most drivers will make a stop at least every two hours, sometimes more often. Remember, stops have to be made for food, fuel, and restroom, not to mention sightseeing. You'll probably find that when more passengers are in your vehicle, the more often you'll have to stop.

The second question is more difficult because most of us tend to overestimate our endurance. When I took my first roadtrip, I assumed I could begin about 4:00 a.m. and drive until about 10 or 11 at night, and that was a solo trip! Needless to say, that didn't happen. That would have made for an 18-hour day. Not only is that kind of driving unsafe, it nearly guarantees that you'll be miserable by evening. Remember, this is supposed to be a vacation!

When the plan involves a quick, one-day drive, it's not unreasonable to arrive in one long, 15-hour day. On multi-day trips, though, plan to drive no more than about 10 or 11 hours each day. Although this might not sound like a lot, being on the road much more than 10 hours a day can tire a driver very fast. Even if you have several drivers switching off, you'll likely need to spend time outside the car to truly enjoy your roadtrip.

Now, how many miles can you reasonably drive in one day? If your answer is anywhere close to 1000, then you seriously need to rethink your possibilities. Most experienced roadtrippers average about 55 miles per hour over the course of a driving day. In rural areas, this value may be as high as 57 or 58 miles per hour. Now, these average speeds include stops for meals, fuel, and other necessities. Lengthier stops for sightseeing or side trips are not included. This means that a driver who plans to be on the road ten hours a day can cover a little over 550 miles.

I've heard several ambitious drivers over the years tell me they can cover much more than 550 to 600 miles in a day. But remember, although the speed limit may be 70 miles per hour or higher in some places, it is virtually impossible to average that speed over the course of an entire day. Traffic will slow you to much less than 70 mph, and work zones will do the same.

Each stop, even for a quick restroom break, will take at least ten minutes. Even motorists who drive well over the speed limit hit the same traffic bottlenecks, take the same stops, and pass through the same work zones as other drivers. In other words, no matter how fast you try to drive, you will be hard-pressed to average much more than 57 or 58 miles per hour over the course of a day.

What Attractions Do You Want to See?

America is full of interesting attractions for every taste. Do you want to explore cities? Or would you rather spend the bulk of your time in rural areas? Perhaps you could enjoy the treasures available in the increasingly-popular National Park system. Maybe you want to visit the desert. How about a scenic drive or hike through the Rocky Mountains? Maybe you could search out museums along your route. Art or history buffs will find enough museums to keep them occupied for any length of time.

Many travelers make food the center of their trip. They quite literally eat their way across America. Interesting locally-owned eateries seem to invite road travelers with home cooking, friendly service, and regional specialties simply not found in the chain restaurants. Some roadtrippers even plan their meal stops long before making hotel reservations.

You'll find plenty of unusual roadside attractions along the way as you motor across America. From the *Cadillac Ranch* in the Texas panhandle to *Wall Drug* in South Dakota, unusual stops can make for an interesting diversion along the road. Although *The Thing* along I-10 in Arizona may not be as culturally stimulating as visiting an art museum or a national park, roadside oddities might make a trip that much more memorable. Many of these places predate the interstate highway system and are destinations unto themselves. Others may just warrant a half-hour stop to look around and see what the fuss is all about.

Whether you plan to make your roadtrip a quest for culture, a search for tasty food, or simply a hunt for roadside Americana, make a list of the places you want to visit. Don't be surprised if you have to narrow your destinations by half or more.

How Much Time Is Available?

Great roadtrips don't require a month on the highway. In fact, I've devoted a chapter specifically to short jaunts. Still, you'll need to know how much time is available for your trip. To make sure you have enough time, do the following quick calculation: How far from your starting point is the farthest destination on your list? Take that mileage and divide it by 200. The answer is the minimum number of days you will need to make the trip comfortably.

For example, if you live in Houston, and you're planning a roadtrip to Washington, DC, your destination is about 1400 miles from home. That means you'll need *at least* seven days for this trip. By the way, those seven days count drive time, and some minimal sightseeing. Even then, most travelers will want more than that minimum time for their trip. Once you get on the road, you'll find sights worth exploring more closely, and you'll likely want *more* time for your trip, not *less*.

How Fast Do You Have to Get There?

If your roadtrip is taking you to an important meeting, family event, or other engagement, you may be looking for a more direct route with fewer intermediate stops. Your sightseeing along the road may be limited to a few carefully chosen attractions. If time is an issue, stick to the interstate highway system as much as possible. Although the majority of roadtrip 'purists' loathe the interstates for their uniformity and lack of character, when you're in a hurry, they can't be beat. However, planning ahead can reveal lots of hidden treasures along your route, even when traveling the interstates.

Due to the high speed involved in driving the interstates, it is possible to cover a longer distance in a day. If you ever find yourself in the difficult situation of having to cover 800 or 900 miles in one day – which I don't recommend – the interstates are really the only way to make the trip. It's possible to travel 200 miles or more without stopping, and due to the quality engineering of most interstate highways, they truly are an architectural marvel.

However, interstates, due to design requirements, tend to showcase less of an area's natural beauty. Since lanes must maintain a certain width and grades can only be so steep, interstate highways tend to look very similar to each other, even in remotely different areas of the country. Also, since these superhighways require much more than a 100-foot right-of-way, highway developers tend to find inexpensive, less scenic areas much easier for road building. Mountain highways cost much more to build than flatter roads, so interstates tend to wind *around* the scenery, instead of passing *through* it.

Although interstates have a reputation for being somewhat boring, a number of them break that stereotype and are scenic roads in their own right. Some of these are discussed specifically later in this book. Interstate 70 through Colorado and Utah, Interstate 64 through West Virginia, and Interstate 80 through eastern California are roads that are worth a look, simply for their natural beauty.

If you don't have any particular place to be, and your roadtrip *is* the destination, you can take my favorite kind of roadtrip, which is a *slow*

2-Lane or 4-Lane?

Two-lane roads let you drive closer to the scenery. Most four-lane roads actually take you *around* the scenery. If your schedule allows you leisure time
to explore and enjoy the surroundings a bit more, follow two-lane highways
and byways. Many road atlases – such as Rand McNally's national atlas –
specifically identify highways known for their scenic nature. If you're in any of
the following three situations, though, seriously consider sticking to the interstates:

1. When driving in bad weather
2. When driving at night
3. When you're short on time

---

wander across the land. When time abounds, you will likely find two-lane
roads to be more memorable, where it feels like your car is actually closer
to the surrounding terrain.

Even in areas where the interstate highway seems bland, veering
onto a two-lane highway will often completely change the scenery. For example, many travelers dislike Interstate 70 through Kansas, because it
seems empty and flat. If you dislike level land, Kansas may not be for you,
but the natural beauty of this state is better appreciated by taking the
southern route, U.S. 400. The distance is nearly identical, but the two-lane
road will let you soak in the towns, villages, fields, and rolling hills of this
region.

True, taking the two-lane road is slower. You may get behind a slow-
moving truck, and giant gas stations – or *travel centers*, as they are now
called – may be scarcer. But the two-lane roads are where roadtrip
memories are made. So, try to include regional two-lane highways on your
trip if time allows.

How Carefully Do You Want to Plan?

Part of the fun of a roadtrip is the freedom to choose where you want
to travel, how much time to spend, and the route to take. Because of that,
many roadtrippers start out with only a vague, general sense of where they
want to go. They meander across a few states, making stops in places that

interest them. They literally decide where to go when they see the road sign. This kind of spontaneity makes for a fun and relaxing trip, but it works best with just one or two people in the car.

I'll admit that some of my favorite roadtrips are those where I got into the car at the beginning of the ride without knowing where I would end up. When you take that kind of trip, you really *do* feel a sense of adventure as you wander into your very own uncharted territory.

If you choose this spontaneous type of trip, be aware that you may pay more for lodging than you would by reserving ahead. Still, I'll discuss ways later in this book to save money, even on last minute hotel rooms.

If you really want to plan your roadtrip carefully, be aware that it's possible to plan nearly every detail of your journey, down the very last fuel stop. Planning ahead can save money, especially when reserving hotel rooms and show tickets. A little planning can help save fuel, especially if you study the map to ensure taking the shortest route.

Most roadside attractions have websites. Those that don't *will* have numerous online reviews, so you can decide which places are worth your time. When planning a roadtrip, I like to plan for one or two attractions a day. More than two attractions can be very tiring, especially if you have plans to advance down the road any significant distance. Making two sightseeing stops in a day, one in the morning and one in the afternoon, helps keep the trip from getting monotonous; it really helps to break up the day.

What do you do if there are no attractions along a significant portion of your route? In this case, I recommend making your own attraction. Try discovering the downtown area of a small town. Even the smallest of cities are trying to revive their downtown shopping districts. You may discover a quaint antique shop, a local history museum, or an interesting cafe. These are also some of the best places to meet and interact with locals, who can also give you tips on other places to visit that may not be listed in the guidebooks.

Try planning your route around some places you want to visit, and not vice versa. As an example, suppose you want to take a roadtrip around Arkansas. This state, though small in population, hosts some real natural wonders and interesting tourist attractions. Much of the state can be en-

joyed easily in a one-week roadtrip. List some of the attractions you want
to visit:

- Clinton Library in Little Rock
- Little Rock Central High School
- Crater of Diamonds State Park – dig for your own diamonds!
- Hot Springs Park
- Wal-Mart Birthplace Museum in Bentonville
- Ozark Mountains, Eureka Springs
- Texarkana – where city hall is split between Arkansas and Texas

Now, maybe these attractions aren't what you would have chosen.
Still, these are just examples. Next, make a dot on your map for each attraction you want to visit. Try to have at least one attraction – but not
more than two – for each day of your road trip. Now comes the fun part!
Use roads to connect the dots on your atlas, trying to include as many
scenic roads as you can.

You may want to calculate your daily mileage with a computer program or even with the atlas itself. Try to keep daily mileage less than 600,
and certainly well under 500 for a sightseeing trip. In the example I plot-
ted above, you could very well enjoy this roadtrip for seven days without
driving much more than 200 miles in any one day.

As you decide where to finish each day of your roadtrip, visit an online hotel booking website. Not only can you reserve a room online, you
will be able to compare prices and select the best value for your taste and
budget. If you would rather try camping, try an online or print directory of
campgrounds. You will find that camping can be both fun and economical.
We'll discuss lodging options later in the book....

If you like to plan ahead, you'll want to weigh your lodging options
carefully. This is one area where some forethought and a few minutes of
online research can prevent real headaches. Nothing is more disappointing
than driving all day with plans to stop for the night in a certain town, only
to find that every motel in town is full – or worse, finding that the town
has no motels at all!

Look for Variety

When planning a roadtrip, try taking one route going to your destination and another route returning. The scenery will be different on the return trip, and you will have an opportunity to visit attractions you would have otherwise missed.

If after looking at all the options for roadtrips, you're still not sure where to begin, keep reading! Later in this book, I'll suggest some different routes you might want to take, such as a trip from one coast to the other, a drive along historic Route 66, or even a drive to the beach.

In fact, you'll find plenty of books that suggest routes, stops, and things to see along the way. Visiting the travel section of your local bookstore will lead you to numerous books about Route 66, the Lincoln Highway, and other historic roads. Other books highlight America's scenic roads, and at least one magazine is dedicated to two-lane road adventures.

Don't feel like it's necessary to spend lots of money on books, though, to get an idea of possible destinations. Each state's tourism department offers free travel planning guides with much of the information you'll need to plan your journey.

Probably one of the best ways to get excited about planning your trip is to get on the road and take a short weekend getaway. After experiencing the freedom of the road, you'll likely want to plan a longer trip. Use the ideas and resources mentioned in this chapter, and you should have plenty of tools to make your adventure memorable.

What about your vehicle? How can you get your vehicle ready for this kind of excursion? What if you don't think your car is up to the challenge? The next chapter will address those concerns.

CHAPTER 4

Getting the Car Ready

When it's time to get the car ready for a roadtrip, you know it's almost time to begin your adventure. However, some advance planning can make your trip more enjoyable and reduce the risk of a negative situation ruining the experience.

In Chapter 2, I discussed the importance of not stuffing too many people into your vehicle on a long trip. But the question remains: What is the ideal vehicle for a roadtrip?

Honestly, almost any type of vehicle can work wonderfully on a long drive. The *best* vehicle really depends on the driver and the passengers. Instead of recommending one type of vehicle over another, I'll simply discuss the pros and cons of each main type of vehicle: cars, pickup trucks, and vans/SUV's.

Cars

If you plan to take a typical family-sized sedan on your roadtrip, you're in good company. Since sedans are the most common vehicles on the road today, it's no wonder that they're the most popular type of roadtrip vehicle, too. If you drive a particular car every day, you'll be more comfortable with it when in unfamiliar surroundings. You'll be able to spend more time enjoying yourself, instead of trying to adjust to a different type of vehicle.

I prefer to drive a sedan on my roadtrips. They usually get better gas mileage, and I also like how they handle – at least from my own experience. Since just about everyone has his or her own door, passengers often feel less cramped in a car. If one to three people will be on your trip, you'll likely have more than enough room for your gear.

On the other hand, with four people on a long trip, a car can get cramped pretty fast. Especially if one (or more) of the passengers hasn't grasped the concept of packing light, you may find yourself running out of room in the trunk. True, you may physically be able to *fit* all your stuff back there, but *finding* something may be nigh impossible.

Pickup Trucks

Most people don't drive pickup trucks on roadtrips unless they are traveling alone or with one other person. Although many pickups of yesteryear made for uncomfortable driving and were better suited for hauling wood and working around the farm, today these trucks can be just as comfortable and roomy as larger vehicles.

However, note this rule of thumb: The roomier and more comfortable the interior of the pickup, the worse the gas mileage will be. Many larger pickup trucks are known for pitiful gas mileage, hovering around 15 miles per gallon, sometimes even less. Light trucks, especially the four-cylinder variety, can be quite economical, some even getting as high as 30 miles per gallon. These light trucks may not be as roomy or comfortable as their larger counterparts, but it is a give-and-take proposition. Give up some space, improve fuel economy.

Of course, if you really need to move a larger amount of luggage, maybe because you're moving a long distance, a pickup truck could be your best bet. Once again, your priorities will dictate which vehicle you take on a long trip.

> ### *Roadtripping by Motorcycle*
>
> In good weather, roadtripping on a motorcycle can be one of the best ways to experience the spaces around you. Although room for luggage will likely be limited, you'll save on fuel and have nearly unlimited travel options. Dozens of riding clubs organize annual roadtrips along some of the most scenic highways in the country.
>
> Visit www.moto-directory.com/touring.asp for more information on taking a motorcycle trip.

Vans and Sport Utility Vehicles

Vans, minivans, and sport utility vehicles are also common roadtrip vehicles. Trips with the family – especially three or more children – will be the most comfortable in these types of vehicles.

When it comes to gas mileage, most minivans outperform full-size vans and SUV's. However, the extra room the other two offer make them worth your attention. Large families and groups of five adults or more will be most comfortable in an SUV or van, where there's plenty of room in the back for luggage and other roadtrip necessities.

Although most vans and SUV's can carry the same number of passengers, be aware that most larger vans may not handle as well as an SUV; sometimes vans feel a little 'top heavy'.

In short, if you're looking for the best gas mileage among larger vehicles, minivans get the nod. However, if you need the maximum amount of space possible, go with a larger SUV.

Red Tape

The last few pages have assumed that you will have the luxury of choosing among various vehicles to take your roadtrip. In reality, though, most people have only one or two vehicles parked outside their homes, so the choice is simpler.

If you have one vehicle, then the choice is already made for you. Of course, if someone else is going along, perhaps he could offer his car. Still, the fact remains that the 'perfect roadtrip vehicle for everyone' doesn't exist. After taking your first journey, you'll find things about your vehicle you wish you could change. Those may be features you'll look for in your next car – or even add to your current car when you get home!

No matter what car you drive, though, make sure your legal bases are covered. Check your driver's license to make sure it hasn't expired, and carry it with you at all times while on the road. Make sure your car has current registration and insurance forms in the glove compartment. In fact, put those two documents in an easy-to-access location in the glove compartment. For a few dollars, you can purchase a small vinyl pouch to hold your registration and proof-of-insurance forms. You don't want to get stuck in a situation where you can't find these forms when you need them.

As an added security measure, make a copy of your license and keep it in the glove compartment with your other important documents. In the event your license is lost or stolen, it may be invaluable for getting a replacement in a hurry.

Don't forget to check your license plate to be sure the registration sticker is current. Also, make sure the entire plate is visible. It is illegal in many places to cover any part of the plate with plastic covers or other decorations.

Will My Car Make the Trip?

If you have any doubt as to whether or not your vehicle is ready for a roadtrip, you need to stop driving it immediately! Take it to a mechanic's shop and get it fixed today!

Am I overreacting? Not really. If your car can't be taken on a long roadtrip, then it probably shouldn't be driven on local streets around town. In fact, highway miles driven on a roadtrip are normally some of the easiest miles a car will ever experience.

Why do I say this? Well, when driving on the open road, a car uses its brakes very little; many drivers use cruise control instead of keeping their foot on the accelerator. On the other hand, driving on local streets requires constant acceleration, deceleration, braking, and turning. So, if your car is truly safe to be driven around town on a daily basis, it should be fine on a roadtrip.

Consider Renting

If you don't have a car or simply don't want to drive your own, you may want to think about renting a car. When renting, you will have the advantage of not putting extra miles or wear-and-tear on your own vehicle. Still, renting *does* add to the total cost of the trip, and the car you rent may not have all the features you want.

One case in which renting would be the best option, though, is for foreign visitors. If you're from somewhere other than North America, bringing your own car to the United States will be difficult and costly. Therefore, renting a car is often the only option for European visitors.

Now, I've said that renting may be the only option for foreign visitors. Foreigners may find it very difficult to purchase a vehicle here, because registering one in the United States is nearly impossible without a permanent U.S. address. In addition, insurance on a purchased vehicle is available only to those with a valid U.S. driver's license. Recent laws have made it almost impossible for individuals from abroad to obtain a license without some kind of permanent visa (or work visa, in some instances).

Of course, I'm not a lawyer, so this information is certainly not legal advice. Still, the fact remains that foreign visitors who wish to take a roadtrip in the United States will probably have to rent a vehicle.

If you decide to rent, remember that weeklong rates are often cheaper than booking a weekend rate under some circumstances, so shop around. Also be aware that adding extra drivers may cause your rental fee to increase significantly. If you're under 25, be prepared to pay much more to rent a car. If you're under 21, you probably won't be able to rent at all.

Should you pass on the 'optional' insurance (sometimes called CDW, for *collision damage waiver*) offered at the counter? It depends. If the insurance on your personal car has full coverage, that coverage *probably* travels with you to a rental car, but check your policy to make sure. If you drive with just liability coverage back home, you may be well-advised to buy the rental insurance.

Sometimes, your credit card will include CDW insurance. Check the fine print of your card's benefits package to see whether you have this cov-

---

RV's

Recreational vehicles can eliminate the need to stay in hotels. These rolling homes give their owners the comforts and conveniences of home, but they come at a steep price. Although simple, towed RV's and pop-up campers can be had for less than $20,000, luxury motorhomes often cost upwards of $100,000. If you can't afford to buy a new motorhome, used RV's are constantly available on the market and often a good deal. If you'd like to experience the RV lifestyle without committing to a long-term investment, though, consider renting. Most RV's can be rented for less than $200 a day, which isn't that expensive if divided among several friends or a large family.

For more information on RV's, see Chapter 10.

---

erage. Even if you do, credit card CDW insurance is used only as a last resort, after your other options, such as your own auto insurance policy, are exhausted. Once again, a call to your auto insurance agent or to your credit card company will save some anxiety at the rental counter. When in doubt, though, it is usually better to have too much insurance than not enough.

Make sure your rental car contract includes unlimited mileage. Most do, except for a few places out West. If you need to take the car out of state, make sure your contract allows for that. Arrange to drop off your car at the same location where you pick it up, or be prepared to pay an expensive one-way drop-off fee. And of course, return the car with a full tank of gas, because rental car companies will charge you outrageous fees if you don't!

Mechanical Preparations

If you decide to take your own car, you'll want to get it serviced before embarking on your journey. Many quick-lube places will service your car in 30 minutes or so for less than $40. If you don't know much about cars, this is probably your best bet. For that small fee, they'll change your oil, top off essential fluids, check your tire pressure, and basically make sure that the car is in good working order. They usually change filters, lamps, and windshield wiper blades for an additional fee.

If you're unsure of a vehicle's mechanical health, it may be wise to take it to a trusted mechanic and ask him to check the car from top to bottom. If he finds any problems with the transmission, motor, or exhaust system, the small fee you paid will be well worth it. Even if your car is in perfect shape, it's worth the peace of mind to know that it will be less likely to break down at an inopportune time. Since you're taking a long roadtrip, it's usually better to discover vehicle problems near home rather than hundreds of miles away.

Even drivers who know little about cars need to be able to check basic items on their vehicles. Arguably, the most important mechanical check a driver should perform is the oil level. When you pop the hood, look for a removable dipstick, probably labeled "Oil Level". Pull out the dipstick, and make sure the level is up to the top of the shaded area near the bottom of the stick. If the level is low, add a little oil at the screw-on engine oil fill.

Know how to check your tire pressure. In fact, check your tire pressure often. When on a roadtrip, I check my tire pressure every third tank of gas. Since underinflated tires will reduce gas mileage significantly, keeping tires inflated to the recommended pressure (around 30 pounds per square inch for most tires) will save you money!

Tire pressure gauges cost only a few dollars, so it's wise to keep one in your glove compartment while on the road. If you don't want to check your pressure that often, you can buy special valve caps that change color when your tire pressure falls below a certain level. These caps cost around five dollars and do come in handy!

Another easy inspection every driver should make is to check the wheel alignment. If your car pulls to one side, your wheels may be out of alignment. When you drive down a straight stretch of highway and release the steering wheel for a few seconds, the car should not drift much, barring any heavy winds. If it does, your wheels could need realigning. Wheels that are out of alignment will cause your tires to wear unevenly and very quickly. In extreme cases, a tire may need to be replaced after less than 1000 miles of being driven on unaligned wheels!

When you pack your vehicle, remember to include some basic tools. Although auto supply stores will sell you a 'safety kit' or 'emergency kit', it's easy to assemble your own from items you likely already have. Make sure to include these basic items in your kit:

Essential Tools for Emergencies

- Spare Tire (inflated) and Jack
- Can of Emergency Tire Inflator (Fix-a-Flat or similar)
- Lug Wrench
- Pry Bar or Crowbar
- Hubcap Key (if you have special hubcaps)
- Screwdriver
- Tire Gauge
- Mini Air Compressor (to inflate a tire from your cigarette lighter outlet)
- Jumper Cables

The need for most of these emergency items is obvious; so don't leave home without them!

If you're planning for emergencies and aren't a mechanical expert, arguably the most important item you can take along is an auto club membership. The most popular one in the United States is AAA, and most of their members seem to be satisfied with their service.

In an emergency, you get free tow truck service, up to five miles, to the nearest shop to get repairs. If you are locked out of your car, they will send a locksmith to help, free of charge. If you run out of gas, they will send someone with enough gas to get you to the next station – you pay for the gas, though. If your battery fails, they will send someone to give you a jump-start.

All in all, it's not a bad deal, especially if you drive an older car. AAA can help with trip planning, also, with free travel guides, maps, and personalized TripTik maps. Showing your membership card will also score discounts at many restaurants, hotels, and other attractions. Of course, AAA is not the only auto club available, but it is the most popular. Other clubs are available which provide similar services, so shop around and see if membership in an auto club is for you.

Once your car is mechanically ready to go, it's time to start packing! What do you want to take along? Before you start packing clothes and shoes, think about some gadgets that you may want to consider that may make your ride more enjoyable.

Every experienced roadtripper has a special item or gadget to make the time on the road more fruitful. In the 1970's, the CB radio was the gadget to have. Cell phones later took their place. Whatever gadget you already own for your car, below are three that you may want to consider acquiring before your journey.

Satellite Radio

One of the greatest innovations of the last several years for people who spend a lot of time in their cars is satellite radio. In the United States, it is now possible to listen to the same station from coast-to-coast without losing the signal for more than a few seconds at a time. Whatever your personal taste, you'll find something on satellite radio you enjoy. Commercial-free music, news, talk radio, play-by-play sports, weather, and even local traffic reports are available on both of the major satellite services.

Both services, XM and Sirius, form one company, Sirius-XM Radio. Both services cost about $13 per month, with discounts for those who commit to yearly subscriptions. Although the audio quality is not nearly as good as listening to a CD, satellite radio is the easiest option for those who want the greatest variety of listening options on the road.

Which service is best for you? Really, it depends on your personal tastes. Since the two companies merged, offerings on both services are *very* similar. I subscribe to both services, and since I listen primarily to talk radio and news stations, both services are just about equal for me.

If you are a sports fan, keep this in mind: the NFL and NASCAR are on Sirius, while XM hosts major league baseball and NHL hockey. Both services feature different college sports conferences throughout the year, so check with the providers to see which service has your favorite team.

Talk radio and news offerings are similar on both services, with this exception: Sirius seems to have slightly more non-political talk stations, while XM has more political talk. Once again, it depends on your preference.

If you're traveling with the kids, you might want to remember this: Many talk shows on Sirius are 'Sirius-exclusive', which means that they are not carried on terrestrial AM/FM radio. As a result, these programs are not subject to FCC regulations regarding the use of offensive language. Many of these shows, even those on 'mainstream' talk and political talk channels, throw around foul language freely.

Howard Stern is on Sirius, Oprah is on XM. On XM, every station that uses offensive language is designated by an 'XL' label; not so on Sirius. As a result, XM tends to be more family-friendly.

Again, both services are great, and most travelers will enjoy either one. Satellite radio may not be for everyone, though. If your Ipod or CD collection *really has* 10,000 songs on it, and you don't care for news or talk radio, then skip satellite and stick with what you want to hear. On a roadtrip, you should be able to enjoy what you choose to listen to.

GPS Navigation

GPS (Global Positioning System) is a free satellite service operated by the U.S. government that determines your location to within a few feet. Although the service is free, you do have to buy a receiver. Receivers range in price from just over $100 to over $1000, depending on the features and convenience desired in the device.

A simple $200 GPS receiver will plug into your car's cigarette lighter outlet and offer turn-by-turn directions and maps of the continental United States. They can be mounted directly onto the dashboard or placed temporarily on the inside of your windshield with suction cups.

More advanced GPS devices offer the capacity to play MP3's, find local attractions and services, pronounce local street names, and even capability to download audiobooks or play games. Although the possibility of playing a game on a GPS device may seem exciting at first, the screen is really too small to be of much use at a distance. Likewise, anyone who has an appreciable MP3 collection already has his or her own dedicated player. And really, do I need to mention the fact that using these other features on a GPS device keeps the screen from being used for its intended purpose, actually getting somewhere?

MP3 Players

Dozens of MP3 players are on the market today, many with similar features. All of them play audio files in the MP3 format. If you don't have an MP3 collection, it's easy to start one from albums you already own. If you have a computer, just place your CD's into your system's optical drive, and it will 'rip' the tracks on that particular disk to the hard drive.

At that point, connect your MP3 player to the computer via a USB cable. It should be easy to transfer – or drag – the digital files to your player.

If you already have a large MP3 collection, go for a player with a large hard drive capacity – like Microsoft's Zune or Apple's Ipod, both of which are available in 120-gigabyte versions. If your music collection is smaller, or if you normally take only a couple dozen CD's along, a smaller player should be fine – such as SanDisk's Sansa players, the Ipod Mini, or smaller versions of the Microsoft Zune. These players utilize flash memory and are usually much smaller, more portable, and consume battery power more conservatively. Look for specials – both online and in stores – when shopping for MP3 players. It's possible to find a 4-gigabyte player for as little as $30 if you're willing to shop around.

If you're interested in video capability, look for players with larger screens – most of those will be the larger, more expensive players. It's possible to transfer videos and DVD's to these devices and even watch movies on them.

Your MP3 player will need a good set of headphones, as built-in speakers are not standard on most models. Consider a pair of noise-reduction headphones, which not only produce high-quality sound, but also reduce ambient noise from the road, engine, and fellow passengers.

Personally, I keep a portable GPS system attached to the windshield most of the time when on the road. It's easy enough to enter the next destination into the unit and let it guide me through complex street patterns and unfamiliar areas. Although I don't rely on the GPS much in rural areas, it's invaluable in cities and even in smaller towns, especially when looking for a specific street address. Usually, when searching for a hotel or attraction, if all you have is a street address, the GPS will find it without a hitch.

Especially in rural areas, sometimes I decide not to take the route recommended by the GPS unit. Most often, if I opt for a two-lane highway instead of a four-lane expressway, the unit will try to 'guide' me back to the interstate. If I'm confident enough of my whereabouts and get tired of hearing the GPS unit tell me where to go, I'll just turn it off. That's always an option.

If you choose to buy a portable GPS unit, be aware that thieves in many areas have been stealing them for easy cash. When you park your car for the night, remove the unit from the car, and wipe off the suction cup marks from the windshield. Thieves often look for suction cup marks on a windshield as a sign of expensive portable electronics in the car.

Radar Detector

In the last chapter, I briefly discussed why it doesn't really pay to speed. Any amount of stopping, even if just for using the restroom or re-fueling, will consume any advantage you may have had speeding on the open road. Add even a small suburban traffic jam or construction zone, and you'll find that speeding doesn't really get you to your destination any faster.

All that being said, why would a driver even consider a radar detect-or? Well, even the most conscientious drivers have a lead foot at times and find themselves speeding. It's better to have some advance warning of the officer ahead rather than pay a hefty fine, along with increased insurance fees and points on your license.

In addition, it's always useful to know where police are patrolling an area of highway several hundred yards ahead of time. Whether police departments wish to admit it or not, out-of-state vehicles *are more* likely to be targeted for infractions than local motorists.

If you are a minority, take further note: Police officers in many areas, especially a few places in the rural South, are not as accepting of outsiders as the state welcome centers would have you believe. Racial pro-filing is still practiced in many areas – not just the South – as many minor-ity drivers have personally experienced.

As a person of mixed heritage, I've experienced it, too. Driving through Arkansas one morning with my cruise control set to the speed limit, a state trooper parked under an overpass proceeded to pull out and follow me for several miles. Although my cruise control was still set to 70 –

the posted speed limit – the trooper pulled me over, asked me to step out of my car, and told me that he clocked me at 74 miles per hour.

After talking for a few minutes, he says he will 'let me off with a written warning.' This type of action is common when police have little or no reason to stop a vehicle, but simply want to investigate to see if everything is 'normal' with a motorist. Some officers try to find an excuse to stop a car when they see a person of color driving a fairly nice, newer car, especially if it carries out-of-state license plates. Perhaps they suspect that the car is stolen, because after the officer sees a valid license and registration, he usually ends the traffic stop, normally politely.

On two other occasions, both in Texas, I was stopped by police officers claiming they had run a license plate check in their system and found no registration matching my plate. I find it hard to believe that officers in Texas run a check on *every single car* that passes by. So evidently, I was targeted – or *profiled*, if you prefer that word – for a traffic stop well before they even checked my license plate. In both cases, after showing the officers my license and registration, they politely let me go on my way.

In none of these cases had I broken any law. Still, I was stopped three times, needlessly wasting my time. I've been stopped on other occasions under similar circumstances. It would have been much more convenient for me if I had been able to anticipate the officers' presence and react accordingly, maybe even slowing down to a few miles per hour below the speed limit when approaching the patrol area.

Sometimes, there is nothing a motorist can do to avoid being stopped by the police. Most police officers do not take advantage of outsiders, but be aware that some do. Racial profiling is real, although thankfully not practiced everywhere. Profiling of motorists is normally not an official practice, but subject to the individual biases of the individual officer. I'm not saying this to make people afraid of police or to distrust them, but rather, to remind them to be careful on the road and try not to give an officer *any* reason to stop them if at all possible.

All that being said, it's not necessary to buy an expensive radar detector if you simply want to be aware of police presence in an area along the highway. Many simple models produced by *Whistler*, *Beltronics*, or other manufacturers can be had for well under $200. Several of them will also alert you to traffic jams or ambulance presence on the highway, as well.

Radar detectors are not a surefire way to avoid being stopped for speeding, though. Be aware that police in some areas use aircraft speed detection or laser detection, both of which are difficult to near impossible to detect.

In Virginia and the District of Columbia, using a radar detector is illegal, so be especially aware of your speed in those areas. Remember, when far from home, fighting a ticket in court is virtually impossible. Being fined several hundred dollars is not the way to enjoy your time on the road, so be careful!

What to Pack?

When it's time to pack up the car, a few things are obvious: Take clothes, shoes, and basic toiletries. Take along a cell phone, and don't forget your car charger. Before leaving, make sure your wireless plan includes coverage in the areas you plan to visit. If it doesn't, you could be hit with hefty roaming fees. Instead of changing plans just for a roadtrip, consider buying a cheap, prepaid cellphone. For example, *Net10* provides nationwide prepaid cell service for ten cents a minute, all the time, with no roaming charges anywhere in the continental U.S. The phones are pretty cheap, too, starting at about $30 with no contract required.

After you've packed the basics, it may be a little more difficult to think of other necessities to take along. Remember, though, to pack light! Even when traveling alone, I try to fit all my belongings into one duffle bag (sometimes two). It makes stopping for the night much easier when you can take just one bag into the hotel, instead of making multiple trips to the car. If several people are traveling with you, the 'one bag' guideline makes for an easy way for everyone to manage their own luggage.

If you'll be storing luggage in the trunk, or in some other way separated from you while in the car, think about taking along a small personal case or messenger bag with roadtrip essentials. Use this secondary bag to store your music player, earphones, sunglasses, reading material, and camera, along with anything else that really needs to stay at your side throughout the trip.

Speaking of things you'll need to keep at your side, definitely remember to take a camera! Unless you're a photography buff, a simple digital camera should be sufficient to document your travels. Remember to take enough batteries to last your trip, or else bring along a small charger. For most people, a 2-gigabyte memory card will be more than enough to store snapshots from your journey.

Dressing for the Road

When packing clothes, remember to be comfortable. Sitting in the car for hours at a time means you'll want to wear comfortable pants, although shorts can actually make you feel cold if you're sitting in front of an air conditioner. During cold months, I prefer to wear a sweatshirt while driving, and I usually wear t-shirts during the summer.

Even during warmer months, you may want to consider taking along a long-sleeve shirt or sweatshirt if your plans include driving north or west. Locations in the northern and western halves of the nation, as well as any area over 3000 feet in elevation, may experience cool, even cold temperatures at night during the summer.

Personally, for not having planned better, I've ended up shivering while camping in Utah during June, and even in Nevada during July. You've heard it before, but I'm saying it again: Mountain and desert areas *really do* get cold at night, year round. So take a blanket and appropriate clothing if planning to travel to those areas.

For the car, consider taking along a few pillows. People do like to sleep in the car sometimes, and a comfortable pillow can make a long trip that much more comfortable. A small cooler with a few snacks and drinks can help bridge the gap between meal stops.

Even if your plans primarily include staying in hotels at night, consider taking along a tent, especially if there's plenty of room in your vehicle. Camping, even if for only one night during your trip, can be fun, memorable, and an easy way to save money while on the road. It's also a great way to enjoy nature on a level you just can't experience from a hotel room.

When preparing for the trip, make sure the car has a durable cup holder. The driver will need to stay focused on the road and probably won't have an extra hand to balance a soda or cup of coffee. If your car doesn't have a cup holder, or if the one if your vehicle is just too flimsy, consider buying a small console for your car that includes a quality cup holder. It's a small expense, but it will make a big difference – especially for the driver.

One last comfort item needs to be mentioned in this chapter. No one likes to spend hours in a dirty car, so buy a small trash can or litter bag for your vehicle. Instead of throwing snack bags and empty cups on the floor, use the trash bag. And try to empty it at least once a day. By keeping the inside of your car relatively clean, it will be that much more enjoyable for traveling. Remember, you will be living out of this vehicle for several days, so try to keep it neat!

Is the car ready to go? Have you packed everything? Now comes the exciting part – let's hit the road!

CHAPTER 5

Behind the Wheel

If you've spent a while preparing for your journey, the day before leaving will be hectic. You'll likely be busy packing your luggage, deciding what to take and what to leave behind, and preparing your car for the trip. The day before I leave on a long roadtrip, I have my own 'routine' for getting ready, both physically and psychologically.

Since I know I'm going to be sitting in the car for a long time, I try to take a long walk the day before a trip. It's good to exercise, both before and during a roadtrip. To get psyched up, try watching a roadtrip movie. Nearly every traveler has his or her favorite movie about traveling the road. Some favorites include *Fandango*, *Dumb and Dumber*, and *Rain Man*. Depending on your taste in movies, you're sure to find one that will get you in the mood for being on the road.

Another part of my ritual is preparing a music playlist for the first hour or so of my trip. Ipods and other MP3 players make this task simple. Certain songs will put you into the traveling mood, and a string of 20 roadtrip songs can really get your mind ready for the road ahead.

Last-Minute Errands

Before rolling out of the driveway, don't forget these important errands:

- ❏ Put a hold on mail and newspaper delivery
- ❏ Put lamps on timers – to give the house a 'lived-in' look
- ❏ Pay bills ahead of time – to avoid late fees
- ❏ Turn thermostat to low-energy mode
- ❏ Turn off all appliances, except refrigerator
- ❏ Lock all doors and windows

Getting Onto the Road

Now that you've packed every last item, checked your car, and prepared your mind and body for the trip, you're ready to go!

If you've filled your gas tank before leaving home, you won't have to worry about buying fuel for several hours. Still, you may need to stop to pick up a few snacks at the store or run an errand before leaving town.

On the open road, make good use of cruise control. Driving long distances is much easier with cruise control, and as long as your route has little traffic and the weather is agreeable, cruise control can actually make you a safer driver. By maintaining a constant speed, you are free to watch for obstacles on the highway, not to mention the fact that you can enjoy the scenery on the road that much more.

In the last chapter, I mentioned the wisdom of driving at or near the speed limit. Speeding doesn't usually get you to your destination much faster, and speeders potentially face time-wasting traffic stops or expensive fines. However, some drivers may find themselves in an area with an artificially low speed limit. If you really feel that you need to drive faster than the posted speed limit, try to follow another car, and match that car's speed. Normally, the car at the front of a group of speeding vehicles will be the one that gets stopped by the police. In any case, the lead car will probably see the patrol car first and slow down, giving you the signal to do the same. Remember that most officers will allow you a tolerance of at least five mph over the speed limit. Still, you speed at your own risk.

Don't Be Aggressive

After driving for a few hours, you'll begin to notice how other drivers react to what they experience on the road. Many drivers let their impatience rule their behavior, and the result is the road rage so common on today's highways. Smart roadtrippers won't let rude, impatient behavior on the part of other motorists bother them.

Try to drive courteously, staying in the right lane except to pass on divided highways. Flashing high beams at slower drivers not only shows a lack of patience, it's downright rude. Slower drivers may be elderly, have mechanical problems, or have some other legitimate reason to drive slower than surrounding traffic.

Tailgating, or following another vehicle too closely, is the leading cause of rear-end collisions. Try to stay at least two seconds behind the car in front of you. In other words, when the car ahead of you passes a fixed object, such as an overpass, you should pass the same point no less than two seconds later. Never tailgate another driver, and don't allow other drivers to tailgate you. If another driver is following you too closely, slow down little by little until the car is either able to pass or moves back. Although you may be tempted to slam on your brakes if another car is tailgating you, don't! Doing so could cause a collision.

Watch for Obstacles

On the open road, you will find a surprising number of potentially dangerous obstacles. In rural areas, for example, deer and other animals can cause severe hazards on the highway, especially at night. Hitting a deer can cause thousands of dollars worth of damage to a car, ruining an otherwise well-planned trip.

Auto supply stores sell high-pitched 'deer whistles' that can be attached to the front bumper of your car. These special whistles claim to repel deer, and I know many people who swear by them. If you plan to travel through an area with a high concentration of deer, such as the Midwest and much of the South, consider investing a few dollars into this device. They are very cheap and can be installed in about 30 seconds.

When driving at night in rural areas, keep an eye out for stray animals, both wild and domestic. Even if deer, elk, or moose are uncommon along your route, hitting a large dog can do nearly as much damage. Watch for animals running or standing along the shoulder of the highway. If you see one, don't swerve! Instead, slow down and hit your horn a few times to scare the animal away.

In urban areas, obstacles on the road usually consist of traffic jams or emergency vehicles. When you see an emergency vehicle stopped on the side of the road with its lights flashing, move over to the next lane of traffic. Most states now require drivers either to move over for emergency vehicles or to slow down drastically.

Another obstacle found mainly during summer months is the construction zone. Remember not to speed in areas where construction workers are present. Most states are getting serious about speeders in work zones. Illinois, for example, now levees $375 fines against work zone speeders for their first offense. Speeders are increasingly being caught with unmarked patrol cars and speed cameras. And motorists in that state who hit a worker, even on accident, will go to jail for 14 years and pay thousands of dollars in fines.

When driving through construction zones, move over to the available lane well ahead of time. If you see a sign instructing vehicles to "Merge Now", merge immediately. Drivers who attempt to pass other vehicles instead of merging could be cited for aggressive driving. Be patient in work zones, and expect delays. You'll be pleasantly surprised if the work zone doesn't slow you down as much as you thought!

Buy Gas Often

Every driver knows not to let the gas tank run empty. Common sense, though, can be complicated by being in unfamiliar surroundings. Drivers who are used to filling up at a favorite corner gas station may be surprised to see 100-mile stretches of highway without any fuel services in many parts of the West.

Most of the time, you'll be fine if you start looking for gas when the tank drops to about ¼ tank. Out West or in especially remote areas, start looking around the ½ tank mark. It's much better to fill up often than to run out in the middle of nowhere.

Start Early, But Not Too Early

The beginning of a roadtrip is one of the most exciting parts of the adventure. The anticipation of the journey ahead makes the first few hours of every long trip special. A commonly asked question is, "What time of day should we start our trip?" Is it wiser to start early in the morning or later in the day?

Personally, when making a multi-day drive, I prefer to leave in the afternoon on the first day. It helps me sleep easier if I know I won't have to leave at the crack of dawn the following day. Leaving on a late afternoon after work can help you get a head start of a few hours on your journey. I find that starting a roadtrip with a short driving day gets me used to being behind the wheel, so I'm more adjusted and ready for the longer day to follow.

If you're a morning person, though, you might prefer to hit the road earlier. I've done this many times, too, and beginning a roadtrip in the early morning can save money, since you're not paying for a hotel room after only a few hours of driving. A word of caution, though: Don't leave too early. Drivers that leave home at 4:00 or 5:00 in the morning tend to get tired very early in the day.

On one occasion, I left home just before 4:00 a.m. and ended up having to take a nap by 9:00 in the morning. The reason? I didn't get a good night's sleep before the trip. Leaving too early in the morning can leave a driver tired and lethargic, especially by mid-afternoon. If you decide to leave in the morning, I don't recommend leaving much earlier than 7:00 a.m. Try to eat a good breakfast before leaving in the morning. Remember, it can be extremely tiring to drive more than 10 to 12 hours in a day.

Enjoying Yourself on the Road

If you rarely drive for several hours at a time, you may find it difficult to keep your mind occupied while behind the wheel. If you have friends riding along on the trip, you'll have plenty of conversation to stay occupied for a while. For those times when the others in the car want to sleep, listen to their music, or just enjoy the scenery, make good use of your satellite radio or audiobooks.

If your road trip is for leisure, take advantage of every chance to enjoy scenic overlooks or other natural wonders along the way. Many states deliberately build interstate rest areas in spots known for their natural beauty. Most states also feature welcome centers shortly after crossing the state line along the interstate. Stop at these tourist information centers and pick up a free map and state visitor guide.

Even if you're not spending much time in a particular state, the free resources found at state welcome centers can familiarize you with the attractions worth a visit in the area. They also make great souvenirs of your roadtrip, and they may even give you some ideas for future trips.

You'll probably find that two-lane rural roads offer a more relaxing, scenic drive than most interstate highways. Although there are exceptions, interstates were designed for speed, safety, and efficiency, not for their aesthetic value. Even though the trip along two-lane highways is usually slower, they make up for it by taking you through quaint places the interstate forgot. They also make up for it by bringing you much closer to the scenery that the interstates only show you from a distance.

If you're in a hurry, the interstates will normally get you to your destination faster. If you have time, though, try to include two-lane highways in your travel plans. It may be possible to find non-interstate four-lane highways, which are a happy medium between the interstate and two-lane roads. These 'other' four-lane roads give motorists the chance to pass slow cars, with the advantage of being able to experience communities along the way, almost always with less traffic than the interstate.

Traveling through the rural West is a bit different, though. In several western states, just about the only four-lane rural highways you'll find are interstates. Don't worry, though, because the speed limit on two-lane rural highways in many of these states is 65 or 70 miles per hour. Because of this difference, driving through western states like Nevada is usually about as fast on a two-lane road as it is on the expressway. Just remember to slow down when passing through the small towns along these highways. Although having to brake to 25 miles per hour may seem like a crawl after cruising along at 70 for nearly an hour, small towns out West are usually well patrolled and strictly enforce their speed limits.

Fighting the Boredom

Honestly, even the biggest roadtrip enthusiasts get tired of driving for long hours each day. That's one reason I wouldn't take a long trip without my satellite radio. Even the radio, though, doesn't always fight the tired feeling that extended driving days can bring. So, it's important to pace yourself. Take breaks often. When you stop to use the restroom during the day, park far from the building and force yourself to walk. Walking will help keep you alert without draining your energy.

When you make a stop, don't just walk. Take some time to sit on a bench and relax for a few minutes. After sitting in the car for hours on end, though, why would you want to find a bench and sit some more? Mainly because sitting on a bench lets you sit in a different position and stretch your muscles with more flexibility. When in the car, especially if you're the driver, your legs and back are in a set position for hours at a time. Moving around, even if sitting down in a chair or bench, makes a big difference.

How often should you stop? To be honest, when I drive alone, I stop every 2 ½ to three hours. When others ride along, though, I stop more often. On average, I stop once every two hours. And I stop even more often in the morning. Personally, it's all about pacing myself during a roadtrip. If I'm going to enjoy myself on the road, I have to *do more than just drive*. I stop as often as I can, even if just to look at the local historical landmarks found along the side of the road. Instead of rushing, remember that a roadtrip is more about the journey than the destination.

Should I Drive Straight Through?

All too often I hear of roadtrippers that get in too much of a hurry. They assume they can drive 1000 miles in a day. These are the guys that fly down the highway at 85 miles an hour, tailgating and flashing their lights at anybody in front of them. These are the people that probably shouldn't be on the road at all. They're in so much of a hurry that they probably should have taken a plane instead of hitting the highway.

In the Event of an Accident

If you're involved in an accident, try to steer your vehicle out of traffic and onto the shoulder or another safe place, if possible. Make sure that no one involved in the accident is hurt. Call 911, and don't discuss who's at fault; let the police and insurance companies handle that. Cooperate with all authorities. Of course, keep your insurance information handy. Although minor damage can be repaired, allowing the trip to continue, be aware that if the damage to your vehicle is severe enough, the remainder of the roadtrip may have to be cancelled.

This type of driver often thinks he can drive straight through the night and get to their destination that much sooner, without having to pay for a hotel. For most drivers, though, driving through the night is not only a draining experience; it's a risky proposition.

I don't recommend driving through the night under most circumstances. Most late-night drivers have already been awake all day. Even if you feel alert, you're probably more tired than you realize. Consider the hazards present on the road during the daytime, and then add wandering wild animals and the fact that hazards are simply harder to see at night. Headlights shining in your eyes will tire your vision even faster than usual. In short, night driving requires a higher state of alertness than daytime driving. If you've already been on the road all day, driving through the night without additional rest can be very dangerous.

In fact, some stretches of interstate highway have so many crashes resulting from driver fatigue, that a few areas, such as I-95 through central North Carolina, are labeled 'Dead Zones' by safety organizations and state police patrols. I mention I-95 because thousands of people each year drive between South Florida and New York without stopping. If they start driving mid-afternoon, they expect to arrive at about the same hour, the following day. Although many of them make it through the night, fatigue overtakes some in the early hours of the morning, usually between 4 and 8 a.m.

Drowsy drivers cause so many fatalities in the early morning that many state troopers are on the lookout for signs of fatigued motorists. If you're tempted to make that 1000-mile drive by driving straight through the night, remember that you'll arrive more rested and more relaxed by spending a few bucks on a roadside motel. Remember, it's better to get where you're going a few hours later than not at all.

If You Have to Drive Through the Night

If lack of time or other circumstances force you to drive straight through the night, consider the following suggestions:

1. Never drive alone. If your companion can't help you drive, make sure someone else in the car *will stay awake with you the whole time* to keep you company. If you have other drivers in the car, switch off every hour or two while the other drivers rest their eyes or sleep.

2. Take advantage of your satellite radio if you have one. During the overnight hours, listen to talk radio to stay alert. Relaxing music or rock music will make you sleepy and tire your senses.

3. Make frequent stops. Try to stop every hour to use the restroom, walk around, and stretch. Stopping often will keep you from getting *too* comfortable and dozing off.

4. Stay hydrated. Drinking lots of fluids will help keep you alert. Drink caffeine in moderation; it will keep you awake, but too much of it can make you jittery.

5. Keep the temperature in the car relatively cool, even during cold weather. Turning the heat too high will make you drowsy.

6. Most importantly, if you feel drowsy, don't risk it! Take the next exit, pull off the road, and take a quick nap. A 20-minute nap often makes a world of difference. Not only will you get a little rest, you'll improve your own safety on the road.

Hopefully, your circumstances won't force you to drive through the night. Under most circumstances, you'll enjoy your trip much more if you limit driving to 10 hours per day. Most motorists would consider 15 hours on the road to be an *extremely* long day. Back in Chapter Two, we stated that over the course of a driving day, it's reasonable to average between 55 and 57 miles per hour. That means that 550 miles would be a reasonable distance to cover in one day. Driving 15 hours *could* translate to covering as much as 850 miles of interstate driving, but that would be one extremely long day.

So when should you stop for the night? My recommendation is to stop around sunset. Night driving is more stressful (and more hazardous) than daytime driving, so stopping around dusk helps ensure that you get a good night's rest. Driving all day often leaves your arms and legs tense, and it's sometimes more difficult to go to sleep right after stopping for the day. It's best to have two or three hours to unwind, make phone calls, watch TV, or just relax before going to sleep. In most cases, stopping around sunset – or shortly thereafter – will give you enough time to relax before starting again the next morning.

Challenging Situations: City Driving

If you're driving in an unfamiliar city, you may find it a real challenge just to find your way across town. Finding a specific address or location in a city far from home can be even more difficult, even with a map, but if you have a GPS system, the task becomes much easier. Just enter the street address, and the navigation system will give turn-by-turn directions to your destination.

Many drivers unfamiliar with a city are unsure of which lane to stay in. If you are navigating along city expressways without much knowledge of the area, my advice is to stay in the center lane. By staying in the center, you will avoid the merging traffic to your right, and you will keep from blocking faster traffic to your left. In addition, by staying in the center, you will never have far to go if you need to change lanes to merge for an exit.

Mountain Driving

If you plan to do any significant amount of east-west driving across the United States, you'll experience a fair share of mountainous terrain. Although mountains usually provide the most beautiful scenery on a roadtrip, driving across mountain ranges requires some forethought. Don't be afraid, though, because today's vehicles have no trouble maneuvering over mountain highways. Remember, too, that today's mountain roads are safer than ever before, with more lanes, wider shoulders, and safety features that make accidents rare.

When climbing a mountain, be on the lookout for slow moving trucks in the right lane. Interstate highways are limited to 6% grades (occasionally 7%), which make the climb in elevation relatively painless. You won't need four-wheel drive or a special vehicle to cross a mountain range on an interstate highway. When climbing a steep grade on a two-lane road, though, be careful not to pass slow-moving trucks. Those trucks will speed up significantly on the downward slope, and they may not be able to pass you, possibly causing a collision.

Most cars will have no problem with mountain driving. If you are the slightest bit unsure of your vehicle's abilities, though, turn off the air conditioning or defroster. Those features pull power from your engine, so turning them off could give your car some more pep to go up the mountain.

When descending the mountain, start slow. Try not to ride your brake down the mountain, but if you feel the need to slow down, tap your brakes gently, especially just before approaching curves. Some larger vehicles may need to shift into a lower gear on the descent, but passenger cars are usually fine in normal gear.

When driving at higher elevations, you'll notice that gasoline has a lower octane rating than what you may be used to. Your engine needs less octane at higher elevations due to the lower concentration of oxygen in the atmosphere higher up. No need to worry, though, since 85-octane gasoline works just as well at higher elevations. Personally, I've seen no decrease in fuel efficiency at higher elevations, even with lower octane gas.

When crossing mountains in wintertime, you may be required by law to carry tire chains. You can buy inexpensive tire chains (or cables) at nearly any auto supply store. They normally include installation directions, and most of the time tire chains can be installed in just a few minutes. Before ascending peaks in the Rockies, for example, you will find parking areas labeled "30 minute Chain-Up" especially for this purpose.

Desert Driving

Crossing the desert isn't as big a deal as it used to be, when cars overheated more often and air conditioning was still a novelty. Today's modern cars will have no problem crossing the desert during hot weather, as long as you keep a few things in mind.

1. **Check your fluids.** Make sure your antifreeze level is adequate, as well as engine oil and transmission fluid. Most likely the attendant already checked these fluids when you had your vehicle serviced before the trip. Still, it doesn't hurt to double check before crossing the desert.

2. **Take plenty of water.** Well, not really for the car. Intense sunlight and heat can leave you dehydrated. Drink plenty of fluids. And yes, in an emergency, water can be used to mix with antifreeze if you need to top off your coolant levels.

3. **Stop often.** These days, even the most inhospitable desert roads will have rest areas and scenic overlooks. These give the driver a chance to rest, and they also give your car a few minutes to cool down.

4. **Keep an eye on the temperature gauge.** If you notice your car starting to overheat, turn off the air conditioner. Turn on the heater instead! By turning on the heater, you give your hot engine a chance to release whatever heat it's built up. If the vehicle has a tendency to overheat, you may have to drive without air conditioning.

5. **Turn your air conditioner to "MAX" or "RECIRC".** These settings cool the air already inside your vehicle instead of cooling hotter air from outside. By recirculating the cool air, your engine works less and actually keeps you cooler!

6. Consider crossing the desert in the early morning or late evening. Temperatures are usually the hottest between 10:00 a.m. and 4:00 p.m. By avoiding these hours, you'll not only be more comfortable, your car will work less on your drive across the desert.

Driving in Poor Weather

When most of us think of roadtrips, leisurely drives in perfect weather come to mind. Most people don't enjoy roadtrips as much in inclement weather, and for good reason. Poor weather can turn an otherwise fun ride into a dangerous obstacle course.

Most travelers plan their roadtrips for the spring and summer, when weather is usually the best. However, storms can pop up in any state at any time. Being prepared and being aware of your surroundings are the best ways to drive safely through bad weather.

Before leaving on a trip, check the weather ahead of time. The Weather Channel's website (www.weather.com) has an excellent national overview, called "Interstate Forecast". This national map color-codes areas where the most hazardous driving conditions are likely. By pinpointing areas of bad weather, you can plan an alternate route or postpone your trip by a day or two, if necessary.

Much of the time, though, you'll have no choice as to the weather you experience on the road. One of the best ways to prepare, though, is to get your car ready to handle bad weather. Keeping an ice scraper, snow brush, and a can of deicer in your car makes sense anytime between October and May. Treating your windshield with a liquid water repellent, such as RainX, greatly enhances your visibility in the rain. And of course, make sure your windshield wipers are in good shape. Have the blades replaced if they're more than a year old.

When driving in the rain, the most important tip I can give you is: Slow down! Drive significantly slower in the rain. In fact, during rainy weather, *the speed limit is usually way too fast.* Keep your headlights on, and even use your hazard flashers if you're driving slower than surrounding traffic. Remember, roads are slickest when rain is just starting to fall.

Oil mixing with precipitation can cause very slippery conditions, causing your vehicle to hydroplane. So drive slowly, especially as it begins to rain.

If your roadtrip brings you to an area with snow, you'll also need to drive much slower. Don't get in a hurry, and leave much more following distance between you and the next car. Snow and ice reduce your traction, so it will require much more time to stop. Whatever you do, don't slam on the brakes. If you need to stop in the snow, start tapping the brake gently *long before* you have to stop. At the same time, don't accelerate quickly. Making sudden moves, like slamming on the brakes or jackrabbit starts, will likely make you slide (or worse).

The worst kind of winter weather for drivers is ice. Freezing rain, sleet, and ice storms are rare in America's coldest climates; they're more common across the Central Midwest and South. Ice storms can completely paralyze a region, shutting down schools and businesses for days at a time. The worst ice storms can even bring down trees and power lines, leaving an entire region in the dark. If a significant winter ice storm occurs, you won't want to be in it. While snow brushes off easily from a car, a half-inch of ice can literally leave you frozen out of your car, and it could take you a while – up to an hour – just to open the doors and get the windshield defrosted.

My recommendation is to avoid ice storms if at all possible. This is not the kind of weather that lends itself to a leisurely roadtrip. If you *must* travel in an ice storm, drive *very* slowly. Don't brake suddenly. In all honesty, if you encounter a major ice storm along a winter roadtrip, you may be better off just getting a hotel room and enjoying a couple of days indoors.

Enjoy the Road

Hopefully, your roadtrip won't include any winter weather events or severe thunderstorms. If you're lucky, the worst weather you'll experience will be the glare from the sun. And all you'll need for *that* weather event is a good pair of sunglasses.

When you travel the road, relax and enjoy your surroundings. Savor the freedom of being able to wander scenic country and unknown back roads at your leisure. Don't be afraid of taking that road you've never traveled before. Of course, after a few hours behind the wheel, you're bound to get hungry. What should you do for food on the road? That's what the next chapter will cover.

CHAPTER 6

Eating on the Road

Driving around an area and exploring its scenery from your car is just one way to enjoy your travels. For most of us, hitting the road is also a great way to enjoy new tastes and favorite foods. Eating on a roadtrip is more than just a way to stay nourished; it's recreation unto itself.

In this chapter, we'll be discussing the vast array of food options you have when on the road. Whether you're eating healthy, want to pig out at buffets, or just want to sample local cuisine, there's something for everyone to enjoy.

Packing Your Own Food

One of the best ways to save money on food is to take your own. When preparing your own meals, you have the option of purchasing the food you want at your local supermarket. You'll get to shop around for the best prices and be in control of your own nutrition.

If you decide to take along prepared meals from home, remember that you probably won't want to eat every meal out of a cooler, unless you're seriously strapped for cash. When you get tired of self-prepared meals, remember that low-cost restaurants are in abundance these days, and they provide a nice break from eating out of the cooler.

You'll want to invest in a quality cooler that's the right size for your needs. Notice the word *invest*. That means you'll have to pay for quality when buying a cooler. Cheap foam coolers can be had for as little as two dollars, but you'll wish you had paid more when it topples, and ten pounds of melting ice are now saturating your car's interior.

If you're traveling solo, a small cooler will work fine. For my solo roadtrips, I take a small cooler that's about 12 inches in length. Larger groups will need a larger cooler. My favorite cooler is designed to store beverages in ice, but it has a small plastic shelf that keeps sandwiches elevated above the ice. These types of coolers keep drinks ice cold without making the rest of your food soggy.

It's much easier to carry cans of beverages instead of larger 2-liter bottles. Although 2-liter bottles are cheaper per serving than cans, pouring a bottle into a cup in a moving car can cause a sticky spill. Think seriously, though, about carrying drinks with little or no sugar. Riding in a car doesn't burn many calories, and you may start to feel jittery if you drink nothing but soft drinks all day. Consider buying juice and bottled water instead of just soda.

When preparing meals to take on the road, don't just limit yourself to sandwiches. Sandwiches do tend to get soggy or stale after the first day, and you'll want a greater variety, too. Consider taking cheese and crackers, fresh fruit, potato chips, fresh vegetables with dressing, salads, and beef jerky. Many of these foods, when sealed and kept in a cooler, will last several days.

Salads, sliced fruit, and vegetables will stay freshest in a cooler if you store them in plastic zippered bags. Buy several of the one-gallon variety, and you'll be able to store as much fresh fruit and vegetables as you want.

Shopping for Groceries

If you're concerned with food spoilage, you might want to consider stopping at local grocery stores or supermarkets along your route. You'll be ensured fresh food every day, and buying foods in local markets brings you closer to the communities you pass through. Shopping at local stores is also a great way to meet locals and get tips on area attractions.

If you get tired of eating food you've prepared yourself, try stopping at a local supermarket's delicatessen for a prepared sandwich or salad. Most supermarkets sell simple prepared meals for much less than you would spend in a restaurant. You'll likely find that five dollars can buy a fresh, tasty, locally prepared meal.

If your trip takes you by parks or other roadside stops, you might want to consider having a barbecue. Most parks provide barbecue pits; you provide the charcoal, lighter fluid, match, and the food. An impromptu barbecue is a fun way to relax after spending the day on the road. You'll have to take your own seasonings and sauce, but if you like to barbecue, enjoying one away from home is a great way to unwind.

Most people, though, aren't going to want to haul a big bag of charcoal, seasonings, and raw meat in the trunks of their cars. If you'd still like to enjoy a picnic on the road without the hassle of having to cook it yourself, try stopping by a local supermarket and picking up a bag of chicken, along with your favorite side dish. A simple picnic is an easy and memorable way to eat while on a roadtrip.

Quick Meals

Most roadtrippers are in a hurry when they stop to eat. That's probably why so many of us choose fast food restaurants when on the road. They're familiar places, they're quick, they're convenient, and they're usually cheap. Still, eat fast food in moderation when traveling. The high fat, high calorie, low nutritional value of many fast foods can keep you from feeling your best, especially if you're sitting in the car for long periods. And remember that you're on the road to discover something new, not to eat the same food you had for lunch last Tuesday.

Many fast food restaurants, especially at lunchtime, can be so busy that the crowd detracts from the experience. If there's a line, you may find that eating fast food may actually take just as long as a sit-down meal. And watch those prices! Many of the *combos*, *value meals*, or *specials* at that fast food place are just as expensive – if not more so – than a filling plate lunch at a sit-down restaurant. The service will probably be better at the latter establishment, too.

If you really need to get a quick meal, and the fast food place is the restaurant of choice (or necessity), try to eat as healthy as you can. A big cheeseburger may have more fat than you should eat *all day*. Choose a salad instead, and go easy on the dressing. Remember, regular salad dressing may easily have ten times the calories of the entire salad. If you really want a burger, a plain hamburger is healthier than one that's loaded with cheese and special sauce.

When looking for variety on the road, and you need it in a hurry, consider stopping at a buffet. Most buffets can get you to a table and to your meal within a few minutes of arriving. The variety of buffet-style restaurants is much greater than just a few years ago, too. Although most feature Chinese food or typical American food, many also offer seafood or ethnic foods not commonly found at this price point. And speaking of price, most buffets provide a full meal at a very reasonable price, usually in the 10-dollar range.

As every road traveler knows, buffets are easy to find. They're often advertised on billboards miles ahead. Most of us are familiar with the common buffet chains: Hometown Buffet, Old Country Buffet, Ryan's, Golden Corral, Sirloin Stockade. Some of the best buffets I've tried, though, are of the non-chain, local variety. So if you're thinking of stopping at a smorgasbord, don't be afraid to try a place you've never heard of before. Stop by the restaurant, and ask to see what's on the buffet. A reputable restaurant will allow you to look before you decide. Check to see if the place looks clean. If it's not what you're looking for, just say "Thank you" and leave. You'll find something better down the road.

If you decide to try a buffet, remember a word of warning: Don't eat too much! Unless you really plan to do some serious exercising, you'll be sitting in the car for hours, and you won't be burning many calories. Many cheaper buffets feature items chocked full of bread and carbohydrates. Although they'll fill your stomach fast, they may also make you regret eating so much. So go easy on the heavy foods!

Full-Service Restaurants

If you're not in the mood for a buffet, but don't want fast food, either, you'll find a plethora of choices available on the road.   Local diners and

Roadside Restaurants Worth a Visit

The following restaurants are all located along Historic Route 66. You'll find other great places to eat in your travels, but these three diners are not to be missed.

Cozy Dog – The famous restaurant known for its special deep-fried corn dog. This place has been open since the 50's and the recipe hasn't changed a bit. Along Historic Route 66 in Springfield, Illinois.

The Big Texan Steak Ranch – Known for the 72-ounce steak, free if you can eat it in an hour. The food and ambience will give you a real taste of Texas, even if you're just passing through. Located along Route 66 – I-40 as it's called today – in Amarillo, Texas.

66 Diner – Located in Albuquerque, New Mexico, along Historic Route 66 – Central Avenue – this classic diner is a good place to try old-fashioned American food cooked the New Mexico way. Hot chilies are ground into the meat here to give the cheeseburgers an extra kick. And the ambience makes it feel like you've gone back to the 50's.

other family-style restaurants welcome travelers, and you'll probably find these restaurants a good option at mealtime.

Plenty of mid-range casual dining chains have dotted cities, suburbia, and even rural America over the last 15 years or so. At most of these spots, you'll pay about ten dollars for even the simplest of meals, if you include a drink and tip. However, these chains, which include restaurants such as Applebee's, Rafferty's, Olive Garden, Cracker Barrel, Chili's, and T.G.I. Friday's, still have deals, and you're likely to get a reasonable, predictable experience when dining there. However, much like the fast food chains, these restaurants thrive on consistency, so the location in Miami is likely to have the same menu, food, and even décor as the location in Boise.

Think about the purpose of your roadtrip. If you're simply traveling to get somewhere in a reasonable amount of time, the chain restaurants will give you what you want at a reasonable price. If you're driving to really get a glimpse of culture in different parts of the country, you'll probably be missing out on local cuisine and homemade specialties by visiting the chains exclusively.

Although I enjoy going to the chain restaurants, especially if there's a special deal, the fact is that the experience is practically identical no matter where you go. So, when on the road, visit locally owned restaurants and diners when possible. Let your meal choice be influenced by your location; you'll get a better feel for where you are, and the meal will be more memorable.

For example, when in the South, try southern cuisine. Eat Cajun food in Louisiana. Eat Chicago style pizza in, you guessed it... Chicago. Have a cheesesteak in Philly. Eat seafood on the coast. You get the idea. Meals like these are often cheaper than the chain restaurants. Even if the food isn't exactly what you were expecting, the meal will be a lot more memorable than just a stop at another fast food place.

Be Flexible at Mealtime

Don't feel that you're tied to any rules when eating on the road; you aren't. If you really want to eat fast food at every meal, to the tune of a now-famous documentary, you're free to do that. If your budget dictates that you can only subsist on cereal and baloney sandwiches out of a cooler, then you're free to do that. The suggestions in this chapter are just that – suggestions. Hopefully, you'll find an idea you can use to discover more dining options on your next roadtrip.

One area in which flexibility really pays off, though, is the time you choose to eat out. The same restaurant that was filled to capacity at noon may be practically empty two hours later. You may have to wait an hour to get a table for dinner at 7:00, but you might walk right to a table at 5:00. Since you probably don't want to spend your precious vacation time waiting in a restaurant lobby, try stopping for meals at off-peak hours. You'll likely get more attentive service mid-afternoon, and prices are often lower, too.

Staying Healthy

Anyone who has traveled extensively knows that you're more susceptible to acute illness and general malaise while away from home. The combination of different foods, different drinking water, and a general change of routine can be a shock to your body. The foods you eat really *do* have an impact on how you feel. That's why roadtrippers should be careful to stay healthy and eat healthy on the road.

Although you'll want to try new foods, not all of them will necessarily be good for you. That's okay, but remember that *whatever you eat, do so in moderation.* If you treat your roadtrip as a vacation, then don't stress about eating a few tasty, high-fat foods here and there. At the same time, eating foods that are *extremely* out of the ordinary for you, especially when spending hours seated in the car, can make you feel lethargic, achy, or even nauseous.

Of course, there are several things you can do to eat healthy and maintain your general well-being while on a roadtrip. Consider drinking bottled water if you're sensitive to tap water, and drink lots of it. Drinking plenty of fluids will keep you from getting dehydrated. If it's a good idea for your daily routine, it's an even better idea to drink plenty of water while away from home.

If you plan to eat seafood, stick with the kind that's been cooked thoroughly. Fish, shrimp, and crab legs are normally pretty safe. Seafood or shellfish that's undercooked or raw, such as oysters, may be best to avoid, especially if you happen to be far from the coast. In that situation, your meal might not be very fresh. Avoid heavy seafood meals after 8 p.m. Your body requires extra time to digest these meals, and going to bed less than two hours after this kind of meal may make you sick.

When on the road, pack a few Pepto-Bismol tablets (they're not as messy as the liquid form) and a few antacid tablets. If your meal doesn't agree with you a few hours down the road, at least you'll have a quick treatment.

Food that's Good. . . for You

Most food at roadside restaurants is sold based on convenience. It's quick to prepare, it's quick to serve, and it's usually quick to eat. Although it may taste good, it might not be quite as good from a nutritional stand-point. Many restaurants load their food with fat and grease. Some still use the dreaded *trans* fat, the type that should really be avoided completely.

If you're on a diet, or you just want to eat better on the road, you have plenty of options – and they don't involve eating a salad three times a day, either. These days, most national chain restaurants provide nutrition information for all their items in small leaflets that are readily available to customers. If you don't see this information when you go in, ask your server. Many restaurants, especially at the mid-level casual dining chains, identify low-fat dishes on the menu with some kind of mark, making it easy to identify food that's good for you.

Local, non-chain restaurants and diners may not have as many health-conscious options. Even at these places, look for the words *grilled* and *fresh* on the menu; they often identify meals prepared with your health needs in mind. When in doubt, ask your server. It's their job to describe the menu if you need help. Your server can suggest low-fat items or other foods that meet your dietary restrictions. Remember, an otherwise unhealthy meal may suddenly become a better choice once you hold the gravy, special sauce, or dressing.

Eating can be as much a part of the roadtrip experience as the destination you choose or the sights you see along the way. If you end up at a restaurant you regret later, don't stress over it too much. Take it with a grain of salt – no pun intended – and just consider it part of the ride. It's part of the roadtrip experience, and you'll probably laugh about it tomorrow. Try to pick eateries that you don't get to visit in your own neighborhood, and don't be afraid to try something different.

CHAPTER 7

Where to Stay

If your roadtrip is going to last more than, say, one day, you're going to need a place to sleep. Unless you're planning to bunk with friends or relatives, you'll likely stay in hotels. This chapter is designed to help you find the best lodging for your circumstances – and budget – and get the best deal in the process.

Nearly every hotel booking engine has a separate way of classifying hotels according to amenities, price, or some other specification. I have my own way of classifying hotels, too, but there are no stars, no thumbs up, and no dollar signs used in my rankings. It's much simpler than that. Here are my four classes of hotels.

High-End Hotels

These hotels are the most elegant and most expensive. They include everything from a typical Hilton all the way up to the Ritz-Carlton. They also include most full-service hotels such as Marriott, Hyatt, Sheraton, Radisson, and Crowne Plaza. These hotels almost always charge at least $100 a night, and in city centers, they can cost up to four times that.

Although these hotels bill themselves as full-service, be aware that at this level, you will pay extra for that service. Breakfast will cost extra, you will usually pay extra for parking, and you will likely even pay extra for Wi-Fi internet service.

High-end hotels are perfect for couples who want a weekend getaway or vacation. They are also designed to suit the needs of business travelers. At this class of hotel, full-service business centers and even convention facilities are common. Many guests at high-end hotels are traveling on someone else's dime, though, so they don't mind the $10 parking, the $10 internet charge, or even the $15 breakfast. (By the way, those charges are *per-day*, and they *are* typical.)

What you need to know is that high-end hotels are *destination* hotels, not the best places to stop alongside the interstate to catch a few winks before continuing along the highway. Don't be surprised if, when checking in at these places after a long day on the road, you get funny looks from other guests in the lobby. Don't worry; they may just think you're lost. Nothing against these hotels; they're just meant for a different purpose.

Roadside Chains

These hotels are the typical chains you find at interstate exits, and the price should be less than $100 per night. The number of hotels at this level are too numerous to list entirely, but some familiar names include Best Western, Super 8, Comfort Inn, Microtel, Hampton Inn, Fairfield Inn, Baymont Inn, La Quinta, and Days Inn. There's a somewhat more complete list in the "Roadtrip Resources" chapter at the end of this book.

I'm using the word *hotels* mainly for convenience. Technically, a *hotel* is a lodging establishment with interior corridors, whereas a *motel*, short for *motor hotel*, has exterior corridors. In other words, at a motel, the door to your room will open directly to the great outdoors. At a hotel, though, the door will open into a hallway. The chains listed above are a mix of hotels and motels, and many of these chains actually have some hotel locations, with motel locations in other cities. The La Quinta brand, for example, operates most of their locations as motels, with other, newer properties as hotels.

Many travelers prefer the added security of the hotel setup. At a motel, any stranger can knock on your door. At a hotel, though, visitors have to get past the front desk first. Hotel-type properties tend to have cleaner carpets in the rooms, simply because guests have to walk farther to access them.

Roadside chains always welcome roadtrippers. In fact, highway travelers are the bread and butter of these hotels. They will nearly always be full near the holidays and on the weekends. When these properties are full, the parking lot will be full of cars and vans filled with fellow roadtrippers' gear.

Often, hotels at this level offer the best bang for the buck. Your rate will nearly always include free parking, free Wi-Fi, free local phone calls, and some type of free breakfast. Whether it's called a continental breakfast, a deluxe breakfast, or something else, it's worth it to have the most important meal of the day included in the price of your room, especially if you've got a group of three or four traveling.

Most roadside chains offer at least a minimal discount, 10 to 15 percent, to guests who present a AAA or AARP card at check-in. Be aware, though, that this discount is off the rack rate, or most expensive rate, so you may be able to secure a better deal elsewhere.

What roadside chains do well is offer a predictable, reasonable level of quality at a fair price. The President probably won't be staying there when he's in town, but you're likely to be quite comfortable at a roadside chain hotel. The rooms are often identical in design to those at high-end hotels, and you may find that some properties actually give you *more* room.

Is one of the roadside chains any better than another? In my opinion, yes. Since nearly all of these properties now offer Wi-Fi, free local calls, and free parking, our attention turns to room quality and breakfast quality.

Fairfield Inns, Hampton Inns, Holiday Inn Express, and Comfort Inns seem to offer excellent quality across the brand. I've had the fewest problems with housekeeping issues and general cleanliness at these hotels. And their breakfasts offer quite a variety, with both hot and cold items on the buffet. In fact, one of the best hotel breakfasts I've ever had was at the Holiday Inn Express in Ciudad Juárez, Mexico. Breakfast was served daily in the hotel's grand atrium, complete with servers bringing drinks and clearing dishes. The buffet was complete with both Mexican and American breakfast items, tropical and traditional juices, fruits, vegetables, and meat items, completely free for hotel guests.

Not all hotels offer this level of service or variety on their continental breakfasts. I've stayed at a few motels that promise a continental breakfast, but deliver only a paltry selection of donuts and coffee. Better hotels at this level will offer an inviting breakfast room, instead of just a couple of tables strewn about the lobby.

Most of my hotel stays on roadtrips are at roadside chains. They usually offer a predictable product because they have a corporate image to maintain. If you're not sure about a particular property, search for it at travel review websites like tripadvisor.com. Although one or two bad reviews shouldn't bother you, any property whose negative reviews outnumber their positive ones should raise eyebrows.

Mom-and-Pop Motels

You know what I mean. I'm referring to those motels you see on the side of the road, usually in small towns, that advertise those really cheap rates on billboards alongside the highway. Often, they really are run by Mom and Pop, or Grandma and Grandpa, or some other family combination, complete with help from the rest of the family and a few other local employees.

Although Mom-and-Pop motels don't belong to any corporate chain, they may be operated by a local business in conjunction with a restaurant or even another motel. The decorations may be dated, but the price usually can't be beat. And you're likely to find many of the same amenities here as you will at roadside chains.

Most Mom-and-Pop motels charge less than $60 a night. Motels at this level throughout the South may charge as little as $20 a night during the winter or midweek for single occupancy.

Many travelers avoid these places, because there is a certain risk to staying at Mom-and-Pop motels. Since they have no corporate reputation supporting them, they have to attract customers with lower prices; hence, the highway billboard advertisement is necessary for these motels.

The quality at non-chain motels varies wildly. You may find one that's as nice as any chain motel, if not nicer. But there are plenty of dogs out there, too. If you stop at a Mom-and-Pop motel and aren't sure about the quality, ask to see one of the rooms first. A reputable motel won't have a problem with showing you the product *before* you commit.

Since the cost is less at Mom-and-Pop motels, the amenities will likely be fewer, too. You'll probably have to forget about a free breakfast, and the furnishings may not be as new or as good as at a chain property. You may find that the rooms are a little worn; maybe the towels are thinner and the walls still have 80's-style paneling. Although more and more motels offer Wi-Fi, you should never have to pay for it at this level of motel. And if the manager tries to charge you for parking at one of these places, it's a good sign you should just walk away and look for something else down the road.

Extended Stay Properties

Ten years ago, extended stay hotels were virtually unheard of. Today, they're popping up increasingly in suburban areas where individuals often need to stay on business for weeks at a time. Sometimes, these hotels are found at interstate exits, but more commonly they're located near business campuses and even residential areas.

The concept of the extended stay hotel is markedly different from the other three categories; that's why I think they warrant a separate listing. Extended stay properties give you a room with a small living area and kitchen, complete with utensils, pots, and pans. It's almost like a studio-size apartment, except in a hotel environment. Housekeeping service is provided only about once a week. If you're staying for less than a week, you're expected to take out your own trash, make your own bed, and wash your own dishes.

Extended stay properties have amenities that are different from most other hotels. Although you'll probably get free local phone calls, you may have pay for the Wi-Fi. Extended Stay America, for example, charges guests $5 *per stay* to use the internet, so you could stay a whole month and pay only a one-time charge for unlimited web access. Room rates, though, are usually quite reasonable, with typical rates well under $80 a night.

On the other hand, you can forget the free continental breakfast, but you do get your own kitchen to prepare any meal you want. This can be handy, especially if you need to prepare lunch for the next day on the road. The fridge is normally full-size, so it's easy to keep drinks or other perishables cool overnight.

The furnishings at most extended-stay hotels are basic but functional. Expect one bed in the room; extra bedding usually costs extra. Expect a very simple check-in area with limited hours. The front desk at these properties may close as early as 8:00 p.m. with little recourse if you arrive late. Under the best of circumstances, a security guard may be able to let you into your room if you have a reservation.

During the week, extended stay properties may be lined with pickup trucks and other heavy-duty vehicles. Construction workers and other laborers often stay at these places when on an extended assignment. You may find that guests treat these properties just like their own homes; they'll wash clothes, have a barbecue in the lawn, or even sit in front of their door and drink beer.

Extended stay hotels can provide a good value, especially on the weekends, but be aware that the ambience may make some travelers nervous. I've been to some extended stay properties that felt more like a run-down apartment complex; others have a more upscale feel. Use your best judgment to decide whether this class of lodging is for you.

What Amenities Do You Want?

Almost every hotel or motel can be classified into one of the four groups just described. Some hotels, though, straddle two of the levels. Courtyard by Marriott, for example, is not exactly a roadside chain. Because it caters more to business travelers, Courtyards tend to provide the amenities business travelers need (free Wi-Fi, comfortable desk and office chair, business center, meeting rooms), but you'll have to pay close to ten bucks for breakfast, something roadtrippers usually try to avoid. Most Holiday Inn hotels (not to be confused with Holiday Inn Express) are similar. Although they usually provide free Wi-Fi, some Holiday Inn's still charge for local calls, and they usually charge for breakfast, too.

Think about the amenities that are important to you before making a reservation or booking a room. Do you *have* to have breakfast included with your room? Is free wireless internet a must? Or would you forgo one or more other amenities to have a nice workout room and indoor pool? Maybe you really need a kitchen in your room. Each of the four levels of lodging has features that the others usually don't. Below, I've listed what I think to be the most attractive amenity at each level of lodging:

High-End Hotels	Indoor Pool, Whirlpool, & Workout Area
Roadside Chains	Free Breakfast & Wireless Internet
Mom-and-Pop Motels	Really Low Prices
Extended Stay	Kitchen Facilities

Depending on the kind of traveler you are, a different level of service may appeal to you. Be flexible, and you'll find plenty of places along your route that will fit your preferences.

To Reserve or Not to Reserve?

Many travelers like the security of knowing where they'll be spending the night several days ahead of time, so they reserve their rooms, either by phone or internet, before leaving home. However, if you're on a long roadtrip, you might not know exactly where you'll end up each day. Many roadtrippers like the freedom of being able to travel until they decide to stop for the night. Be warned, though; you *may* pay more looking for a room late in the evening.

If you decide to reserve a room a few days in advance, make sure that the rate you accept is cancelable. If not, your plans may change, and you'll still be stuck with a charge for a room you never used. When in doubt, ask. Often, the absolute cheapest rates a hotel offers are non-cancelable or non-refundable. Some of the deals with online booking engines, like Expedia or Orbitz, are prepaid or non-cancelable. If you choose to accept these rates, your plans become set in stone.

Some of the best rates, though, can actually be had by *not* reserving ahead of time. If you've stopped at an interstate rest area or a large gas station, you've probably seen those small brochures filled with hotel coupons. Those coupons usually offer the lowest rate provided directly by the hotel. Even if you decide not to use the coupons, these brochures can give you an idea of the hotels available in an area.

One word of caution when using these coupons, though. Most of them have restrictions on when they can be redeemed. For example, one roadside chain hotel may advertise a rate of $49.99 in the coupon book. Read the fine print, though, and you may see that that rate is good Sunday through Thursday only; weekends are $10 extra. The rate may also state "1-2 people", which means that if you bring a third person into the room, you'll pay $10 more. So a Friday night stay with three people now becomes $70 before tax. The rate may still be decent, but nothing special. The lesson? Read the fine print, and be aware of any restrictions *before* you use the coupon.

The coupons are also void if the hotel happens to be more than about 85% full that night. If the parking lot is full when you arrive, it's likely that the rate won't be honored, if there's a room available at all.

Most brochure coupons have blackout dates, too. The fine print will often read "Not valid during holidays or special events." If there's a convention in town that week, the hotel can refuse to honor the rate. And what constitutes a holiday? Christmas is obviously a holiday, but what about Columbus Day? And how about President's Day?

The point is this: the hotels will honor their coupons when they want to. If you've been driving all day, you won't want to schlep around an unfamiliar town looking for a place to stay, only to be told they're not accepting the coupon. Call ahead! Use the phone number printed on the coupon. You don't have to make a reservation, just ask if they're accepting the coupon rate of X dollars tonight. You'll save time, and it will give you a little peace of mind to know that the hotel you want is offering a good rate.

Getting the Best Rate Without Coupons

Even if you don't have a coupon brochure, you're likely to get a discount at a hotel by simply asking for one. If you choose this route, though, be aware that you could actually pay *more* by waiting until the night of the stay to ask for a discount, unless you are armed with information.

1. Midweek is cheaper. Most roadside chain hotels offer lower rates midweek, Sunday through Thursday. Be prepared to pay more on the weekends. An exception to this rule would be high-end hotels, especially those that cater to business travelers. Those hotels, especially those in downtown areas, often have better rates on the weekend.

2. Check out the parking lot. When you drive up to a hotel in the evening, take a quick drive around the parking lot. If it looks full, the hotel likely has few vacancies, and you will probably pay more. When the hotel is near its maximum occupancy, there's less room for negotiation. If you're looking for a deal and the parking lot is full, it may be worth it to try the next hotel, or even the next town.

3. Travel in the off-season. In most of the country, hotel rooms are cheaper in the fall and winter, when fewer people are on the road. Some holidays, though, are major road travel times, so prices will be higher then, too. Plan for hotels to be packed in the days leading up to Christmas, Thanksgiving, New Year's, Fourth of July, and Labor Day. In traditional vacation areas, like much of Florida, there's not much of an off-season, since people tend to go there year-round.

4. Try not to pay rack rate. The rack rate is the highest price a hotel charges for a room on a given night. The only thing you really need to know about the rack rate is that *you don't want to pay it*! Most hotels give discounts of at least 10% for members of AAA and senior citizens. If you ask and are friendly, many desk clerks will give you a small discount just for asking. Discounts usually *are* available, even when the rack rate is high.

5. Stay in the suburbs. If you plan to spend the night in a major metropolitan area, be aware that suburban hotels are usually much cheaper than hotels in the city center. In addition, suburban hotels rarely charge for parking, while downtown hotels may charge as much as $40 per night for this privilege. A suburban hotel may be going for $80, while the exact same hotel chain may be charging twice that price for a similar room downtown.

6. Be prepared to walk away. If you don't like the rate, that is. When you're looking for a deal, you may have to try two or three different hotels to find what you want. If you've been driving all day, you may be tired. So don't attempt to go bargain hunting for a hotel room much after 8:00 p.m. In fact, start looking much earlier. The earlier in the day you start looking, the less chance you have of acquiescing to an expensive rate because you're simply too tired to keep driving.

7. **Get away from the interstate.** Hotels within sight of an interstate exit often attract more traffic and can afford to charge guests more. Properties a little farther off the expressway, especially those in towns not served by the interstate at all, are likely to charge much less.

Online Deals

These days, most savvy travelers book their hotel rooms online. Websites such as Expedia, Orbitz, Hotwire, and Priceline make it easy to compare prices and amenities for different hotels. If you've used these booking engines, you know that all you need is a city and a date, and it's easy to find dozens of hotels that meet your criteria.

Some of these sites have sales and coupons that can save you even more money. Each of the major booking engines has a weekly e-mail newsletter. Sign up for it, and you'll receive notification of major sales or special deals on hotels, as well as other travel products. In the next chapter, we'll go into detail on how to save serious money by booking hotels online, especially at the last minute.

Alternatives to Hotels and Motels: Campgrounds

Hotels are good at providing a predictable level of comfort when you need it. Sometimes you need – or want – something different. Part of a roadtrip is discovering new places and relaxing in your surroundings. And what better way to relax and enjoy your surroundings than to go camping?

It's easy to find campgrounds. They're advertised in most states on interstate exit service signs, and print directories can be found in the travel section of most libraries and bookstores. Today, most campgrounds have an online presence, too. You'll find lists and reviews of campgrounds readily available on the web, complete with directions and pricing information.

Even if you plan to spend most of your nights in hotels and motels along the way, it's well worth it to consider camping, at least for one night. Not only will you save some money, you'll get to enjoy the outdoors and get some well-needed exercise.

If you plan to go camping while on the road, you'll need a tent. Sporting goods stores and even discount chains carry plenty of tents. Make sure that your tent will hold as many people as there are traveling with you. Beware, though: most tents, when occupied by the number of adults specified on the label, make for a *very* tight squeeze. For example, I have a tent that states '3-4 adults' on the label. This tent measures about eight feet by six feet, and I'm not sure that four adults could fit in that tent. Two adults, maybe. Keep this in mind when shopping for a tent. When in doubt, get a tent that's a little bigger than you think you'll need. It's always better to have too much room than not enough.

If you're traveling in a smaller car, is it still possible to go camping? Definitely! Camping out of a smaller car may be a tight squeeze, though, especially with more than two or three travelers. Tents and other camping gear *do* take up space in the trunk, so vans or SUV's may be better suited. For one or two people, though, there should be plenty of space for basic camping gear in an average-sized car.

Camping Gear

What other camping gear should you take along? You'll need a sleeping bag or some other type of bedding. Be aware that most places do get a little cool at night, except in the warmest nights of summer, so consider taking a blanket, even in early summer. Lying directly on the ground, with only a sleeping bag and tent fabric separating your body from the hard earth, will be very uncomfortable after the first 30 minutes. So spend a few dollars on a good camping pad or air mattress; your back will thank you. And don't forget to take a comfortable pillow, preferably one from home.

Most tents are easy to set up, and one or two people should be able to handle the job in about 20 minutes. Practice putting up your tent in the backyard at home. It can be frustrating trying to read the directions in an unfamiliar location, especially as it's getting dark. By practicing with your tent ahead of time, you'll be able to set up camp faster, leaving more time for enjoying your new surroundings.

Speaking of putting up your tent in time, be aware of the time you'll be stopping for the night. If you plan on camping, you can't afford to drive until 8:00 p.m. if sunset is at 8:30. Make plans to stop at least *two hours* before nightfall; otherwise, you'll likely be setting up the tent in the dark. Keep an eye on the local weather forecast, too. If it calls for anything more than light rain, you might want to rethink camping, at least *that* day. Otherwise, you'll need extra time in the morning to let your tent fabric dry before repacking.

Where should you plan to camp? Fortunately, there's a myriad of options. Commercial campgrounds, such as K.O.A., are a great choice if you've never been camping before. You'll pay more at these campgrounds, sometimes as much as $40 a night, but often much less. For your money, though, you'll get much more. Commercial campgrounds are equipped with full electric hookups, so you won't be isolated from civilization. Many also feature swimming pools, hiking trails, game rooms, general stores, and even wireless internet.

Beyond the amenities, though, commercial campgrounds usually have a full-time staff whose job it is to assist guests and maintain security onsite. Since these places are private property, only paying guests are allowed to enter the campground.

Public campgrounds are very common in rural areas and offer some amenities, too, though not quite as extensive as commercial grounds. State and national parks offer campers reasonable prices, usually well under $25 a night. Be aware that many of the more popular national parks – such as Yellowstone and Yosemite – get *very* busy in the summer months, and you'd be well advised to reserve your campsite months ahead.

Most public campgrounds have a ranger or other employee who will collect your camping fee and provide help in emergencies. Otherwise, you normally won't find swimming pools or Wi-Fi on these facilities. You'll usually have access to an electric hookup and bathhouse at your site, but other than that, you'll be 'roughing it'.

If you want even more of a wilderness experience, try camping in national forests. Most national forests offer campgrounds for less than $15 a night. The campsites will be simpler, and you might not have an electric hookup. The bathhouse may not be very inviting, and it may not offer complete shower facilities. Instead of a paying a full-time ranger, you will usually put your camping fee into an 'honor box' upon entering the campground. If you're on a very tight budget, you can't beat the price of the national forests.

Another secret about national forests: they allow *dispersed camping*, and you don't even have to pay. In other words, unless you see a sign that specifically prohibits camping, you're normally allowed to camp anywhere in a national forest outside the 'official' campground, completely free of charge. It's the best camping deal out there, and most people don't know about it. Of course, you won't have a bathroom, electricity, or running water, but you'll get a lot closer to nature. If you choose the dispersed camping option, though, remember to clean up after yourself! You're expected to take *all* trash when you leave your site and *completely* extinguish any fire you may start.

Hostels: Another Option

Visitors from Europe often ask about hostels when visiting the U.S.A. The fact is, hostels just aren't that common in the United States, and most Americans have never stayed in one. If you look for them, though, you'll find a few hostels scattered about the land, usually in larger cities.

If you've never heard of a hostel, it's basically a communal hotel. In most hostels, up to eight guests – often strangers – share a room filled with twin beds. Hostels usually offer a modest living area and internet access, too. Obviously, they're great places to meet fellow travelers, and they're more popular among travelers under 30. Essentially though, you're paying for a bed and a place to sleep.

Most hostels also offer more private accommodations as well. They have a few 'suites' that mimic regular hotel rooms designed for couples and small groups traveling together. These mini-suites usually start at around $60 a night. If you don't mind sleeping in the communal area, expect to pay at least $20 *per person*.

My recommendation? If you're a young, solo traveler who wants to meet new people, go ahead and give the hostel a try. However, if the idea of sleeping around strangers makes you nervous, hostels might not be for you. If your car group includes three or more people – or even as few as two – you may actually pay *more* at a hostel than you would at a Mom-and-Pop motel (sometimes even a roadside chain). Although there aren't

---

Sleeping on a Couch?

If you're low on cash, but would rather not sleep in your car, have a look at CouchSurfing's website, found at www.couchsurfing.com. Hundreds of thousands of hosts from around the world have opened up their homes to travelers at no charge. All they ask in return is that you fill out a profile and offer to host travelers, as well.

The system seems pretty safe, as there's a 'vouching' system, similar to Ebay's feedback system. Those who've successfully hosted travelers earn a higher score and are considered to be 'safer' bets than newbies to the site. If you're not sure about the concept, take a look around the website; it's a great way to make friends on the road!

---

many hostels in this country, many travelers and backpackers swear by them.

What About Sleeping in Your Car?

Although this is not the best option for road travelers, the fact is that many roadtrippers have done this at one time or another. In fact, sleeping in the car is really quite a popular option. Just stop by nearly any interstate rest area between the hours of midnight and 4 a.m., and you're likely to see several vehicles parked. Their occupants are probably trying to get a few hours sleep before continuing on their journey. Sleeping in the car is arguably the most uncomfortable, worst way to get rest while on the road. But I know people do it, so let me offer my advice on how to do it safely.

The car *is* the cheapest place to sleep when on a roadtrip – absolutely free. Is it legal, though? Yes. It is completely legal to sleep in your car. As long as the car is your property, you're free to eat in it, sleep in it, and so forth. Really, the more important part is making sure your car is *parked* legally. In a few states, it is illegal to park overnight at a rest area. In every state, it is illegal to trespass, or to park your car on someone else's private property without their permission. So where should you park, if you decide to sleep in your car? More about that later. . . .

The big question is: Is it safe to sleep in your car? The answer is: it depends. It's a lot safer to find an exit and sleep in your car than it is to drive drowsy. Most highway patrolmen would agree. They would rather see a motorist sleeping for a few hours in his car than seeing him crash into a tree because of drowsiness.

If you need to pull off the highway and sleep for a few hours, most highway rest areas are safe. Those that aren't will be heavily patrolled by law enforcement. In most states away from the two coasts, it is perfectly legal to park at a rest area. Check the signage; if overnight parking is prohibited, it will be stated prominently. Remember to lock your doors, leave the windows cracked, with the keys in a handy place in case you need to leave quickly.

After being at the rest area for a few minutes, try to gauge the mood. If you get a bad feeling or see anyone suspicious, feel free to drive away. That's one advantage that sleeping in your car *does* have; you can drive away if you sense trouble, something you can't do in a hotel room or campground. Remember, though, that sleeping at a rest area is not something I recommend; it's simply a last resort if you need to catch a few hours' sleep before moving on.

If overnight parking is prohibited at rest areas in your locale, where can you park? Often, truck stops or large 24-hour gas stations permit drivers to park for a few hours and rest. Since these are on private property, ask permission before doing so. It may be harder to rest well at these places due to truck noise and bright lights, but they generally are safe.

It's been said that large Wal-Mart parking lots permit overnight parking. Sometimes up to a dozen RV's can be found in a Wal-Mart parking lot on a summer night. Most Wal-Mart stores allow this practice, but it's best to ask a manager before doing this; some local ordinances prohibit overnight parking on large lots in their city limits. Some travelers prefer hospital parking lots, but the same advice applies: Don't draw attention to yourself; be inconspicuous.

The few times I've had to sleep in my car for a few hours, I've found a quiet country road – plentiful and easy to find in the midsection of the country – and parked there. Look for a lightly traveled gravel road, pull far to the side so cars can pass, and park for the night. You probably won't be bothered; if anyone knocks on your window, they're likely to be friendly people asking if you need some help.

Are there any places you definitely *shouldn't* park to sleep? Of course. Never park on the shoulder of an interstate highway – or any other major highway – to sleep. And never park in someone's driveway overnight; you're likely to be asked to leave, or in the worst case, you could be fined or taken to jail for trespassing. Try to avoid businesses that normally have empty parking lots at night; a stray car on the lot could arouse suspicions.

If you sleep in your car on a roadtrip, do so out of necessity only. The rest you get in the back seat of a Chevy will not make you well rested and cheery the next morning. If you're in a sedan, only one or two people can even rest overnight after reclining the seats. Maybe three or four people, at the very most, could sleep in a larger SUV or van. But remember, sleeping in your car is not the way to enjoy your roadtrip. If you have to sleep this way one night, opt for a motel room or campground the following night. Remember, sleeping in the car is a last resort, something to hold you over until you can get some *real* rest, not something you'll want to do every night.

Make Lodging Part of the Fun

No matter where you choose to spend the night, make it part of the fun. When you stop for the evening, try to get out and explore your surroundings. Don't stop so late at night that you're completely drained of energy. And be open to new options, like camping or hostels, which will help you meet new people and relax while on the road.

Now that you're well on the way to your destination, you've probably spent quite a bit of money. How can you save some of that hard-earned cash while on the road? Read on, road warriors! That's what the next chapter is about.

CHAPTER 8

Saving Money on a Roadtrip

Roadtrips can get expensive. Really expensive. In fact, let's pause for a minute and think about all the plans we've talked about making. Spending nights in hotels, paying for gas, buying tents, eating out – all these activities cost money. In fact, on a roadtrip you could easily spend $200 *per day*. Your roadtrip, though, doesn't have to be that expensive. This chapter will offer you 40 suggestions to save money at every step along the way.

Saving on Gasoline

1. Pay attention to gas prices, and fill up where it's cheaper. This bit of advice seems like common sense, but you'd be surprised how often people don't even pay attention to the price of gas. Since every gas station in a town might be charging a different price for essentially the same product, it pays to keep an eye out for the spots where gas is cheaper. If gas is more expensive in one town, it may be several cents less a few miles down the road. Watch your gas gauge, though! Don't let yourself run out of gas trying to find a better price.

2. Look for gas stations away from interstate exits. Gas stations adjacent to the freeway exit tend to charge more because road travelers usually don't stray from the interstate much more than a third of a mile. If you take an exit near a town, try driving toward the business district. You're sure to find gas stations, likely with less traffic and lower prices.

3. Get a gas discount card. If you have a favorite gas station chain, sign up for its charge card. Pay it off every month, and you'll save up to 10% on your gasoline purchases, both on your roadtrip and after returning home. Nearly every major fuel chain offers a credit card, and applications are usually available right at the pump.

4. Use the internet to look for cheaper gas. The best place to explore gas prices online is GasBuddy.com. GasBuddy is an excellent site to find regions of the country and even individual stations offering a better deal. Since gas stations change their prices daily, focus on the 'Gas Price Temperature Map', which gives an idea of states and counties where gas is cheaper – and places where it's more expensive, too. Determine which areas offer the best gas prices and plan your fuel stops accordingly.

5. Check your air filter, change your oil, and make sure your car is tuned up. A dirty air filter decreases fuel economy. Likewise, old, misfiring spark plugs will lower gas mileage. And get your oil changed before a roadtrip, since dirty oil also affects fuel use. These three minor maintenance repairs may improve your fuel economy 10% or more.

6. Inflate your tires properly. You already know this, but it's worth repeating. Underinflated tires may waste 10% or more of the gasoline in your tank. Follow the instructions in your vehicle's owner manual, but keep in mind that most car tires need to be inflated to at least 30 psi. Keep a tire gauge in your glove compartment, and check your tire pressure periodically while on the road. Very wide temperature fluctuations can also affect your tire pressure (e.g. driving from a very warm climate to a very cold one), so check your pressure again after driving into a different climate area.

7. In warmer weather, when using the air conditioning, set the control to "MAX" or "RECIRC" to recirculate air already inside the vehicle and save energy. When the weather isn't as warm, but you still want a little ventilation in the car, turn on the vent instead of the air conditioner. You'll save gas by keeping the air conditioner off.

8. Skip the premium gas. Regular unleaded is fine for most cars and is just as good for gas mileage as more expensive grades. In my personal experience, premium gasoline may eliminate spark knock, but does little to nothing for gas mileage. In fact, the few times I've tried it on a trip, my gas mileage actually went down! Regular grade gas is just fine unless your vehicle's manual specifies otherwise.

9. Slow down. Keeping your speed to 55 really does save gas. If you don't believe it, try it! Keep your speed to 55 miles per hour for an entire tank of gas, and monitor your gas mileage. Look at the tachometer on the instrument panel; the engine works hardest at speeds above 55. Since interstate traffic moves much faster than that, consider taking two-lane roads instead. Nearly all two-lane highways east of the Mississippi cap speeds at 55, and those west of the Mississippi usually keep speeds to 65 or below. Even if slowing down doesn't improve your gas mileage, driving the speed limit *will* save money in the long run. Speeding tickets are expensive!

10. Consider driving fewer miles each day. If your destination is negotiable, seriously think about driving significantly fewer miles per day. When gas is $3.00 a gallon, each hour of interstate driving costs about $7.00 (assuming fuel economy of 25 mpg). So, planning for shorter days puts money back in your pocket. Try stopping for the evening two hours earlier each day. Not only will you save about $15.00 a day, you'll also leave more time to explore the local area. Now, if you have a specific destination in mind, this suggestion won't work too well, but for roadtrips where you're 'wandering' around an area, it works just fine.

Ways to Save on Lodging

11. Take advantage of free Wi-Fi. In the last chapter, we discussed free wireless internet as one of the amenities offered at nearly every roadside chain hotel. But what does it have to do with saving money on your hotel room? Well, some of the best hotel deals are found online. (More about that later.) And if you can't get online, you won't have access to those prices. So if you have a laptop computer, search for a Wi-Fi signal.

One of the best places to get online is in your hotel room itself. Get in the habit of looking for hotel deals at tomorrow's destination *today*. You'll save yourself the hassle of having to get online to make a reservation late in the afternoon, when you're already getting tired. Other spots offer a free wireless signal, too. Many restaurants are attracting customers with free Wi-Fi. For example, most Burger King restaurants now feature free wireless internet, and some other fast food places are thinking of following suit.

While many businesses charge customers for internet access (McDonald's and Starbucks come to mind), many other places offer free Wi-Fi as a municipal service and don't mind if you borrow access for a few minutes. Many public libraries, hospitals, schools, interstate rest areas, and even churches now have open Wi-Fi signals. Although it's not a service that's likely advertised on billboards, like it is at motels, many places, especially libraries, welcome motorists who need to use the internet for a bit.

12. Use Priceline.com to save money on hotels. Every hotel has days when its occupancy is low. Many hotels, from extended-stay properties to high-end hotels, auction off their unoccupied rooms at Priceline.com. If you're somewhat flexible with your plans – and most roadtrippers are – Priceline is a great way to save up to 50% on even the lowest advertised rate available. Of course, to use this website, you'll need a computer with web access and a major credit card.

To bid on a hotel room, input the dates you want to check in and check out. Enter a city or town, and the number of rooms you need. Look for the "Name Your Own Price" option. After you click "Enter" or "Bid

Now", you'll see a list of neighborhoods and star levels. Click on the neighborhood where you want to stay.

"Star levels" refer to the level of amenities available to guests. They don't necessarily refer to the quality of guest rooms. In other words, a room at a 4-star hotel may not really be any nicer than a room at a 2-star hotel. What's the least you need to know about Priceline's star levels? High-end hotels are generally found in the 5, 4, 3 ½, and 3 star levels. Most roadside chains fall into the 2 ½ and 2 star levels. Extended stay properties are normally 2 stars, but they're occasionally rated as 1 star. Although Mom-and-Pop motels are usually not available on Priceline, when they are, they'll probably be rated as 1 star, along with the cheapest of the roadside chains.

After you've decided where you want to stay and the star level you want, decide on a fair price to pay. How much should you offer? This is the tricky part of the bidding process. Offer too much and you'll have overpaid; offer too little – your offer will be denied and you'll have to wait 24 hours before trying the same offer combination again. If you don't want to wait, it will be necessary to change dates, neighborhoods, or star levels. Under some circumstances, though, you can immediately get a chance to rebid without waiting 24 hours – something called a 'free rebid' – and it involves recognizing that certain Priceline neighborhoods don't contain hotels at the star levels on which you're bidding.

Be warned, though! Priceline is not for the extremely picky or for anyone who *has* to stay at a certain hotel; you won't know which hotel you'll be staying at until your bid is accepted. And once your bid is accepted and you learn the name of the hotel, your credit card is charged immediately, and there's no turning back – no refunds or changes.

Sound complicated? It can be, if you've never tried it before. Priceline is almost like playing a game, and you need to know the rules before you play. Fortunately, Priceline's website interface is quite intuitive, and there are at least two discussion forums dedicated to helping people get the best prices for hotels on Priceline – betterbidding.com and biddingfortravel.yuku.com. Both forums are quite large and should help anyone who wants to learn to use Priceline most effectively.

Bidding on Priceline involves taking a risk, namely, trusting that your $50 bid on a 4-star hotel is really going to land you at a 4-star hotel. Usually it does; but that 4-star hotel might have a few crummy rooms. Some hotels assign their worst rooms to Priceline guests, but most hotels treat winning bidders just like anyone else. Personally, I use Priceline to book as many as 80% of my hotel stays. If you travel often, it could easily save you thousands of dollars a year. Over the years, I've stayed at some very nice hotels for very little money.

The savings are real: How about Nashville's Sheraton Music City for $31 a night? I've stayed at the Venetian Las Vegas for $99. The Hyatt Regency Chicago O'Hare was only $45 a night. My stay at the Sheraton Suites Houston Galleria? $40. The Hyatt Suites Atlanta? $40. My lowest price of all time? Just $22 a night at a Quality Inn in Dallas. Although you might not get these same low prices, they're a sample of the amazing savings you can rack up on Priceline.

In each of these cases above, the hotels were worth every bit of what I paid – much more, in fact. The rooms were clean, and I was never discriminated against because I got a low rate. Personally, using Priceline is my top way to save money on lodging while on the road. It not only offers flexibility and savings, but it's also works well for last-minute lodging decisions.

If you like to decide where to spend the night at the last minute, take a laptop along and search for an open wireless internet signal (see the last tip for details). Once connected, you're ready to 'Priceline' a hotel. Since you're bidding, quite literally, at the last minute, you won't be able to wait 24 hours to bid again if your offer is unsuccessful. And you may need to make use of the 'free rebid' strategy in order to win a hotel. To make the most of your bidding opportunities, try consulting one of the aforementioned discussion boards to see what the 'going price' is for certain zones and star levels in a particular city.

Make no mistake, though: bidding for hotel rooms on Priceline at the last minute is risky. If you use all your free rebids without getting an offer accepted, you're out of luck. You'll have to book conventionally or walk up to a hotel and ask for their best rate. Be aware, also, that many hotels at Priceline's 2- and 1-star levels are extended-stay properties, which

---

Priceline Same-Day Bidding

Priceline.com allows you to bid for hotels up to 11:00 p.m. Eastern time the day of your intended stay. In other words, it's possible to bid for a hotel while online in the parking lot of a hotel, have your bid accepted at that very hotel, then go inside five minutes later to check in. If it sounds like a seamless process, be careful – there are a few potential snags that could happen.

Don't make a same-day bid much later than 6:00 p.m. local time. Priceline may claim the hotel has rooms available, but when you arrive, they may already be sold out – it's happened to me. If you must make a same-day bid late in the evening, stick to 3-star properties or higher. Many hotels below this level are extended-stay properties, which don't even have 24-hour front desk service. Your bid might be accepted, and your credit card *will* be charged, but no one may be at the hotel to retrieve your reservation and check you in. It's a lesson I learned the hard way.

---

typically provide only one bed per room. These hotels just don't work well for groups of three or more.

If you decide to use Priceline to book a deal at the very last minute, try to book the room before 6:00 p.m. It takes the hotels a few minutes to get your reservation from Priceline. More importantly, some hotels put their front desks on 'autopilot' at night and aren't ready to handle new reservations, although Priceline has already charged you for the room. If you're assigned to an extended-stay property, for example, the front desk may close completely after 8:00 p.m. Even if Priceline faxes your information to the front desk – which they usually do – there may be no one at the front desk to get your reservation. Once again, you're just out of luck.

13. Use Hotwire to save on hotels. The savings at hotwire.com on hotel rooms are not usually quite as great as on Priceline, but they're nothing to sneeze at, either. Some travelers feel more comfortable with hotwire.com because you're given a list of amenities and a fixed price; you either take it or leave it. Hotwire is often a better choice on the road, because you don't have to make several bids before winning a room, or worse, having all your bids denied. With Hotwire, you make one 'bid', and after it's accepted, you find out the name of your hotel.

Since there's less guesswork with Hotwire, the prices are a few bucks higher, but often it's worth the money to know approximately what you're getting in advance. One area where Hotwire really shines, though, is when traveling with a group of three or more. Priceline guarantees only that your room will hold two people, but with Hotwire, you can specify a room for up to four adults. That's an important feature, because with Hotwire, a group of four people won't be assigned to an extended-stay property designed for two.

So, what's the verdict? Priceline and Hotwire are both great ways to save money on hotels, but if you're traveling alone or with just one other person, Priceline will net the better deal most of the time. If you don't have the time to worry with bidding, or if your group has more than two people, the nod goes to Hotwire.

14. Book with Expedia, Orbitz, Travelocity, or another site. With these online booking engines, your savings won't normally be as great as with Priceline or Hotwire. However, you will know exactly which hotel you're getting before making the purchase. Occasionally, these websites will offer coupons to save up to $100 off a stay of three days or more. If you stick with roadside chains, that $100 savings may even beat the lowest rate available on Priceline or Hotwire. Although most people don't stop at an interstate motor inn for three nights, deals like these can be useful at your destination. Keep your eyes open for these coupons, sometimes they're advertised on the front page of the websites under "Deals".

15. Stay in Mom-and-Pop motels. If you're willing to stay at locally owned, non-chain motels, it's possible to save up to $20 off even the best Priceline or Hotwire rates for roadside chains. Although the amenities may be fewer, you won't have to worry about making a bid or scrolling through lists of hotels when you're already tired and would rather be *in* your hotel room. If you're not planning on traveling with a laptop, this is probably the cheapest way to sleep, not counting hotel/motel alternatives.

16. Use coupons or other discounts available to you. In the last chapter, I mentioned the coupon booklets available for free at larger gas stations and rest areas. Roadside chain hotels provide most of these discounts, so the hotel names will likely be familiar to you. If your roadtrip takes place around the holidays or some other high-occupancy period, though, most coupon discounts will be null and void. In that case, you'll have to rely on some other discount method. If you're a member of AAA or a senior citizen, most hotels will give you a discount for showing your membership card. If you're not a member, ask the desk clerk for a discount anyway. Usually, he or she has the final say as to the rate you'll pay.

17. Join frequent-stay programs. If you have a favorite hotel chain, join their frequent-stay program. It may make you eligible for discounts or other perks, such as free breakfasts or room upgrades. Stay often enough, and you'll earn free hotel nights and even better perks. It's usually free to join these programs, and rewards usually start flowing after just a few stays.

18. Think about traveling off-season. January and February are slow months for hotels in most parts of the country. It's no coincidence that those are the months when the best deals are available. Most areas usually have deals in the autumn, too, so consider traveling in September or October. The weather is still agreeable in most of the country in the early fall, and prices usually are, too. Likewise, midweek prices are normally lower for roadside chains than they are on the weekend.

19. When visiting the city, stay in suburban areas. Downtown hotels often cost twice as much as suburban hotels. Staying in the suburbs not only saves money on the hotel rate itself, but it also keeps you from paying for parking in most cases. Even if you drive to the city center for sightseeing, the money saved by staying out of town outweighs what you'll pay to park for a few hours. Suburban hotels usually offer more dining and shopping options in the evenings and on weekends; most downtown areas go dormant after 5 p.m.

20. Look for cheaper cities. Some cities are just more inexpensive for lodging than others. Kansas City, Dallas, Chicago, and Atlanta are a few cities known for low hotel rates, especially if you're willing to stay in the suburbs.

If you're searching for a low rate alongside the interstate, look for small towns located about halfway between larger cities. These 'halfway' towns often have lots of rooms for little money. About halfway between Albuquerque and Amarillo, for example, you'll find the little town of Tucumcari, New Mexico – home to over 1000 motel rooms, most of them very inexpensive. Halfway between Nashville and Chattanooga is the town of Manchester, Tennessee; rooms start at $23. Texarkana is on the Arkansas/Texas state line about halfway between Little Rock and Dallas; rooms are advertised starting at $29.99 a night.

21. Try camping. Campsites cost less than hotel rooms, and they give you a chance to connect with the outdoors and enjoy your roadtrip that much more. Be aware, though, that camping isn't recommended in the wintertime, and many campgrounds close for the season after October.

22. Sleep in the car. When all else fails, you can always sleep in your car. You probably won't sleep too soundly, but it's free. This is really a last resort, though, and should only be attempted in safe places. See the previous chapter for details.

Ways to Save on Food and Drink

23. Make lunch your big meal of the day. Instead of pigging out in the evening, try eating a substantial lunch and a light dinner. Especially if you plan to be in the car for a while, you won't have the time to burn as many calories from a heavy dinner, so it's actually healthier to eat a bigger lunch when you're on the road. Prices are usually cheaper at lunchtime, too, so you'll save money. Some restaurants have their biggest crowds around the noon hour, though, so visit between 1 and 2 p.m. to avoid the masses.

24. Stay at hotels with free breakfast. If breakfast is the most important meal of the day, then it's even more important when on a roadtrip. A hearty breakfast is the perfect way to start your travel day, and it's even better when you don't have to pay. Four people eating breakfast in a restaurant could easily pay $30 or more, even in an inexpensive diner; save that money and take advantage of your hotel's free breakfast. Never skip the free breakfast offered at a hotel; you've already paid for it with your room rate. Even if you're not hungry or a big breakfast eater, take a piece of fruit or two along for when you *do* get hungry.

25. Visit supermarkets and buy your own food. Supermarket deli sandwiches cost less than most restaurant lunches. Drinks and snacks, like candy bars and chips, will be much cheaper at a supermarket or even a convenience store. To avoid searching for a supermarket twice a day to look for snacks, do your grocery shopping on the first day of your roadtrip at a market near home. By shopping close to home, you'll know where to find your favorite snacks without wasting time or money.

26. Fill your own water bottles. Bottled water is one of the most overpriced products available on the market today. If it tastes any different, it's because the bottled water has been filtered or boiled – two steps you can do at home for much less money. Install a filter on your kitchen faucet at home and purify your own water. Another option: instead of paying close to $1.00 a bottle, fill your own empty bottles with water from a drinking fountain. If you *must* buy bottled water, buy it by the gallon at the supermarket and fill your own smaller bottles as needed. One gallon of water from a grocery store costs less than a 16-ounce bottle at a convenience store.

27. Carry restaurant coupons. Most chain restaurants offer coupons through their websites that are accepted nationwide. Take a few minutes before your trip to look for coupons you might use on the road, and print off as many as you can. Each chain has their own website, and most coupons are featured quite prominently. You may already receive some in the mail or in your local newspaper.

If you're thinking of finer dining on the road, check out the options at **www.restaurant.com**. Their site features discounted gift certificates for finer independent restaurants across the country. Although most of the restaurants featured on the site are in large cities, the savings are hard to beat. Menus are available for most of the restaurants, and you can even make a reservation online. And what about the discounts? For most restaurants, $25 gift certificates are available for $10, and sometimes even those prices are discounted. So, look around for coupons and other deals; they *are* out there.

28. Visit local diners. At locally owned eateries, you're likely to eat where the locals do, and the meals are probably a little cheaper. You're also more likely to sample regional specialties at these places. The desserts are usually better, too.

29. At fast food places, check out the value menu. Most fast food restaurants now offer a 'value menu' or 'dollar menu' for budget-minded customers. Often, the value menu can net you a cheeseburger, small salad, and small drink for as little as $3.00. Or substitute the small drink for another dollar item and drink water instead. It may not be the most elegant of lunches, but the price is perfect for those on a budget.

30. Order a big meal and split it. Many sit-down restaurants provide big servings – too much, especially, for one person who will be sitting in the car for the next several hours. Instead, try ordering one big meal and asking for a second plate. You're likely to eat just as well – better, in fact – as you would having eaten the big meal by yourself. It's cheaper, too. One big meal costs less than two big meals, and in most cases, it's even less than two small meals. Just don't try this at a buffet!

31. If you're *really* hungry, look for a buffet. Buffets offer wide variety and good value. Everyone in a group can get what he or she wants. At lunch, when prices are cheaper, it's possible to enjoy a full meal, with dessert included, for well under $10. Just be careful, though, because it's easy to overeat at these places. For this reason, when on the road, I recommend buffets primarily for lunch, because you'll have more time to burn those extra calories.

32. Order water. Aside from the obvious health benefits of avoiding sugary soft drinks, water is usually free at restaurants. If you have a favorite soft drink, you're probably carrying it in your car anyway, so wait to enjoy it *after* your meal. Have you noticed that most sit-down restaurants don't even include soft drink prices on their menus anymore? They've learned that if customers knew ahead of time what drinks cost, they would order water instead. Drinks are one of their major profit centers, and it's not uncommon to be charged close to $2.00 for what amounts to a few cents worth of syrup. Save yourself the empty calories and the money, and just ask for water instead.

33. If you *must* buy fountain drinks, get them at convenience stores. Many convenience stores advertise low prices on fountain soft drinks to get customers in the door. Whereas the smallest soft drink at a fast food restaurant will cost at least $1.00, convenience stores usually offer drinks that are twice as big for the same price. So, if you've run out of cans in your cooler and need a fountain drink, find one of these stores.

Saving Money at Your Destination

34. Visit free museums and historic sites. Some cities have more free museums than others. Museums in Washington, DC are practically all free, as are most of the major museums in St. Louis, Missouri. Even if the museums you visit charge admission, they're likely more economical than going to a theme park or even a trip to the mall. Historic sites, such as those found in most state capitals, are fun, educational, and almost always free. Other sites worth mentioning include Civil War battlefields, ghost towns, national forests, and beaches. You'll save money by visiting places like these.

35. Ask for a discount. Many museums and theme parks offer discounts to senior citizens, children, and AAA members. Likewise, if you're

---

Budget Cities

Some cities tend to be cheaper for road travelers. Here are a few cities where you're likely to spend less on your visit:

St. Louis – Lodging is abundant and inexpensive, especially in the suburbs. The zoo, science center, and art museum all offer free admission.

Washington – Lodging in the suburbs is less expensive than in the city. Forget parking in Washington; park in the suburbs and take the Metro into town. All the Smithsonian museums and most other major sites are free to visitors.

Dallas – Plenty of cheap lodging options at all levels. Most museums here do charge admission, but consider taking the DART light rail, which is inexpensive, convenient to downtown, and quite new.

Las Vegas – Some of the most inexpensive lodging in the nation, that is, if you're willing to stay off the Strip or at smaller properties. Dining options range from the dirt cheap to the utterly expensive. For the best deals, be willing to dine at odd hours. If you have a car, think about staying in Laughlin, instead, an hour to the south, where hotels start at $19 a night.

Atlanta – Hotels here, especially in the northern suburbs, are quite inexpensive. There are plenty of things to see and do in the downtown area, too.

Orlando – If you're going to see the Mouse or hit another theme park, try visiting during the fall. October and early December offer some great deals in this popular tourist city.

---

in the military, full-time student, teacher, in-state resident, or AARP member, you're likely to get a discount, too. Ask before you pay admission; the discount could range anywhere from 10% all the way up to free admission.

36. Go downtown on the weekend. Most cities don't charge to park on downtown streets during the weekend. You'll likely find downtown less crowded then, and cheaper, too. Beware, though: although choices for visitors are abundant in most downtown areas, a few cities empty out on the weekends, especially in the evening. You may find fewer dining and shopping choices, too.

37. Look for discounts online. Many museums, theme parks, and other attractions that charge admission offer discounts if you buy your tickets through their website. It's convenient, because you can print tickets at home, and you save time, too, avoiding lines at the ticket counter onsite. Even if the online price isn't discounted, it's a good idea to print your tickets ahead of time to allow for more time sightseeing and less time standing in line.

38. Take pictures. Instead of buying expensive souvenirs you're likely to lose or never use, take lots of pictures on your roadtrip. With digital cameras and memory now very inexpensive, anyone can take dozens, even hundreds of pictures with ease. Remember the batteries – preferably quality rechargeable ones – and keep a charger on hand. Take snapshots of anything you'd like to be reminded of when you get back home. Taking pictures and reminiscing about the excitement of a roadtrip is almost as thrilling as being there. Your pictures will bring back memories and help you remember the stories you'll want to tell your friends back home.

39. Avoid the crowds. Steering clear of typical tourist trap crowds will help prevent you from feeling stressed while on your trip. You'll save money, too, because high prices tend to follow crowds. Most major tourist attractions are surrounded with high-priced food, overpriced drinks, gouged parking fees, and expensive souvenirs. Instead, opt for a park, a hiking trail, or one of the less-frequented museums in town. It's less stressful, less crowded, and it will likely be cheaper.

One Last Idea to Save Money

40. Stick to a budget. Hopefully, you've already planned how much money is available for your trip, and you've allotted it accordingly. A very wise person once said, "Take half as many clothes, and twice as much money." And in many respects, that statement is true. Roadtrips can easily go overbudget, especially if hotels end up being more costly than planned, or if gas prices spike during your trip.

Even with unexpected expenses, you can still save plenty of money, especially by sticking to lower-end hotels, getting deals online, and watching your dining expenses. But don't feel that you have to save so much money that you stop enjoying your roadtrip. Sure, eating peanut butter sandwiches and sleeping in the car will save money, but after two days of that, will you *really* be having a good time?

Make your trip relaxing; splurge on occasion, without breaking the bank, of course. Keep an eye on the budget, and if you're cutting it close, keep a 'little black book' with *all* expenses listed. Total your expenses every day, and if you're going over your daily allotment, cut back a little. But most of all, have a good time! If you follow the tips in this chapter, you can save money and have the time of your life, too!

CHAPTER 9

Short Roadtrips

The last eight chapters have discussed strategies to plan and enjoy a typical roadtrip. When I say "typical roadtrip", I'm talking about a trip where a couple spend a week on the road to discover the South. Or the group of four friends who take two weeks to wander around the West. Or the family that's driving up to New England for a few days to admire the leaves in October. Or something similar to that. Those are the most common types of roadtrips, or at least the ones I've kept most in mind in the previous chapters.

But a roadtrip doesn't have to last a week. A roadtrip is more a *state of mind* than a number of miles traveled. Some of the best trips involve getting away for a day or two and exploring places close to home. You can enjoy a great roadtrip in as little as a few hours, and it's not necessary to travel very far, either. In this chapter, I'll be reviewing four ideas for short roadtrips that may give you some ideas for taking a short trip of your own.

The Daytrip

Even if you've never taken a longer roadtrip, you probably have gone on a daytrip, that is, a short roadtrip where you leave home in the morning and return home that same day. Usually, daytrips have a specific destination. Some travelers take daytrips to a state park, a nice restaurant, or a museum. Most short trips use no more than one tank of gas, making them the most economical roadtrip you can take.

If you choose to take a daytrip, plan to leave at a reasonable hour. If you need to travel several hours, visit an attraction, or run your errand, and return home the same day, you'll need to leave rather early. Like every day on any other roadtrip, start out with a hearty breakfast; it gets the day off to a good start. Then start out on the road to your destination.

How far should you go on a daytrip? Be careful not to overestimate your driving ability. If you have a specific destination, make sure it's no more than a four-hour drive from home. Anything longer than that, think about spending the night. A four-hour drive from home means you'll be driving eight hours in one day. That's a lot of time on the road, considering you'll presumably be doing something – sightseeing, eating, meeting with friends – at your destination. It's actually preferable to travel much less than that. Really, some of the best daytrips are just an hour or so from home.

Another type of daytrip with considering is something I call a "triangle trip". This type of journey involves traveling to a destination no more than two hours away, visiting a place of interest, then driving to a second destination another hour or two away, but somewhat in the direction of home. After you visit that second place of interest, you drive home, which shouldn't be much more than an hour or two from your second destination. In other words, when looking at a map, your route looks like a big triangle.

Since you're traveling between two nearby destinations on this type of trip, you're more likely to drive roads you've never explored before. Instead of driving several hours, then turning right around and heading home, each leg of the 'triangle' is different, so you'll experience distinct scenery on each part of your journey. Since you'll be visiting two destinations instead of one, you'll probably spend more time *there* and not as much time worrying about how to *get* there.

Whether you plan to venture far from home, or just plan to explore highways and byways closer to home, daytrips have their advantages. Since you don't have to worry about lodging, there's very little to pack. Most people can take a daytrip with little notice on a Saturday or day off.

And since there's no luggage to take, four adults can fit comfortably in most cars for a daytrip, something that might be tougher on a longer trip. If you've never taken any roadtrip before, start with a daytrip.

The Overnight Trip

If you want a longer 'getaway' than a daytrip, think about taking an overnight trip. A typical overnight trip involves leaving in the late afternoon on a weekday, driving a couple of hours, enjoying a leisurely dinner, then driving a little farther before spending the night at a hotel. The next day, you can do some sightseeing, visit a park or museum, and enjoy lunch before driving home that afternoon.

When you decide to take an overnight trip, think about how much of a getaway you want. When you get to your destination, what do you want to do? What museums will you visit? Will you go shopping instead? Or will the hotel be your destination? Depending on your budget and plans, you may decide to stay at a different type of hotel than you would on a longer roadtrip.

If the hotel is really your destination, and you don't have any serious sightseeing plans, think about reserving a room at a high-end hotel (see Chapter 7 for more details). In many cities and suburban areas, high-end hotels, especially in the off-season, don't cost much more than a room at a roadside chain. And if you're looking for a quick getaway, high-end hotels often include more amenities to help guests relax, such as a workout room, jacuzzi, indoor pool, and more comfortable beds.

For a quick overnight trip, don't plan on driving much more than three to four hours from home. Remember, this is supposed to be a getaway, a chance to relax; you don't want to be on the road until 2:00 in the morning trying to get to your hotel. A short overnight trip should leave you refreshed and ready for the week ahead!

The Weekend Getaway

For some families and groups, a quick overnight roadtrip just isn't quite enough. That's why a weekend getaway may be more attractive, especially if you want to see more than one or two sights in a city. It's similar to an overnight trip, except you'll spend two nights instead of just one, giving you a full day for sightseeing.

A typical weekend getaway starts late on a Friday afternoon. Travelers will most likely leave home after work, drive for a couple hours, have dinner, and then drive on to their hotel in the evening. Up to this point, it's identical to the overnight trip. The major difference is that the entire day Saturday is available for sightseeing. After another night in the hotel, there's still time left early Sunday for more sightseeing before driving home that afternoon or evening.

Most families have done a variation of the weekend getaway. It's perfect for families, because it doesn't require taking vacation days from work in most cases, and it gives everyone a chance to relax for a couple days and do something out of the ordinary. Kids get excited about staying in a hotel, especially if it has a pool. And what better way to enjoy a Saturday than a trip to a zoo, park, or museum?

You have plenty of options when planning a weekend getaway. Instead of staying at a hotel, you could try camping for a couple nights, especially if the weather is good and the campsite isn't more than a few hours from home. If you opt for a hotel, be aware that downtown hotels may be significantly cheaper on the weekend, with rates that even rival roadside chains, especially if booking through an opaque booking site like Priceline or Hotwire. Before deciding to stay downtown, check into hidden fees, like parking, that could drive up the cost of your stay.

Like the other short roadtrips mentioned previously, weekend getaways work well for short jaunts – those under four hours are best. If you're traveling much more than four hours from home, you may be better off spending at least three nights.

The Weekend Drive

If your goal on a short trip isn't really to visit a specific destination, but rather to wander along highways and back roads for a couple of days, consider taking a weekend drive. This style of short roadtrip is more like a 'typical' roadtrip, just shorter. It can be done in a weekend, and if you've never taken a long, multi-day roadtrip, this is the one to try before attempting anything longer.

Typically, a weekend drive begins after work on a Friday afternoon. Drive for a few hours, have dinner, and then keep driving until you're ready to find a place to stay. When it's time to stop for the night, use one of the strategies in the previous chapter to get a great deal on a hotel room, if you haven't already made a reservation. The next morning, keep driving and make a few stops along the way. Somewhere around midday on Saturday, start to turn back, making a circle toward home. Enjoy the scenery. Take in a hearty meal at a local diner. Find a historical site of interest. Saturday night, find another place to stay. On Sunday morning, make your way back home, leaving enough time to relax that evening.

Weekend drives, like other roadtrips, are about the journey, not so much the destination. In fact, this type of trip may not have a specific destination, yet you'll find places along the way to discover. There's no need to be shy about making stops; if there's a town that seems interesting, or a billboard announcing a place you'd like to see, get off the highway and look for it. That stop may turn out to be the highlight of the trip.

Of the short roadtrips mentioned in this chapter, the weekend drive is the one that can potentially let you explore places farthest from home. Instead of being limited to a couple hundred miles, this type of drive can let you travel up to 500 miles from home (or even a little more, if you're ambitious). In fact, on a few occasions, I've taken some weekend roadtrips – and driven just over 2000 miles round trip in about three days. Granted, it's not a trip I'd recommend to anybody, but it shows that it *is* possible to drive a considerable distance, *if necessary*, over a long weekend.

Planning a Short Trip

One of the best things about short roadtrips is that very little planning is required. Especially for a daytrip, it's possible to just jump in the car and take off. When planning a route, try following a road you've never taken before. Most Americans live within a couple hours of scenic byways, many of which they've never even discovered. Avoid the interstates, and favor two-lane roads. Check the weather forecast, and pick a day with good, sunny weather to head out. It's not a big loss when one day gets rained out on a longer drive, but when going on shorter jaunts, you won't want the whole experience to be ruined by a major storm.

Even weekend getaways and drives don't have to be planned far in advance. If the weather will be favorable over a certain weekend, try getting away for a couple of days. With last-minute specials readily available online, it's not necessary to book a week ahead of time to get a great deal on a hotel room. Often, the most memorable roadtrips are the unplanned ones, those impromptu journeys where we just get in the car and go.

The sample roadtrips I've discussed in this chapter are just ideas. I've tried all of them, and they're all great ways to get out on the road when you have little time to spare. Still, your ideal short roadtrip may be a conglomeration of two or more of these ideas, or they may be completely different. No matter what your circumstances are, try taking a short roadtrip. It really is true: good things often do come in small packages!

CHAPTER **10**

The Extended Roadtrip

Some of us dream of traveling the road for months, even for a year or more, wandering the country at leisure to fully experience the land. Although you might think an extended roadtrip is a dream best saved for retirement, more and more people are learning that living on the road – at least for a while – is a dream within reach. With thorough planning and a carefully planned budget, it's possible to spend an extended time on the road without breaking the bank.

Some roadtrippers have big ambitions for the places they would like to see. Many travelers want to visit all 48 of the continental states; others plan a summer trip to Alaska. Maybe a roadtrip to Mexico catches your interest. No matter what travel preference you have, the farthest of destinations require an extended roadtrip. And extended roadtrips require extended planning.

First of all, it requires psychological planning. Think about it – will you *really* be able to spend an extended time on the road? Most travelers enjoy getting away, but after about two weeks, they really start to miss the stability and the routine of being at home. To make sure you can handle a *long* time on the road, try a moderately-long roadtrip, say, about three weeks. How do you feel at the end of those three weeks? Are you ready for more? Or did you really start to miss home? After a three-week trip, you'll know if you're ready for something longer.

Before an extended journey, there's much more planning that has to be done back at home. Being on the road for a month or more isn't as simple as just taking off and asking a friend to watch the house while you're away. If your idea of a roadtrip is one that requires little or no planning, then focus on short jaunts, outlined in the previous chapter. Extended time away from home requires that you take care of business.

Taking Care of Business at Home

It will be necessary to take care of the rent or mortgage payment if you'll be away for a month or more. Most landlords or rental companies will accept your check early, although they may ask you to postdate your check for bookkeeping purposes. Just ask your landlord or building manager, and likely he or she will be happy to help you. Besides, most people would rather get their money early than late, wouldn't they?

Some landlords may even give a discount on rent if you'll be away the entire month. Ask about this possibility; it's an option that may save you several hundred dollars if it's available.

If you own your home, you'll likely have no problem making your mortgage payment in advance. The mortgage company will gladly accept your checks ahead of time, and you won't even have to postdate them. Just send the appropriate month's payment coupon along with your check, and you should be fine. If you haven't already looked into automatic withdrawal or online payments with your mortgage, this is the time to start. By paying your mortgage – and other bills – online, you won't physically need to be home to make payments. You can literally make payments from anywhere in the world.

Other Considerations

Homeowners will also need to make sure the lawn is cared for. Hire a lawn care company well in advance of your trip to keep the grass trimmed and weeds pulled. The cost of this service is small compared to the worry of coming home to an overgrown lawn, not to mention possible code violations, citations, and hefty fines. If you ask a friend to take care of your lawn for you, make sure that he or she knows how to use your lawnmower and that there's enough fuel on hand to last your whole trip.

Both renters and homeowners will need to have someone check on the home occasionally. Make sure to select someone you trust and who won't turn your home into 'party central' while you're away. I know of someone who asked an acquaintance to watch his apartment during an extended trip. Upon his return, he found that nearly every dish in the apartment had been left dirty – but they had all been returned to the cabinets anyway! This 'caretaker' had played a game of darts on the wall; he found darts stuck in the living room wall, the dining room, even in the fish tank! The moral of the story? Don't let just anyone watch your place while you're away; choose someone who's responsible, and preferably older. A trusted coworker or neighbor will often help with this.

If you're going to be gone for a *very* long time, especially from an apartment, it may be wiser to move out, at least temporarily. Landlords usually don't mind if a tenant is gone for a month or two; much longer than that, though, and you may need to give up the apartment and put your belongings in long-term storage. Fortunately, storage units are plentiful and cheap, and they'll certainly cost less than rent. If you're willing to give up an apartment to take an extended trip, putting your possessions in storage will likely save you serious money.

After taking care of matters around the house, remember to stop the mail. The post office will hold your mail for up to one month; for longer trips, you'll have to make other arrangements. If you're going to be on the road for more than one month, you'll be better off forwarding your mail to a commercial mailbox service during your absence.

Notice that I mentioned a "commercial mailbox service," not a P.O. Box number. Although a regular post office box works fine when you're maintaining a nearby residence, they don't work so well when you're away. If you need to have a package delivered, only the U.S. postal service will deliver to a post office box. FedEx or U.P.S. won't be able to complete the delivery. Certain applications or other forms will not accept an address with a P.O. Box number.

Commercial mailboxes give you the benefit of an actual street address, so any courier or delivery service will be able to get a package to you. And as long as you keep the mailbox active by paying the annual fee, you can keep having your mail from home forwarded for up to one year. If you plan on being on the road for more than a year, change your address with the sender. Mailbox services are quite inexpensive, considering the convenience they offer. Although fees sometimes go on sale, expect to pay about $15 a month for commercial mailbox service.

Paying the Bills

When you're away from home for two weeks, paying bills is likely the least of your worries; the mail gets picked up at the post office, and you pay them upon your return. Not so with an extended roadtrip. It's possible for payment due dates to pass without ever seeing the bill. Making payments and avoiding late fees are more of a challenge when you never know what's owed. That's why it's so important to make careful arrangements well ahead of time for your finances when planning for an extended trip.

Most of my advice for paying bills while away from home can be summed up in two words: *Pay online.* Only a few bills can't be paid this way; and many of those services simply need to be suspended during your absence, anyway. Remember that paying bills online will require internet access while you're on the road, so invest in a computer with wireless internet capability if you don't already have one; the computer can be your biggest asset on the road when it's necessary to communicate with home.

Landline telephone. Many phone companies now offer to bill your credit card directly or deduct the balance due from your checking account. Others allow you to pay online. If your company still doesn't allow these options, seriously consider having your landline turned off while you'll be away. Home telephones aren't of much use while you're away, and you could easily save $100 if you'll be away for more than two months. If you don't want to lose your home phone service, even temporarily, seriously consider changing companies; there's no excuse for large telecom companies to refuse online payments these days.

Cell phone. All major cell phone providers accept online payments. If you're not already taking advantage of this service, sign up at least a month before your trip to make sure it works without a hitch. If you don't have a cell phone or use one only in emergencies; seriously consider a prepaid cell phone; some of them, such as Net10, cost as little as 10¢ a minute and never incur roaming charges in the continental United States. Prepaid phones have a significant advantage for the long-term roadtripper: You'll never miss paying a bill.

Credit card. All major credit cards can be paid online. However, log on to your credit card website from your own computer only; some companies require you to re-authenticate your personal data after switching machines. Since paying credit cards online is so easy these days, seriously consider having other bills charged to your card as well. Also, consider charging every roadtrip expense possible to your card, leaving cash just for emergencies or small, convenience purchases. If your card earns reward points, cash back, or airline miles, your daily expenses may actually fund your next vacation.

Electricity. If maintaining your residence back home, you probably won't want to shut the electricity off completely. In fact, it makes sense to keep a few lights controlled by timers for security purposes. Don't shut your heating system off entirely in the winter; your pipes could freeze, causing thousands of dollars worth of damage to your home. Instead, go into 'low energy' mode: turn the thermostat down to 55 (in the winter), shut off the hot water heater, and unplug unnecessary electrical devices. In the summer, most homes need very little, if any, air conditioning; consider shutting it off completely.

Many electricity companies are locally owned cooperatives; others are publicly traded corporate entities. In any case, most people don't have a choice as to which electric company they patronize. Therefore, you're likely to have fewer payment choices with utility bills. Some electric companies allow you to pay bills online, but many do not.

One option for paying your bill is to estimate the amount of your bill and prepay that amount to the company; this method works best for absences of no more than two months. Beyond two months, it gets very difficult to anticipate the amount of a bill, unless you've enrolled in a saver program that keeps your bill consistent from month to month. Some electric companies that don't accept online payments *do* accept credit card payments. Try calling the billing office and paying over the phone with a credit card. If they don't accept phone payments, you may have to call and ask how much is owed on your account. Then, mail the company a check with your account number written at the bottom.

Water. If you pay a separate water bill, it's unlikely that you'll be able to pay it online. Some water districts even hesitate to accept credit card payments. The best option in this case may be to estimate the water bill to the best of your ability and prepay at least twice the normal amount of your bill. Since you won't be home, your water consumption should be very low, and this amount should cover several months of actual usage. If in doubt, call the water district a couple of months into your trip and ask how much you owe, then send them a check.

Trash pickup. If you pay for your own garbage collection, call the company and put your service on hold if you'll be away for a month or more. There's no reason to pay for a service you won't be using. If they won't put a hold on your service, cancel it. Rehire them – or better yet, find a more flexible company – upon your return. Trash pickup is usually paid in advance, so there shouldn't be late fees to worry about, as long as you've put a hold on the service.

Newspaper delivery. Call the newspaper and have them put a vacation hold on your subscription. Otherwise, you may come home to find dozens of newspapers lying on the lawn.

Cable or Satellite television. If you'll be away several months, it may be wise to put your subscription on vacation hold. Otherwise, most cable and satellite companies allow you to pay online or by electronic check.

Auto insurance. Making sure your auto insurance policy is up-to-date is not only wise, it's required by law. Don't let the policy expire while you're on the road, either. Call your agent and write a check, if necessary, or have the premium deducted directly from your bank account. Most companies now let you print your own proof-of-insurance certificates directly from your own computer.

Vehicle registration. Most states allow motorists to renew car registration at least two months before their expiration, sometimes more. If you can't personally go to the D.M.V. to renew, though, most states allow you to renew by mail, sending in a check for the required amount. If you're not sure of the amount owed, call your local Department of Motor Vehicles. If you renew by mail, you will receive the renewal registration form and sticker (or license plate) by mail, as well.

If you're not going to be near your mailbox, it may be necessary to have a friend check your mailbox for you and personally forward the package to you. Vehicle registration is one of the few bills that's best to complete personally. If possible, handle this before leaving home.

Property taxes. If you pay a mortgage, the company should pay property taxes for you out of an escrow account. If you own your home free and clear, though, you'll have to send the check yourself. Most local governments don't take credit cards or online payments, so this is another matter you may have to have a trusted friend handle. Once again, it's best to handle tax payments before you leave; you really don't want the county putting a lien on your house while you're away.

Money Matters

Even before you decide that the bills can get paid during your time away, it's important to think about money issues. Do your finances really allow for this kind of trip? And, just as importantly, what's the longest time you can afford to be away from home? If you're dependent on a regular job, and you feel fortunate to get two weeks vacation each year, taking a month-long roadtrip may simply be impossible. On the other hand, retired couples with a steady pension income may practically be able to live on the road for months, even years at a time.

Other individuals, though, may be able to manage spending a few months on the road without quitting their jobs. Teachers may be able to arrange being away for an extended time in the summer; college students may be able to do the same. If you work from home or perform your duties over the internet, it may be possible to take your work with you – a working roadtrip, if you will.

If you don't currently have a 'portable' job, but you really want to spend months at a time on the road, seriously consider an online occupation. It may be as simple as selling antiques on Ebay, as complex as being a technical writer or translating text, or somewhere in the middle. 'Working at home' and online jobs are becoming more common, and they're more conducive to your dream of living on the road than traditional office jobs.

For those of us who have to work in a fixed location, though, the reality is that your job will have to be separate from your roadtrip. Which means you're going to have to save up to take an extended journey. How much will you need to live on the road? Plan on spending at least $2000 a month, in addition to any expenses you have at home. Now, it's possible to live on less than $2000 when traveling, but it requires some real scrimping and frugality. And it's very easy to spend *more* than $2000 a month, too, but I'll give share a few ideas later for saving money when spending a longer time on the road.

Before you think about spending money, though, make sure you have a place to *get* money. Although locally owned banks usually provide more personal service, they usually won't help you avoid ATM fees while traveling. Open an account at a bank with branches across the nation. When traveling, it will be easier to find a branch where you won't needlessly waste money on ATM fees.

At times, it may be impossible to find a bank or ATM where you won't be charged a fee, even with an account at the most common banks in the country. If you need to withdraw funds from an ATM where you'll have to pay a fee – usually between two and five dollars – withdraw the maximum daily amount from your account, so you won't have to repeat the process in a few days. Remember, it's possible to cut down on ATM fees by avoiding cash and sticking to debit or credit cards as much as possible.

Should I Buy an RV?

Many long-term road travelers decide to buy a recreational vehicle. RV's can range from simple towed pop-ups to rolling luxury behemoths.

But is an RV for you? Before buying one, think about it carefully; this is a major purchase that could easily cost more than an entire year's worth of living expenses on the road. However, happy RV owners state that it's more than just a purchase; it's an investment in a way of life. In other words, if you've decided to adopt the 'roadtrip way of life' and plan to spend a lot of time on the road, and you can afford it, go ahead and purchase an RV.

Keep in mind, though, that the choice of RV's is as nearly extensive as that of passenger vehicles. A simple pop-up camper may be cramped for extended periods, but since it's relatively inexpensive, it may be the perfect choice for the traveler who wants to enter the RV lifestyle on a budget. Since pop-ups are towed, their lifespan will likely be longer than the motor towing it. If a larger motorhome needs significant mechanical repairs, the entire roadtrip may have to be put on hold.

Luxury motorhomes are basically small homes on wheels. Driving a beast like this, you may never again miss the comforts of home; they'll be within easy reach during the whole trip! Be aware, though, that high-end motorhomes cost as much as $250,000. At the high end of the price spectrum, expect satellite TV reception, comfortable furniture, and plenty of space, not to mention numerous other amenities.

If you don't have much experience with RV's, don't buy one until you've driven one and taken a roadtrip in one. It's possible to rent an RV and experience the road in style; you'll have the full support of the rental agency, too, in case of mechanical or other problems. RV's can normally be rented for less than $200 a day. Renting for a week or two on the road is a good investment, as it gives the potential owner a good idea as to how life in an RV would be.

Be aware that most roadtrippers, even those who plan to spend months on the road, don't need to purchase an RV to get the most out of their vacation. RV drivers certainly spend less on lodging than other road travelers, and they may also spend less on their total vacation budget than other people – not counting the actual RV purchase itself. Be aware, though, that the fuel economy for most gasoline motorhomes will be about six miles per gallon; diesel coaches average closer to 10 miles per gallon.

Motorhome resale opportunities fluctuate with gas prices and the economic climate; when gas prices are high or the economy is struggling, fewer families will splurge on purchasing an RV. Recreational vehicles are wonderful for those who will use them and can afford them, but most roadtrippers will be just fine with a van or SUV. For one to three people, a car will even suffice for all but the longest of trips.

Special Considerations for the Extended Trip

Long roadtrips aren't really that much different from shorter ones – you'll spend time on the road and likely at various destinations along the way – but there are special considerations you'll need to keep in mind that make them a little more challenging. Other than the advance planning discussed earlier in this chapter, think about the following needs on an extended trip away from home.

Laundry. Any roadtrip longer than a week should include a laundry plan. Since you won't want to wear dirty clothes repeatedly, nor will you want to haul dozens of different outfits, plan to take just enough clothes for a week. At the end of the week, look for a local laundromat and take an hour or two to wash clothes. It's a great way to meet locals, and it sometimes can be a welcome diversion just to wait on the dryer and read a magazine. Some hotels have a laundry facility, but most laundromats are cheaper. If you decide not to bring along detergent or fabric softener, most laundry facilities will sell them for a dollar or so. Use the internet or the local yellow pages to find locations.

Cooler. When on the road for weeks or months at a time, you'll want to have a reliable cooler for your days on the road. Many better coolers are actually small refrigerators that connect to a power outlet in your vehicle. These coolers will keep you from having to look for ice constantly to keep food cold if you decide to spend a few days camping. Good coolers may cost upwards of $50, but they're worth every penny.

Luggage. Although a duffle bag may do for a shorter trip, longer journeys require more organization. A three-month-long journey doesn't require much more luggage than a weeklong jaunt, but after the first week or so, you'll want to know *exactly* where everything is. Suitcases, wheeled bags, and computer cases all have small compartments for those little, easy-to-lose items. Use those compartments! You'll waste valuable time – not to mention fraying your nerves – searching for something important when a little organization would have made it much easier to find.

Camping supplies. Even if you plan on staying primarily in hotels and motels on your journey, take a tent if you'll be on the road awhile. Staying in hotels can be tiresome after a couple of weeks, and camping can make your trip more enjoyable and relaxing. It's not necessary to buy the biggest tent on the market; just take one that will comfortably sleep the number of people on your trip. Don't forget sleeping bags, pillows, and an air mattress or tent pad. It may sound like a lot of supplies to take, but if you're traveling in an SUV or van, it won't take up that much space. As long as *everyone* remembers to pack light, there will still be plenty of room.

Reliable internet access. Internet access is increasingly becoming a crucial part of all types of travel in our connected world, not to mention the fact that the best travel deals are found online. When you're on the road for only a week or two at a time, relying on free public Wi-Fi or hotel internet access will work just fine. For extended trips, though, it may be wise to investigate something more reliable. The major cellular providers all offer nationwide internet access through EV-DO, or wireless data cards. Access is available just about anywhere there's a cell phone signal. Prices are reasonable, too; for wireless customers, (nearly) unlimited internet access can be had for about $60 a month.

Mechanical needs. If you're on the road long enough, the car is going to need repairs, or at the very least, preventive maintenance. Every town will have a mechanic in case the car breaks down. If the vehicle was thoroughly inspected before the trip, it's likely you won't have any serious problems. Nevertheless, don't be nervous about getting repairs done on your car while away from home. If you're reluctant to trust a mechanic in a strange town, don't be; just ask around at a local diner or even a laundromat. Local residents will likely recommend their own mechanic.

Don't forget to get the oil changed every 3000 miles. With quick lube businesses in just about every town big enough to have a McDonald's, it's easy and quick to get your car serviced – usually in under an hour. Just like back home, they'll change your windshield wiper blades, filters, and top off other necessary fluids if necessary.

Shopping. Plan to visit a grocery store at least once a week. Restaurants are convenient, but they can get expensive and are not always very healthy. Look for supermarket chains that you're familiar with from home; the prices and setup are likely to be similar to the store you're used to, saving you both money and time. If you need a specific item, your best bet is to visit a national grocery chain like Kroger, Wal-Mart Supercenter, or Safeway.

Staying Within a Budget

Most people will need strict financial discipline to stay on the road for months at a time. All too often, the temptation is just too great, and some travelers end up staying in overpriced hotels or eating overpriced meals, when lower-priced options would have worked just as well.

Your total expenses while on a roadtrip are the sum of your expenses on the road and your bills that have to be paid back home. The latter set of expenses is fixed; the former set of expenses can be kept low *if* you're willing to follow a few rules.

Budgeting on an extended roadtrip can be summed up in two simple equations. They are as follows:

Lots of driving   +   Hotels every night   =   Lots of money

Less driving   +   Budget lodging options   =   Less money

Get the idea? Some expenses can't be reduced much. If the car needs to be repaired, it's an expense that has to be paid – right then. When your clothes get dirty, your car companions will *really* appreciate it if you wash your clothes – laundry shouldn't be eliminated to save money. But some expenses really cut into a travel budget more than others. The biggest chunks of a roadtrip budget are lodging and fuel, and to a lesser extent, food.

Stretching Your Lodging Funds

If you plan to be on the road awhile, you'll have to seriously stretch your lodging budget. Hotel expenses can get out of control very fast, especially with some roadside chains charging upwards of $100 a night for walk-up rates. In fact, at that rate, lodging could easily consume half or more of an entire vacation budget! The same thing can be said for gasoline expenses. When gas prices are high, it can easily cost $20 just to drive 100 miles in an SUV.

Instead of driving a couple hundred miles every day, getting a hotel for the night, eating in a restaurant, then repeating the process the next day, why not try staying in one place for a few days? Many hotels and motels, especially at the extended stay level, offer weekly rates. By staying in one place for a week, it's possible to save $100 or more on lodging – plus you'll have more time to explore the area.

Extended-stay hotels offer another benefit: the ever-coveted kitchen. With a kitchen in the room, you're never stuck eating fast-food. Stop by the grocery store, and everyone can take turns cooking dinner. Having a kitchen in your room could easily save $100 a week in restaurant meals. At the same time, don't get burned out on eating in, either. At least once every other day, plan for a hearty lunch at a local restaurant with reasonable prices; remember, you are on *vacation*!

Camping provides another opportunity for low-cost lodging. Although this was discussed earlier in the book, it's worth repeating that state parks, land areas managed by the Army Corps of Engineers, lakes, and national forests are great places to camp, often for as little as $10 a night. If you're looking for a serious deal, try dispersed camping in a national forest, which is absolutely free – of course, you won't have any amenities, either.

Renting a room at a resort or condominium is also a surprising option for budget lodging.   Many resorts, especially in the off-season, rent

---

Living on the Road for $500 a Week – Plan No. 1

Think it's possible for someone to spend $500 a week or less while on an extended roadtrip? It certainly is, if you're willing to economize and try a budget like this one. The prices are for a single traveler; they'll need to be adjusted for groups of two or more.

Gasoline – 500 miles total	$ 70
7 Nights in resort won on SkyAuction.com	$ 270
Groceries	$ 50
4 Restaurant Meals	$ 60
Miscellaneous Expenses	$ 50
Grand Total for the Week	**$ 500**

---

rooms in tourist areas for a fraction of their normal rate. It's possible to spend as little as $300 on a week in one of these resorts, which is really a bargain. Websites such as SkyAuction.com often offer resort rentals like these at the last minute, so keep an eye on this option. You may be surprised at the deals available!

Try Something Different!

Spending two months on the road *is* definitely out of the ordinary! Still, being on the road for an extended time, especially if traveling alone or with only one other person, can become an isolating experience. So it's important to get out and meet people, talk to others, and enjoy the places you visit. When you eat out, talk to people. Ask about places to visit; often they'll recommend places the guidebook never mentioned.

If you're passing near an area where friends or relatives live, pay them a visit. Spend an afternoon, a day, or a few days, whatever is most appropriate. Find people you know along the way; it will keep you from feeling isolated. If you're a member of a church or religious organization, look for the local congregation in the phone book and attend local services or meetings. You're likely to make new friends, and it's possible you may even have some common acquaintances.

And even though you're on a roadtrip, don't feel you have to travel exclusively by car. If you're on a strict budget, try bus travel. It's safe to say you'll find a wide variety of people on a bus. Even if you decide you hate it, traveling by bus is an experience you'll never forget.

If you don't want to take a bus, try traveling by passenger rail. Amtrak, America's only nationwide rail system, passes through almost every state and will take you directly to the center of many major cities – no taxi required.

Amtrak is probably one of the best-kept travel secrets in the country, since most Amtrak stations, especially those in smaller towns, offer free long-term parking to train travelers. You can park your car at the Amtrak station, ride the train to the center of a major city, and spend a few days exploring. You won't pay any parking charges, and you won't have to fight any city traffic. It's possible to discover most city centers by public transportation and, perhaps, a few taxi rides. Lodging deals, even in downtown areas of major cities, are plentiful on websites such as Hotwire and Priceline.

I highly recommend traveling by train, especially as a complement to a roadtrip. On the train, it's hard *not* to meet people. The mood is much more relaxed than on an airplane. When passengers get hungry, they can enjoy the lounge car for snacks, or the dining car for full restaurant-style meals. If you're willing to splurge, try the train's sleeping accommodations. For as little as $60 it's possible for two people to rent a miniature private room for the night, with all meals included; ask the conductor about upgrading to sleeper service if you're interested.

Don't Get Overwhelmed!

Some people start an extended roadtrip with the intention of seeing *everything*. They want to go to every major attraction in the country. They want to visit every state. They want to stop at every kitschy roadside attraction ever built. If that's your intention on a roadtrip, you're likely to be disappointed. Most people who live 100 years never see all that.

If you drive all over the country in a zigzag pattern just to say you've set foot in every state, in most cases you're shortchanging yourself. Although the car is one of the best ways to get to the places you want to see, most of America can't be experienced from *inside* one. You're going to have to get out and discover what's *outside* the car; that's what's great

---

Living on the Road for $500 a Week – Plan No. 2

Here's another possibility for living on the road for $500 a week.

Gasoline – 400 miles to 1st destination	$ 50
3 Nights in budget Mom-and-Pop motel	$ 150
6 Restaurant Meals	$ 70
Gasoline – 200 miles to 2nd destination	$ 30
4 Nights camping in State Park	$ 80
Groceries and Supplies	$ 80
Miscellaneous Expenses	$ 40
Grand Total for the Week	**$ 500**

---

about taking a roadtrip. The journey is about more than miles clocked on an odometer or the exits you've passed. It's about stopping and experiencing what's along the way. So, on an extended roadtrip, don't get in a hurry. You'll have lots of time to explore and discover, and if you find a place you like, stay longer!

Plan to drive full days only occasionally. On a weeklong roadtrip, it may be common to drive two or three full days, sometimes more. On a longer trip, though, think in terms of weeks, not days. Instead of spending a day in a place, plan on spending a week. Then, when it's time to move on, go somewhere else, and spend another week. This style of travel will also give you more of a sense of stability than moving from one place to another nearly every day.

If you've thought about taking to the road for months at a time, you're not alone. Hundreds of thousands of 'snowbirds' and others do it every year, often migrating to places where the sun shines and warm temperatures prevail when it's cold back home. Really, an extended roadtrip is more about being able to move from one place to another at will, being able to really experience a place. It shouldn't mean nonstop driving or a vacation to go see superficial tourist attractions. It's about finding a place and enjoying it. It's about mingling with the locals. It could even be about finding a new home. Whatever the case, there's no need to fear taking an extended roadtrip.

CHAPTER **11**

The Roadtrip Packing List

You've planned your route. You know where you want to go. The sights you'll want to see. Even the places you'll stay along the way. After all this planning, it's time to pack. And really, packing is one of the most important parts of planning for a roadtrip, because how well you pack has much to do with how you'll enjoy your trip – for every unnecessary item you take, it means a little more time loading or unloading luggage and less time to enjoy your travels. And think about this: when travelers take more things, there's less room left in the vehicle for personal space. When sitting in the car for hours at a time, personal space gets to be an important factor.

Packing light really *is* a virtue. And although it would be a shame to leave something really important at home – like medication, your driver's license, or important documents – most other things people pack are comfort items and can easily be acquired along the way.

So *do* pack light. And if you can, convince everyone else traveling with you to pack light too. I've been on enough roadtrips to know that one inconsiderate person, who thinks he needs to take three large suitcases filled with every important personal possession and possible clothing item, can spoil the trip for everyone else in the car. Maybe you've been on that trip or traveled with that person. So if you are the 'captain' of the trip or the owner of the car, let everyone know that one suitcase/roller case and one smaller bag should hold every item taken on a roadtrip.

Really, the 'one suitcase plus a smaller bag rule' is not unreasonable. The airlines expect flyers to follow it when carrying luggage onto a plane. If you need more than that, fine, but you'll pay extra.

The packing list that follows is rather exhaustive. In other words, you may not need everything on this list, but few roadtrippers will need much beyond what's on this list. And unless you're moving cross-country or taking an extended roadtrip for several months, it should all fit in a couple of bags, or even just one.

Personal Items

Clothes. We begin with the obvious. Everyone has his or her own fashion preferences, so this area has endless possibilities, but remember to be comfortable. Unless you're planning to attend a business or formal event where dress clothes are expected, leave the suits and dresses at home. Dress clothes tend to take up more room than casual clothes. If you expect to enjoy a 'nice' dinner at a formal restaurant, men can take a blazer, and women can pack a dress or skirt. Except in the most unusual of circumstances – making a permanent move, for example – take no more clothes than those needed for seven days. After a week, visit a laundromat and do a couple loads of laundry.

Shoes. Two pairs should be enough for most people: one comfortable pair for the car and another pair for walking or hiking. Pack a pair of sandals or flip-flops for a trip to the beach or swimming pool.

Towel. Although hotels provide towels for guests, you'll need your own for a camping trip or for an emergency spill. In a pinch, it can even serve as a makeshift pillow.

Toiletries. This would include your toothbrush, toothpaste, shampoo, mouthwash, deodorant, and shaving products. I like to take travel size packages of most of these products. Small toothpaste tubes can be easily refilled by placing the mouth of the little tube against the mouth of a bigger toothpaste tube. Just squeeze the bigger tube to refill the smaller one. Instead of taking a bulky can of shaving cream, look into a product called *shaving oil* – for a couple of bucks, you can buy a few milliliters of shaving oil which will last for months – available at many drugstores and even discount stores.

Soap. Great for cleaning small stains from clothes and invaluable at a campsite.

Fingernail clippers. Aside from their obvious purpose, these can also be used as makeshift scissors to cut threads or other small objects.

Prescription medications. Take the prescription along, too. Along with these, don't forget any contraceptives or personal hygiene items.

Over-the-counter medications. Prepare a small emergency medication kit that includes your favorite pain reliever, diarrhea relief pills, stomach relief pills, and a few sleeping pills. If you suffer from allergies, include allergy medication, as well.

Brush or comb.

Mirror. Sometimes the rearview mirror just won't do. Look for a basic camping mirror or locker mirror; they cost just a few dollars and are quite durable.

Umbrella. Most of the time, a small umbrella costing one to three dollars will work fine.

Sunglasses and Case. These are very useful on the road, especially when driving. The case will keep the glasses from getting crushed. Also remember to take a few lens cleaning wipes.

Luggage: Wheels or No Wheels?

Today's most popular luggage features a somewhat sturdy frame with wheels attached to the bottom. The metal framework extends, revealing a convenient handle. Are these rolling suitcases what you'll need on a roadtrip, though? Wheeled luggage tends to be heavy, and to be honest, wheels are useful only when rolling your case long distances, such as in an airport. Wheels don't handle too well on city streets or up stairs. Consider, also, that the inflexible nature of wheeled luggage makes for less room in the trunk of the car, especially if four people each plan to take their own case. Personally, when on the road, I use a large duffle bag; they tend to hold just as much as any wheeled bag – and they usually weigh much less.

Travel mug. Many convenience stores will allow you to refill your own travel mug for a discount. These are also much sturdier than cheap foam or paper cups, which tend to leak or collapse easily. Remember to wash the mug occasionally while on the road!

Calculator. Great for calculating gas mileage or adding up expenses. Buy a solar calculator, so you won't have to worry about batteries. Don't spend any more than five dollars on this purchase.

Reading material. For those evenings in the hotel when nothing's on TV, and you just want something to read. Good reading material is a must if you're traveling alone; it will help keep your mind occupied while sitting in a restaurant or at other times. Magazines are ideal when on the road; read them, then dispose of them or give them away as you finish them.

Pillow. A pillow from home can make a night's sleep much easier, especially if you'll be away from home a while.

Small fleece blanket. A small blanket is perfect for those times when the air conditioner is turned too low for your comfort. Instead of complaining, just cover up with a blanket. Don't leave this home in the summertime; you may be surprised how often you'll feel chilly, even in warm weather months.

Earplugs and eye mask. Especially if you need darkness and/or quiet, these two items will help you get to sleep, even in the noisiest of roadside motels. If you need to take a nap during the day, an eye mask will make it much easier to get a few minutes sleep.

Plastic bags. We all have these lying around the house. Plastic shopping bags make great litter bags for the car, and they do a good job of holding dirty clothes until you get around to doing laundry. Take several of these.

Clothespins. Perfect for closing a bag of chips, hanging clothes to dry at a campsite, or just keeping the curtains closed in a motel room.

Pocket knife. These are handy for cutting, slicing, even peeling an orange.

Hangers. The hotel may not have enough hangers for everyone, so take a few of your own.

Binoculars. A small set of binoculars will help you appreciate the scenery when riding along in the car or on a hike.

Important phone numbers and addresses. If something happens to your cell phone, you'll need to have the most important contact numbers and addresses available in the event of an emergency. In fact, I take my contact list and laminate it. Keep it in a safe place, such as a purse or wallet.

Checkbook. If you don't plan to be away for an extended time, it should suffice to take two or three checks, instead of the whole book. Although most businesses don't accept checks from out of town, it may become necessary to pay a bill or some other expense.

Envelopes and postage stamps. If you have to pay a bill by mail when you're away, you'll save time by having a few envelopes and stamps available. Or, you may just want to send someone a card or write an old-fashioned letter.

Small notebook. For jotting down expenses, places you've been, hotel confirmation numbers, or anything else that may need to be written down.

Spare keys. If traveling with others, let someone else in the group keep the spare keys.

Documents and Red Tape

Driver's license. Very obvious, but you won't want to be stuck without it. Make sure it doesn't expire while you're away.

Current vehicle registration. Keep the original in the vehicle's glove compartment and affix the sticker to the correct spot on the license plate. Once again, make sure it won't expire during the trip.

Proof of insurance. Keep this in your glove compartment, next to the registration information. In fact, laminate both of those forms and paperclip them together.

Passport, birth certificate, and car title. Under most circumstances, necessary only if you'll be leaving the country with your car. See Chapter 14, "The Mexico Roadtrip."

Copies of all the above documents. Make copies and keep them separate from the originals, preferably in a safe place in your luggage.

Credit card and/or ATM card.

Membership cards. Whether you're a student, a member of AAA, AARP, or a labor union, your membership card may yield valuable discounts. And I suppose you can include your medical insurance card, too.

In the event of illness, you'll definitely want to be considered a 'member' of that club.

Communications and Technology

Cell phone. It doubles as an alarm clock and, possibly, a calculator. And don't forget the car charger!

Laptop computer equipped with Wi-Fi. If you plan to be on the road for an extended period, consider a wireless data plan or EV-DO card for internet access. Otherwise, Wi-Fi should be sufficient for most purposes. If your battery's charge doesn't last as long as it used to, consider buying a new laptop battery before the trip. Of course, don't forget your computer's AC adaptor and mouse. Take your machine's recovery disk and copies of any essential software, in case the unthinkable happens, and the hard drive has to be wiped clean for some reason.

Satellite radio or CD's. Essential for audio entertainment while on the road.

MP3 player and headphones. For the times when you don't want to listen to what everyone else is listening to. Consider noise-reducing headphones; they're wonderful at blocking road and engine noise when you just want some peace and quiet.

Portable DVD player, movies, and car adaptor. Many better MP3 players double as video players, so the portable DVD player may not be necessary. Still the screen is bigger on these, so two or three people can enjoy the movie at once. Be aware that in many states it is illegal to operate a video device such that the screen is visible from the driver's seat.

Digital camera, rechargeable batteries, and memory card. To document all the great times you'll have on the road.

Battery charger. To recharge the batteries for your camera and other sundry devices you may have.

For the Car

GPS device. The more expensive models pronounce the names of streets and towns, and they also have larger screens. For most travelers, a simple model should be fine. They can easily be found for less than $150.

Radar detector. Useful for identifying areas where police are patrolling for speeders. Having one of these devices is not an excuse to speed, though, as many police departments now use laser devices or even aircraft to crack down on speeders; most radar detectors are useless against these methods. Radar detectors are illegal in Virginia, the District of Columbia, and for commercial vehicles nationwide. In Minnesota, it's illegal to attach *any* electronic device – radar detectors included – to the windshield.

DC power inverter. Useful for plugging in a typical electronic device, such as a laptop computer, to a car's DC power outlet. Make sure the rating on the inverter is appropriate for the appliance you plan to run. Blow dryers and microwave ovens were not made to run on these things; keep them for laptop computers and small electrical equipment.

DC power splitter. The radar detector, the satellite radio, and the GPS all require a power outlet. Only have one power outlet in your car? Not to worry, because a splitter will convert one outlet into multiple receptacles. Look for one that has three outlets; these usually have an on/off switch and additional safety features.

Toolkit. Most auto supply stores sell an emergency toolkit that includes basic wrenches and screwdrivers for very simple repairs. Just as important, though, are the jumper cables and emergency air compressor that many of these kits contain. They're essential for jumping the car's battery or inflating a flat tire in an emergency.

Tire gauge. Get in the habit of checking the air pressure in your tires regularly. Well-inflated tires keep your fuel economy at acceptable levels, prevent the tires from wearing out too soon, and are generally just safer.

Ice scraper. Even in the summer, frost can form at high altitudes or at northern latitudes. In the winter, it's essential to scrape the frost from your windshield in the morning. If you want to get a good deal on an ice scraper, make your purchase in the spring, when even the best scrapers are often put on clearance for just a few dollars.

Canned tire inflator. If you run over a nail and need to change a flat tire, it's just not safe to do it on the shoulder of a busy expressway. You're better off calling for help. If you're in a place where it's safe to do so, a can of tire inflator, such as Fix-a-Flat, will temporarily seal your tire, so it's possible to drive to a repair center instead of having to call a tow truck.

Quart of oil. Check your oil level occasionally. If the vehicle is slowly leaking or burning oil, make plans to get it repaired. Until then, add oil yourself and make sure the level stays full.

Deer warning whistles. In rural areas, especially the Midwest, seeing deer on the highway at night is a dangerous reality. A deer collision can easily cause thousands of dollars worth of damage, and in rare cases can even cause motorist fatalities. Deer warning whistles attach to the front of your car and emit a high-pitched noise that supposedly keeps deer away from your car. Many motorists swear by them, and many brands claim to ward off moose, elk, and livestock as well. If you choose to attach these devices to your car, remember that these whistles are still no substitute for a keeping a watchful eye on the road.

Liquid rain repellent. This waxy liquid, of which Rain-X is the most common brand, is rubbed onto window glass with a dry cloth. After the glass is treated, rain beads up on the window, drastically improving visibility in poor weather. It's well worth the few minutes required to treat your car's windows, especially if rain is expected along the route.

Cooler with snacks and drinks. Not only is it convenient to fill a cooler with snacks and drinks, you'll save money, too, by avoiding the drive-thru line every time you get thirsty. Buy ice along the way to keep the drinks cold.

Box of tissues. In addition to their intended use, they can be used as miniature paper towels. Of course, if you plan on doing any major picnicking, take a real roll of paper towels, too.

Roll of toilet paper. Not all public restrooms provide toilet paper. So keep a spare roll in the car, and get in the habit of taking a few squares of toilet paper into public restrooms, just in case.

Liquid hand sanitizer. Most public restrooms aren't the cleanest of places, and sometimes they don't even have proper handwashing facilities. A bottle of liquid hand sanitizer is a must when traveling the (sometimes dirty) road.

Tent. Essential for camping.

Small propane stove. Every discount store with a sporting goods department carries these miniature stoves. They're useful when camping, and even when you're not. It's often easier to cook a meal at a park with one of these stoves than it is to use the park's barbecue pit. Your stove is probably cleaner, too.

Flashlight. A good flashlight is useful for finding something you lost under the seat or in the trunk of your car at night. In an emergency, they're invaluable. Consider a flashlight that uses a hand crank instead of batteries, because Murphy's Law applies to flashlight batteries, too.

Duct tape. We all know duct tape is useful for just about any temporary repair. Keep a small roll in the trunk of your car for emergencies.

Road atlas and other maps. Essential for finding your way on the road. These can be used in conjunction with your GPS device.

Guidebooks. Invaluable for finding attractions along the way. Many guidebooks also recommend inns, hotels, and restaurants. Some even include coupons. Every state has a tourism department that will send you state guidebooks and information free of charge. For more information, see Chapter 15, "Roadtrip Resources."

Coupons for restaurants and attractions. Print coupons from the web for restaurants you may visit along the way. Many attractions also offer online coupons. Keep these in a safe place, such as a dedicated coupon envelope or plastic baggie.

Take What's Important to You

If you take every single item on this list, you'll probably have everything you could possibly need for a typical roadtrip. Feel free to delete items you won't need on your trip. And if there's something you *really* need that's not on the list, then take that, too. Since every traveler is different, it's best to take a list like this and create your own personal packing list that can be revised and reused over and over again for future travels.

If one of your traveling companions feels the need to take excessive baggage on a roadtrip beyond what's really necessary, remind him or her of this fact: Of all the travelers I've met, many of them have told me that they wish they hadn't taken so many things on their trip. I have yet to meet someone who has told me, "I wish I had taken more baggage." It's always the opposite. So pack light, and pack smart.

The next few chapters will discuss something much different: suggestions for possible routes. Of all the popular roadtrip highways in America, one stands out above the rest: Historic Route 66. The next chapter will give you a glimpse of what to expect on this famous road.

CHAPTER 12

Route 66

Route 66 is likely the most written-about highway in history. Since its inception in the 1920's, Route 66 was the highway of choice for motorists heading west to California, either on vacation or looking for a new life out West. The highway was immortalized in John Steinbeck's novel *The Grapes of Wrath*, in which the Joad family leaves the Dust Bowl of Oklahoma in search of a better life in California. In fact, you could say that *The Grapes of Wrath* was the first great American roadtrip novel.

Don't look for Route 66 on your trusty road atlas, though, because you probably won't find it there. The highway started being signed as "U.S. Highway 66" around 1928, shortly before the beginning of the Great Depression. It quickly became the highway to take when traveling from the Midwest to southern California. During the Dust Bowl period, a combination of poor economic conditions mixed with severe drought caused many farmers and their families to abandon their homes in Oklahoma, Kansas, and other rural states in favor of the booming economy of California.

As the economy improved post-World War II, Americans became increasingly mobile and the modern roadtrip was born. They took to the highway like never before, and Route 66 was their road, too. Vacationers headed to California, the Grand Canyon, St. Louis, and places in between.

Route 66 took them where they wanted to go. Traffic was so congested on the highway, in fact, that the road was eventually expanded, and much of it became a four-lane highway.

Many nostalgic travelers feel that Route 66 lost much of its charm when it became a four-lane road, yet progress was inevitable. Four-lane roads became the standard, especially at the end of the 1950's when the Interstate Highway System started to replace many of the older two-lane routes. Sure, the new highways were faster, but they also bypassed many of the small towns that gave the older roads their personality and charm. Many of the small towns the interstate forgot relied heavily on Route 66 traffic to make ends meet. As the traffic from 66 dried up, so did many of the towns. Eventually, in 1985, the federal government decided the highway was unnecessary and removed the designation from the register of U.S. highways.

The Old Road's Revival

Over the past two decades, highway nostalgia has revived Route 66, attracting roadtrippers from around the world. Many bikers flock to the route to experience the "Mother Road" on motorcycle, others make the drive in their automobiles to experience what it must have felt like to travel west decades ago. Most states along the route have made it easy to follow old Route 66, especially as it meanders through smaller towns along the way. Even where the interstate has completely superseded the old road, as you approach medium-sized towns, you'll likely find signs reading "Historic Route 66" that guide motorists along the route through business districts.

As the song says, Route 66 "winds from Chicago to L.A." And yes, it is "more than 2000 miles all the way." If you're really interested in traveling "Main Street of America," as it's often called, visit the travel section of your local bookstore or library; you're likely to find several volumes documenting the trip. I won't try to cover everything that's found along the route, as other books completely devoted to Route 66 do a much better job. In the pages that follow, I'll give a basic summary that may whet your appetite for an exciting trip that truly explores the heart of America.

Following the Route

Thanks to several Route 66 historic societies around the country, it's pretty easy to follow the old highway. In fact, a few sections still have the original pavement used in the 1930's. Traveling from Chicago, most of old 66 parallels Interstate 55 through Illinois. In the city of St. Louis, much of 66 follows surface streets until joining up with Interstate 44 through most of Missouri.

Near Joplin, Missouri, 66 diverts from I-44 for a few miles to take a brief jaunt through Kansas before rejoining the interstate in Oklahoma. The Mother Road parallels I-44 all the way to Oklahoma City. From there all the way west to Barstow, California, Route 66 runs alongside or concurrent with Interstate 40. Beyond Barstow, follow Interstates 15 and 10 for most of the remainder of the route.

For more specific details on following the old road, look for a Route 66 guidebook at your local bookstore or library. Many of them include mile-by-mile maps documenting every town along the route and interesting sights to see along the way. Several documentaries have also been made about 66, and it would be a good idea to watch one or two before planning your trip.

Highlights of Route 66

Traveling south along I-55 between Chicago and St. Louis, you'll notice a narrow two-lane road paralleling the freeway most of the way; that's old Route 66. One small city along the road worth a visit is Springfield, Illinois. Springfield is the site of the only home Abraham Lincoln ever actually owned. The house still stands, and tours are given several times daily. Lincoln's entire neighborhood is a pedestrian mall helping visitors imagine how life in the mid-19th century must have been.

The brand-new Lincoln Presidential Library and Museum is also in the city. If you're into Civil War era history, this museum is a must-see. Also of interest is the Illinois state capitol, located downtown. Route 66 passes almost directly in front of the capitol, not to mention other historic sites in town.

Crossing into Missouri

About 100 miles south of Springfield is the bigger city of St. Louis. An interesting attraction on the north side of the city is the Chain of Rocks Bridge. Originally used as one of the alignments for Route 66 around the city, today the bridge is closed to vehicle traffic and is used as a pedestrian and bicycle path.

About 45 minutes west of St. Louis, near the town of Eureka, Missouri, is Route 66 State Park. The park has a small visitor center and provides access to the nearby Meramec River. Probably the most interesting thing about the park, though, is that it's built on the site of the deserted town of Times Beach. Considered a major environmental disaster, throughout the 1970's the streets of the little town were accidentally sprayed with oil contaminated with dioxin, a lethal chemical.

No one suspected much until dozens of area horses started dying. Shortly thereafter, it was discovered that practically the entire town had been contaminated with the chemical. When the Meramec River flooded in late 1982, dioxin contamination allegedly spread from the streets to the soil and homes of town residents.

In 1983, the federal government decided to buy out the entire town of Times Beach and evacuate the residents. By 1985, the town was shut down and completely sealed off. Only after contaminated soil was removed and incinerated did the state of Missouri decide to open the former town as a state park. Visitors say the abandoned streets in the ghost town are still visible.

Kansas and Oklahoma

Route 66 continues west paralleling Interstate 44 through most of Missouri. Near Joplin, State Route 66 takes over where the interstate leaves off. From here through Baxter Springs, Kansas, it's easy to follow the original highway, as signs marking "Historic Route 66" mark the old route quite well. Even though 66 passes through only about a dozen miles of Kansas, it's said that the Kansas section is one of the easiest to follow.

The state of Oklahoma has made a great effort to encourage visitors to travel the old road.   Nearly every town of appreciable size along the

Destination: St. Louis

Often called the "Gateway to the West", St. Louis, Missouri, has plenty to see and do. Well before crossing the Mississippi River into the city, though, the most familiar landmark is the 630-foot-high Gateway Arch. A visit to the Arch is the perfect way to begin your trip to St. Louis. Even if you don't take the five-minute elevator journey to the top, check out the museum underneath the monument which commemorates America's westward expansion and the Lewis and Clark expedition, which began near here. Admission is free to the museum, and it costs $10 to go to the top.

After visiting the Arch, head toward Forest Park – larger than New York's Central Park – where many of St. Louis' finest museums are found. The St. Louis Art Museum, Science Center, and Missouri History Museum are all located in Forest Park. Each of these attractions require at least two hours to see well, and special exhibitions will require more. Best of all, admission is free to all three museums. The St. Louis Zoo, also located in the park, is normally considered one of the top twenty zoos in the country. Admission is also free.

About a mile southeast of Forest Park is the Missouri Botanical Garden. Admission is $8 for adults and makes for a leisurely afternoon any time of the year. The Garden was founded in 1859, making it the oldest continuously-operated botanical garden in the nation.

Sports fans won't be disappointed with the options in St. Louis, either. All the major stadiums are downtown. The baseball Cardinals play in Busch Stadium, the NFL's Rams play in the Edward Jones Dome, and the NHL's Blues play in the Scottrade Center – all located within a few blocks of each other.

Also located in the downtown area is St. Louis' historic Union Station. Although the old train station may no longer serve passengers, the property has been restored as a lively downtown shopping and dining center. Union Station is home to many chain stores as well as several local merchants. The area's largest mall, the St. Louis Galleria, is located well west of town along Interstate 64; take the Brentwood Avenue exit to access this upscale shopping center.

About an hour to the west of town along Interstate 44 is Meramec Caverns, thought to be Jesse James' hideout. Whether you're interested in roadside attractions, big-league sports, or fine museums, St. Louis has a little of everything, and is worth a stop on your itinerary!

route boasts "Historic 66" signs to make it easy. Many of the original Route 66 travelers were from Oklahoma, as were the Joad family in Steinbeck's novel, invoking the pejorative 'Okies' to refer to Midwestern migrants.

The Texas Panhandle: Cattle Country

Although Texas is the biggest state in the lower 48, Route 66 crosses through Panhandle country for a mere 177 miles. Through most of Texas, the old road runs as a parallel frontage road to Interstate 40. Although the route through the state is relatively short, it's full of interesting sights, many of which are visible, or at least easily accessible, from the interstate. All the way through Texas, Route 66 is pancake flat; only a few rolling hills dot the landscape through here.

About an hour west of the Oklahoma state line, near the town of Groom, Texas, you'll see two roadside attractions that cause many travelers to break out their cameras: a giant cross on one side of the highway and a leaning water tower on the other. The cross welcomes visitors, but the water tower, labeled "Britten USA", used to lure travelers to an area truck stop which shut down years ago.

Almost halfway through Texas is the city of Amarillo. Amarillo really is a cow town, and it's proud of that designation. The Texas area around the city is one of the largest beef-producing regions in the United States, if not the entire world. Don't be surprised to see ranches filled with cattle all over this region.

One of the best places to sample some of the local fare is the famous Big Texan Steak Ranch, located right off Exit 74 in Amarillo. You've probably heard of this restaurant before; it's famous for the free 72-ounce steak. If you can finish the steak dinner in one hour, it really is free. Of course, they offer smaller steaks for more normal appetites, but you have to pay for those. The steakhouse is nearly a destination unto itself; it offers a motel onsite, complete with a swimming pool shaped like Texas. They'll even give you a free limo ride from any hotel in Amarillo.

Also in the Amarillo area is a famous site called the Cadillac ranch. In between Exits 60 and 62 along I-40 lie ten old Cadillacs, mostly dating from the 1950's, buried halfway, face down. It's supposed to be art, a testament to the golden age of the road, most notably nearby Route 66. The cars are covered in graffiti, and visitors are welcome to add some of their own. Although it's a somewhat offbeat place to visit, thousands of people flock to the 'ranch' every year to see it and add their own message.

An hour west of Amarillo, right on the Texas/New Mexico state line, lies one of the casualties of the interstate highway system – the town of Glenrio. Although Glenrio was founded when the railroad went through, well over a hundred years ago, it was Route 66 that made it prosper. Few people actually lived in the little town, but it was a convenient stopping point for travelers along the old highway.

Located exactly on the state line, Glenrio had restaurants, a filling station, and a motel. With the construction of Interstate 40 a few hundred yards to the north, though, Glenrio didn't have enough pizzazz to lure motorists off the expressway. Today it's a ghost town; the buildings still stand, but most of them are abandoned. You'll be hard-pressed to find a single person in town. Glenrio is easy to find; take Exit 0 just over the Texas state line. After looking around at what's left of the town, you may agree that the exit number is eerily appropriate.

New Mexico: The Heart of the Southwest

Through most of New Mexico, Route 66 has been buried underneath the endless ribbons of interstate asphalt, as a testament to the millions of travelers from decades past who discovered an America of yesteryear along this same highway. Although the old road is gone, many of the towns and sights are still there and are worth a visit.

The town of Tucumcari, New Mexico, is located about halfway between Albuquerque and Amarillo. Although it's home to well under 10,000 residents, the little town boasts well over 1000 motel rooms, most of which are locally owned. In fact, you could call Tucumcari the Mom-and-Pop motel capital of America!

Some of these motels are the same ones that operated when Route 66 was in its heyday back in the 50's. Tucumcari's motels, though, were known for their neon signs. At one time, the neon lights of Tucumcari welcomed well over 1,000 visitors every night as travelers stayed here en route to places all over the nation. Even today, many businesses in town have survived the interstate highway. Of course, it helps that it's the only sizable town in a 60-mile radius. Thousands still spend the night in Tucumcari in the Mom-and-Pop motels that dot Old Route 66 through town. In fact, billboards advertising "Tucumcari Tonite!" have invited travelers to spend the night in town for decades.

Once you get past Tucumcari and near Albuquerque, you'll notice the terrain starting to change noticeably. Although the last thousand miles of road have been flat plains, with the exception of a few spots in Missouri, things change considerably about an hour east of New Mexico's largest city. The level land you saw from Illinois all the way through Texas now changes to rolling hills. And the rolling hills suddenly become rugged mountains, before descending into the valley where Albuquerque lies.

Not to worry, though, the grade is much easier than in other places in the country, and even the least powerful of cars will easily handle the mountains along Route 66 / Interstate 40 – one of the reasons the route was so popular back in the day.

Desert Country

After passing Albuquerque, traveling through western New Mexico, the terrain becomes rocky, dry, and relatively flat, except for a few hills. This is the terrain you'll see from here all the way to Flagstaff, as you enter the famous Colorado Plateau, where the high plains and mountains give way to desert. Along that same plateau, about a half hour before arriving at Flagstaff at Exit 233, you'll find an interesting formation. Simply called Meteor Crater, it's the place where a meteor – or technically, a meteorite – crashed into the earth's surface 50,000 years ago, leaving a hole nearly 600 feet deep and a mile across.

Meteor Crater, or the Barringer Crater, as it's sometimes called, is located in the middle of an otherwise flat desert. Plan to spend two hours. During good weather, tour guides will lead visitors on a walk around the rim of the crater, narrating the history of the crater's discovery and subsequent exploration. If you look closely, you'll see where the crater was used for mining in the early part of the 20th century. In fact, the ruins of mining structures are still visible around the rim of the crater. Look for the wreckage of a plane that crashed in the crater back in 1964. And don't forget to ask about the astronaut training that NASA conducted in the crater, due to the similarity of the crater's base to the lunar surface.

About halfway through Arizona is the city of Flagstaff. The highest major town in the state, it's an interesting place to visit, if only for the unusual terrain. Flagstaff is located at over 7000 feet above sea level, and as a result, the city boasts alpine forest, is surrounded by mountains, and has a cool climate different than much of the rest of Arizona. The unusually high elevation keeps winters cold and summers refreshingly cool, and as a result, Flagstaff is a popular summer resort destination.

Further west is the town of Williams, Arizona, often called "Gateway to the Grand Canyon." Although Williams itself is quite small, with only about 3000 residents, it's a popular stopping point for passing motorists, even those not headed to the Grand Canyon, for it's the last town on the interstate for the next 100 miles.

One of Williams' main attractions is the steam locomotive found in town, and it's also the end of the line of the Grand Canyon Railway. An interesting fact about Williams is that it was the last town along Route 66 to be bypassed by the interstate. Due to fierce local opposition, Interstate 40 around town wasn't opened until 1984.

Once you head west out of Williams, you're in the desert. Towns, restaurants, gas stations, and other services are few and far between until the small city of Kingman, more than 100 miles down the road. So enjoy the desert scenery, and take old Route 66 at Exit 139. It's more scenic than the interstate, and you'll pass a few more towns that the interstate forgot, like Seligman, Peach Springs, and Valentine. All used to be important towns along the dusty old road; when you pass through today, you can still visualize the thousands of motorists who passed through every day back in the heyday of Route 66.

At Kingman, much of the traffic turns north, heading to Las Vegas. Others head straight east, making the long, steep descent into Bullhead City and Laughlin, Nevada. Interstate 40 makes a sharp turn to the south, though, as it heads toward Needles, California, and eventually Barstow, where I-40 ends.

From Barstow, continue on Interstate 15, heading south, to experience the scenic vistas for which southern California is famous. You'll pass Victorville and San Bernardino, then head east on Interstate 10. Eventually, you'll end up in Santa Monica, where the old road ended. Although the Interstate superseded the old route in most places, you'll still see signs pointing out the old alignment, especially passing through cities and towns along the way.

The last few pages were really just a cursory glimpse at the endless sights along the Mother Road. True, Route 66 may not be the most scenic way to head cross country, but it is one of the most historic. And it's one of the best ways to get a glimpse of past small-town glory, while still enjoying a leisurely roadtrip in the present.

After driving the route, you may want to come back and do it again. Plenty of Route 66 roadtrippers are repeat visitors, and when you make *your* visit to the old road, you'll see why it's called Main Street of America!

CHAPTER **13**

Coast to Coast:
A Cross-Continent Adventure

Like I mentioned in the opening chapter, the purpose of this book is not to tell you where to go; plenty of books on the market do that. This book primarily gives advice on *how* to plan your journey and get to your destination enjoyably. Still, many readers may want some ideas about places to go, and for that reason, I've included these three chapters on route ideas. These routes – or a portion of them – would make for a great way to spend a week, or even a month, on the road. The route I've included in this chapter is a favorite for many: one that winds from the Atlantic to the Pacific, passing some of America's best scenery along the way.

This route begins in Ocean City, Maryland, at the shores of the Atlantic Ocean. Ocean City is also the eastern terminus of U.S. Highway 50, which we will rejoin later. Highway 50 winds its way westward across the Delmarva Peninsula all the way to the Chesapeake Bay near Annapolis. It's possible to follow Highway 50 all the way into Washington, D.C., right past the National Mall and the Lincoln Memorial as Constitution Avenue.

Before venturing into Washington by car, though, be aware that traffic is often horrendous, and street parking is difficult to find. Parking

Destination: Washington, DC

Our nation's capital is a fun place to visit, especially if you're a history buff. You may be surprised, though, that it's also an inexpensive destination. The most popular museums and sites offer free admission. Lodging can be inexpensive, too, if you're willing to stay in the suburbs.

First of all, getting around Washington is *most* difficult in your own car. If possible, try to park at your hotel or in a lot outside the city – there are plenty of Park-and-Ride facilities in the suburbs near major Metro stations. Take the efficient Metrorail into the city center; most major attractions are within walking distance of a subway station. Remember, it's cheaper to take the subway during non-rush hours.

Some of the most popular destinations are government sites; the Capitol building and Supreme Court both welcome visitors. The White House is open, too, but tickets must be obtained well in advance from your member of Congress. See the Constitution, Declaration of Independence, and Bill of Rights at the National Archives. The Library of Congress is also an interesting destination; look for Thomas Jefferson's first draft of the Declaration of Independence. Admission is free to all these sites.

If you're a museum buff, you won't be disappointed here. The granddaddy of all museum complexes, the Smithsonian, is a collection of over a dozen individual museums, each dedicated to a different facet of American life and culture. Some favorites include the National Air and Space Museum, the National Museum of Natural History, the National Museum of American History, and the National Zoo. The most popular museums are adjacent to the National Mall, within walking distance of numerous monuments, memorials, and government buildings. Once again, admission is free to all Smithsonian museums in the Washington area.

Monuments and memorials abound in the area, as well. The Lincoln Memorial, Vietnam Veterans Memorial, and World War II Memorial are all located on the National Mall, a park located almost exactly in the middle of the city. If you want to ascent to the top of the Washington Monument, a 555-foot stone obelisk also found on the Mall, you'll need to obtain a free ticket at the lodge on 15th Street. Other monuments worth a visit include the Jefferson Memorial, located alongside the Potomac River, and Arlington National Cemetery, found across the Potomac in Virginia.

Although Washington is best navigated by foot and public transportation, there's enough to do in this city to keep roadtrippers of any budget satisfied for a week or more. So plan a stop in our nation's capital and discover one of America's most popular destinations!

garages are expensive near popular tourist attractions. You may be better off driving around Washington on the Capital Beltway – Interstate 495 – and parking your car at the Park-and-Ride complex near Vienna, Virginia. From Vienna, located along Interstate 66 west of the city, you can catch a ride on the Washington Metro into town. The city's relatively new subway system is efficient and certainly beats the stresses of trying to find a parking space near the museum or attraction you want to visit.

Into the Mountains

Leaving the Washington, D.C. metro area on I-66 traveling west, you'll eventually arrive at the town of Front Royal. This town marks the entrance to one of the most beautiful driving tours in this part of the country: Shenandoah National Park's Skyline Drive. Although it costs ten dollars per car to drive the 100-mile long trail, it's well worth the cost.

Once south of Interstate 64, you leave Shenandoah and begin traveling on the famous Blue Ridge Parkway. This scenic, sometimes winding mountain road gives some spectacular views of the Blue Ridge and Smoky Mountains as it makes its way nearly 400 miles through Virginia and North Carolina, almost to the Tennessee border.

Our journey along the Blue Ridge Parkway, though, takes us only as far as Roanoke, about 100 miles from where the parkway begins. Roanoke, the largest city along the Blue Ridge Parkway and the largest city for the next 350 miles along our route, is worth a visit of its own. The city's historic downtown area boasts a popular farmer's market, a science museum, and numerous local shops.

From Roanoke, our route continues west along U.S. 460, paralleling the interstate before turning north to cross the Brush Mountains near Blacksburg. After a short jaunt through the southern tip of West Virginia, Highway 460 turns back into Virginia as a scenic four-lane highway that continues almost all the way to the Kentucky state line.

Highway 460 continues as a mountain road through the Appalachians into Kentucky. The first town of consequence in Kentucky is Pikeville, home to one of the largest land-removal projects in America. In fact, U.S. 460 passes right through the so-called Pikeville Cut-Through, which essentially sliced through a mountain to alleviate flooding in town, increase the amount of usable land in the town's center, and provide a more convenient transportation route. Pikeville is also home to a small college, located atop a steep hill in the mountain town.

Pikeville is in the middle of coal mining country, and mining has shaped the fortunes, or lack thereof, of many of the area's residents. It's been stated that Pike County at one time had the highest concentration of millionaires in the state of Kentucky, and the prosperity can be seen by watching the expensive cars driven by local teenagers as they cruise the streets on Friday nights. The prosperity is in stark contrast to the abundant poverty of the region, though, as cramped trailer parks and run-down housing are common throughout this part of Appalachia.

Keep following U.S. 460 west until nearing the town of Prestonsburg, where you'll turn left onto State Route 114. This highway eventually becomes the Bert T. Combs Mountain Parkway, which winds through the last 50 miles of the Appalachian Mountains, first as a two-lane highway, then widening to a four-lane freeway.

Kentucky's Bluegrass Region

Interstate 64 takes you into the Lexington area, which is known for the two H's: higher education and horses. From the east side of the city, follow U.S. Highway 60; it runs straight through downtown Lexington and is an easy way to see some of the city from your car. Staying on the interstate only shuttles motorists to the north and east of town; highway 60 actually takes you near the University of Kentucky campus and the famous Keeneland racetrack, where much of the movie *Seabiscuit* was filmed.

West of Lexington, continue on U.S. 60; look for the castle on the right side of the highway as you leave the city. It was built in the 1970's and is now a pricey hotel.

West of Versailles (pronounced ver-SALES around here), keep traveling west on U.S. 62. This road features rolling hills across nearly the rest of the state. Bardstown, a town along this route, is known for the My Old Kentucky Home Dinner Train, one of the few dinner trains of its type in this part of the country.

Past Elizabethtown, Highway 62 flattens out a little, but remains scenic as it traverses an increasingly green – not blue – region of Kentucky. Passing towns such as Beaver Dam, Central City, and Dawson Springs, you'll see that we've returned to coal country, although not quite as prosperous as that found in the eastern corner of the state.

The Land of Rivers and Lakes

U.S. 62 eventually takes you over Kentucky Dam along the Tennessee River, which impounds Kentucky Lake. At over 180 miles in length, it's one of the largest artificial lakes in the nation. Nearby is Land Between the Lakes, a federal recreation area which includes hiking paths, camping facilities, horseback riding, and even a planetarium.

If you keep driving west on Highway 62, though, you'll end up along the Ohio River in Paducah, the largest town in westernmost Kentucky. It's home to the National Quilt Museum and a thriving art community near the downtown area.

Past Paducah, follow U.S. Highway 60 toward the little town of Wickliffe and a small archeological site called Wickliffe Mounds. The mounds display what life was like for Native Americans who lived in the area hundreds of years ago.

As you drive past Wickliffe, U.S. 60 turns north briefly to cross the Ohio River. If you look carefully to your left as you cross the river, you'll see the exact confluence of the Ohio and Mississippi Rivers. As soon as you cross into Illinois, turn left to cross the Mississippi River and head into Missouri.

Although U.S. 60 passes through Illinois for only nine-tenths of a mile, there are a couple of interesting places to see along this short route. Right before crossing into Missouri is Fort Defiance Park, located at the confluence of the Mississippi and Ohio Rivers. It was used as a strategic fort during the Civil War, and there's archeological evidence to suggest that the site has been used for warfare for as much as 1000 years. And yes, it's possible to stand at the point where the two rivers converge, which also happens to be at the lowest elevation in the state of Illinois.

About a mile to the north is the town of Cairo (pronounced CAY-ro). The historic significance of this town is highlighted in books such as Mark

Twain's *Huckleberry Finn*. Today, the town is only a shadow of its former glory, but the historic downtown still contains some of the old mansions that exhibit the architecture of the early 20th century.

The Ozarks

Once crossing into Missouri, you'll keep motoring west on U.S. 60. Although the highway does its best to mimic an interstate well past Sikeston, the flat farmland of the Mississippi River valley gives way to rolling hills – and eventually the rugged mountains – of the Ozarks. During the summer, this area comes alive as tourists from all over the Midwest flock to towns such as Van Buren to enjoy some of the best whitewater rafting and camping available in this part of the country.

As U.S. 60 nears Springfield, our route emerges from the curves and hills of the Ozarks in favor of the flat, humid plains that await us for the next several hundred miles of our journey. Springfield is the largest city in southwest Missouri and is a popular gateway for tourists headed to Branson, or a stop for roadtrippers along old Route 66.

For our route, though, we will bypass most of Springfield along U.S. 60, which grazes the southern edge of the city as a four-lane freeway. Eventually, you'll follow Interstate 44 westbound for a few miles before veering onto Missouri Route 96, which intersects old Route 66, mentioned in the last chapter. Just past Webb City, head north on Route 171 for a few miles before crossing into Kansas.

Driving the Kansas Plains

Many casual drivers complain about how boring it is to drive across Kansas, especially if they've seen nothing other than Interstate 70. Much of the state, though, features a tranquil beauty that simply can't be appreciated from the interstate. Most of our trek across Kansas will be on U.S. Route 400 in the southern part of the state through the quiet, rural countryside. Be aware, though, that the first 150 miles of our trip through Kansas will have few services. Fill up the gas tank before getting onto Highway 400, and plan to spend the night back in Springfield or ahead in Wichita.

Wichita, with a population of over a third of a million, is the largest city we've passed on this route since Washington, D.C., and the largest we'll see until Denver. It's been rated as one of the most livable cities in the country, and boasts several art museums, a zoo, as well as a few other places of interest to roadtrippers. If you're interested in a notable piece of roadside history, you can visit the site of the first Pizza Hut, as well as the first White Castle; both were founded in Wichita.

West of Kansas' largest city on U.S. 400, we start to pass a few small towns, mostly farming communities. Kingman, Pratt, and Greensburg are all agricultural towns. Of interest is the town of Greensburg, formerly best known as the home of the world's largest hand-dug well. However, one of the most powerful tornadoes ever measured ripped through the area in May 2007, destroying practically the entire town. Shortly after the tragedy, though, came a city resolution to build all structures in Greensburg to the highest of all environmental standards.

A little farther down the road is the town of Dodge City, the setting for the television series *Gunsmoke*. It's also known as the meat packing capital of America, with one of the largest beef processing plants in the country. Dodge City features a historic downtown area, which gives visitors a glimpse of what life was like back in the Wild West.

Ascending into the High Plains

Although the last 300 miles may have seemed deliberately flat, the fact is that the elevation has increased by 2000 feet from Joplin to Garden City. And the elevation will increase another 2000 feet over the next 250 miles. From Garden City, turn north onto U.S. 83. Traveling northbound toward Interstate 70, you'll sample much of the beauty of the high plains. Many visitors to Kansas expect flatlands; you may be surprised that this area is somewhat hilly. In fact, rocky hills and cliffs are visible in the distance throughout much of this area.

From the town of Oakley, our route continues west on Interstate 70 to make the quiet three-and-a-half hour trip to Denver. Highway 70 crosses into Colorado at an elevation of just over 4000 feet near Burlington. If you need to grab a bite to eat or fill up the gas tank, stop now, because Burlington is the last town of consequence until Limon, almost a hundred miles away. The Colorado state welcome center, located near Exit 438, is a good place to stop for maps and tourist information for the entire state.

Most travelers expect Colorado to be mountainous, but in actuality the eastern two-fifths of the state is flat, almost an extension of the wild high plains of western Kansas. From Burlington to the edge of Denver, expect little traffic, a generally straight and flat road, the occasional hill, and a 75 mile-per-hour speed limit. If you'd rather a slower tour of the Colorado high plains, take Highway 50 west from Garden City to Pueblo, then head north on I-25 through Colorado Springs.

Denver, the 'Mile High City', is surprisingly flat to the first-time visitor. The city lies at the foot of the Rocky Mountains, which are easily visible from nearly anywhere in the city. Colorado's largest city is as modern as any, with fine dining, some of the best museums in the country, major league sports, and fine lodging options. You could easily spend a week here, but if you're just passing through, consider a trip to the state capitol, which marks the exact elevation of 5,280 feet above sea level. The Museum of Nature and Science, Colorado History Museum, and Denver Art Museum are also located within easy access to U.S. 40, called Colfax Avenue as it passes through town.

Into the Rockies

The next hundred miles are some of the most-feared stretches of interstate highway in the entire country. Thousands of motorists drive hundreds of miles out of their way so as not to cross the Front Range of the Rocky Mountains in Colorado. There's really little reason to fear, though, as Interstate 70 is one of the best built and safest – not to mention one of the most beautiful – mountain freeways in the country. Heading west out of Denver on I-70, you'll rise quickly into the mountains. It took nearly 2000 miles from Ocean City to Denver to ascend the first mile in elevation, but you'll climb another mile in elevation in less than 70 miles.

As the road rises, the terrain changes, too. Well into the summer, remmants of winter snow can be found alongside of the interstate. Several rest areas and scenic overlooks have been built along this stretch of road, making it easy to survey the surroundings at this elevation. You'll pass towns with familiar names, such as Breckinridge, Vail, and Avon, all ski re-sort towns high in the mountains. Take note: near milepost 211, you'll go through the Eisenhower Memorial Tunnel, which at an altitude of over 11,000 feet, is the highest point on the entire U.S. interstate system. From here, you'll slowly be going downhill almost all the way to the Pacific Ocean near San Diego.

Glenwood Canyon: A Jewel of the Highway

Shortly after Avon, the road flattens out a bit for a few miles, and it may be easy to think you've finished crossing the mountains. Not so fast, though; you're about to go through Glenwood Canyon, one of the last sections of I-70 to be built. Due to the fragile ecosystem surrounding the canyon, there was much public opposition to building a freeway here. Well into the 1980's, this stretch of the interstate was still in jeopardy, as legal battles and engineering challenges threatened its construction.

Eventually, the interstate was completed, but with the condition that the environment be protected in the process. As a result, the Glenwood Canyon portion of our route is one that showcases the natural, rugged beauty of the gorge like few other interstates do. Be sure to get off at the scenic overlook rest areas – there are four of them – to admire the majesty of the canyon from outside your car. The canyon really is a sight to see, as the rocky walls around you tower 1300 feet straight into the air. It's been called one of the most scenic natural formations on the entire interstate system, so don't miss it!

Into Utah: The Journey Gets Quieter

From Glenwood Springs to Grand Junction, the interstate generally parallels the Colorado River, often passing right next to it. From here west, the interstate levels off at just under 5000 feet in elevation, with deep-red mountains off in the distance. Once you reach Grand Junction – named for the Grand River, what the Colorado River used to be called – your trip through the mountains is essentially complete. Traffic gets very light west of Grand Junction, as do services. Fill up in Grand Junction or Fruita, because you're nearly 100 miles from the next small town: Green River, Utah, population 900.

As Interstate 70 crosses into Utah, the scenery is more subdued and tends to be perceived off in the distance. The scenic overlooks are not to be missed. Along the way, you'll pass massive geologic formations with names such as Ghost Rock, Book Cliffs, and Goblin Valley, with sweeping vistas that live up to their names.

This area of eastern Utah between Salina and the Colorado state line is nearly uninhabited, except for the little town of Green River. In fact, the interstate was the first modern road to be built through much of this terrain. Cell phone signals may be weak, or even nonexistent through this area. But the grandiose beauty of the area is well worth any lack of conveniences.

Eastern Utah is also dinosaur country. This stretch of Interstate 70 is part of the Dinosaur Diamond Prehistoric Highway, and dinosaur remains have been unearthed through much of this area, as well as northwest Colorado. Eastern Utah, especially turning south on U.S. 131 at the Moab exit, is a popular gateway for vacationers headed to the national parks in the region. Arches National Park, Canyonlands National Park, Capitol Reef National Park, and Bryce Canyon National Park are all within easy reach of I-70.

Near Salina, we continue west, rejoining U.S. 50. Through this part of central Utah, the terrain flattens considerably, and the road becomes arid and dusty. Highway 50 joins Interstate 15 for a few miles before heading west again through the little town of Delta. Then, towns and villages become a rarity for the next few hundred miles along our route, especially as we cross into Nevada.

Lonely Highways of the Great Basin

U.S. 50 through Nevada is often called the 'Loneliest Road in America' due to the lack of traffic. This route is worth a trek of its own. The drive from Ely to Reno is over 400 miles long and crosses nine mountain ranges in the process. At times, the view along this highway in the Great Basin is so straight that you can see twenty miles or more of road ahead.

Destination: Las Vegas

In a word, Las Vegas, Nevada, can be described as a *spectacle*. It's a city known for extravagant excesses. It's one of the few places of the world most famous for architecture inspired by – or more accurately, copied from – other cities. Most hotels are based on other places: the Paris, the New York New York, the Sahara, the Luxor; the list goes on and on. It's possible to walk down the Vegas Strip and see the Eiffel Tower on one side of the street, the Empire State Building on the other, with an Egyptian pyramid in the distance.

Of course, this city is built on gambling – or gaming, as it's more politely called – and those extravagant casinos weren't built on the backs on winners. Casinos will do everything they can to lure potential players into their properties. That's why they've traditionally been willing to offer dinner specials or buffets at low prices.

Although Las Vegas doesn't cater to 'cheapskates' anymore, there are still a few inexpensive buffets to be had, mainly at off-Strip locations. Arizona Charlie's, located west of the Strip, offers a prime rib dinner buffet for $7.99 each night. Some off-Strip casinos feature lunch buffets for as little as $5. On the strip, the Sahara Buffet is the cheapest option, at $7.99 for dinner. Most of the higher-quality buffets are found at Center Strip and South Strip properties. One of the best is the Bellagio Buffet, which at $18 for lunch and $26 for dinner, is quite a deal considering the quality and quantity of food available.

After a hearty meal, enjoy a stroll down the Strip – South Las Vegas Boulevard – and gawk at the larger-than-life hotels and architecture that's sometimes even more fun than the original. Enjoy walking through the streets of Venice – town square, gondolas, canals, and all. Take a walk through the streets of Paris and New York. Enjoy the surroundings and feel free to walk the 'streets' of the hotels, most of which are lined with shops akin to an upscale suburban mall.

Once you're tired of the glitz and glamour of Las Vegas proper, get out of town and head south – either to the Grand Canyon or to Hoover Dam. Both are wonders that have to been seen to be believed – one natural and the other man-made – and they're within an easy drive of the city. Las Vegas is a town that's easy to enjoy on a roadtrip, and you won't have to risk a dime!

For our journey, though, we'll be turning left onto U.S. 93 shortly before getting to Ely. Route 93 is almost a 'Loneliest Road' of its own, with so little traffic that one wonders if this road will eventually lead anywhere. This route through the Great Basin curves up and over countless mountains and hills down the state of Nevada before descending upon the towns of Pioche, Panaca, and Caliente.

As you travel the final stretch of Highway 93 before touching the interstate, notice the straight, level road ahead of you. The road runs for nearly 50 miles with little more than a slight curve or two. Eventually, U.S. 93 runs into Interstate 15 and continues south to Las Vegas.

Interstate 15 parallels the Las Vegas Strip, so you'll see the gargantuan hotel-casinos for which the city is famous, from the Stratosphere at the north end of the Strip down to Mandalay Bay at the extreme south end. Although Las Vegas is obviously built around the gaming industry, there's still much to see and do, even if you're not a gambler. The spectacle of the city's architecture is worth a look, and the shopping and dining options are endless.

The Desert

Leaving Las Vegas for the south, take I-215 east until you reach I-515 east. Once you've left the city, our route will continue south on U.S. Highway 95. And all of a sudden, you're back in the quiet, barren desert. As you drive south on U.S. 95, you're about 60 miles from the California state line. You'll pass Boulder City, the 'temporary' city built for construction workers involved in the building of Boulder Dam, today called Hoover Dam. It's one of the few towns in Nevada where gambling is illegal.

Going south on U.S. 95, you eventually cross into California near Needles. Our route crosses Old Route 66 one last time along what's now Interstate 40. South of the interstate, though, the desert continues, as a seemingly endless scene of scrub brush and dry land. As the road keeps going south, we eventually hit Interstate 10, and our route backtracks to the east for nearly 20 miles, and we enter the state of Arizona.

Continuing south on 95 in Arizona, we drive through a sparsely populated, rural region of the west. This is definitely desert, and the elements were traditionally inhospitable to travelers passing through these parts back in the Old West. Today, though, our drive is quick and relatively simple, and we're left to admire the tranquil grandeur of the western desert.

Eventually, U.S. 95 meets the city of Yuma, Arizona, right on the California state line. Yuma is the sunniest city in the world, as the sun shines for over 90% of all daylight hours, according to the Guinness Book of World Records. It's also one of the hottest towns in the United States, as average high temperatures for the month of July average an extreme 107 degrees Fahrenheit!

From Yuma, our route enters its homestretch, continuing west on Interstate 8. This freeway through southern California just about has it all: deserts, mountains, and cities, eventually reaching the San Diego beach. Interstate 8 parallels the Mexican border through nearly its entire journey through California; through Imperial County, the road is as little as a mile or two from the border in places. You'll pass the Imperial Sand Dunes, which give you an unmistakable sign that you're still in the desert.

Of note along this route is the town of El Centro. The name would suggest that the town is located in the center of California, but it's actually one of the southernmost – and actually most remote – cities in the state. Interstate 8 near El Centro also holds the honor of having the lowest elevation on the entire Interstate Highway System, around 50 feet *below* sea level.

After driving through the desert for several hundred miles, you'll be ready for a change of scenery. And I-8 will change dramatically over its final hundred miles. The elevation rises – and then falls – a few thousand feet to cross the mountain pass a few miles before heading into the scenic Cleveland National Forest. The wooded terrain and greenery may make you think you're much farther north, instead of so close to the barren desert.

Descending Toward the Pacific

As you leave the forest near the town of Alpine, it's downhill all the way into the San Diego suburbs. If you choose to continue on Interstate 8 all the way through San Diego, you'll be able to see the Pacific Ocean in the distance just as the freeway ends. At this point, you're within easy access of Sea World, numerous oceanfront parks, and, of course, the beach itself.

If you've followed the route described in these pages, you will have driven nearly 3,500 miles from coast to coast. You'll be tired, but you will have seen a little of everything America has to offer – from desert to forest, from mountains to plains, from ski resorts to beaches, from rivers to lakes to oceans.

Most Americans have never experienced this type of coast-to-coast adventure; to really enjoy it would take at least two weeks, probably more. It could very well be the ultimate roadtrip for many readers. But how about another type of ultimate roadtrip – a trip to another country? That journey will be covered in the next chapter.

CHAPTER 14

The Mexico Roadtrip

Years ago, before I starting taking roadtrips, my impression of driving in Mexico was one that had been shaped by legends and rumors instead of reality. It was an impression that crossing the border meant going into a land of bandits, dirt roads, and danger lurking at every turn. That impression, as it turned out, was a myth. Mexico is a modern country, and although driving down south is different from the U.S.A., it's not dangerous; it simply requires a little more preparation and vigilance.

This roadtrip route is the shortest of the three highlighted in this book – less than 1,100 miles – but it's arguably the most adventurous, too, especially if you've never driven south of the border before. Especially during early spring – February, March, and April to be specific – this route will take travelers from a cold, wintry climate to a tropical paradise where you're surrounded by palm trees and warm sand. Although the trip can easily be made in three days – or even two, in the case of an ambitious speed run – this route is best enjoyed over the course of at least a week, or even more.

Our eventual destination is the picturesque Emerald Coast – *Costa Esmeralda*, as it's called in Spanish – located on the Gulf of Mexico in the central part of Veracruz state. It's a good twelve hours of solid driving from the United States border, but those twelve hours would wisely be divided into two or three days, to best enjoy the scenery that few Americans ever get to see.

Starting Point: East Texas Forestland

The route we have chosen begins in Marshall, Texas, almost 600 miles from the Mexican border. Marshall is a small to medium sized town in East Texas, but it has a rich history dating back to antebellum days. At one time, surrounding Harrison County was the richest in Texas and had more slaves than any other in the state. The railroad also brought a boom to the economy of the area, and later, in the 20th century, oil was discovered, and the prosperity continued. Marshall is also the home of Wiley College, the setting for the movie *The Great Debaters*. For a fairly small town, Marshall has a long, varied history and several attractions.

Marshall is also easily accessible from points north and east of here, via Interstates 20, 30, and 40. Even though the most popular route to Mexico from this part of the country traverses Texas through its middle via Interstate 35, the fact remains that the interstate is heavily congested, often with traffic bottlenecks and urban sprawl from the Oklahoma state line all the way to San Antonio. You'll find Route 59 less stressful, and this road passes through only one major city – Houston.

Our route generally follows U.S. Highway 59 south straight through Houston, and at Victoria, the four-lane expressway continues as U.S. 77. Although the entire route boasts four lanes, it isn't controlled-access most of the time, which means you'll experience many small towns and villages along the way.

Starting out in Marshall heading south, you'll pass the towns of Carthage and Nacogdoches. The latter claims to be the oldest town in Texas, having been the site of a Spanish mission established in 1716. Still, archeological evidence supports the idea that the area has been settled for thousands of years.

On down the road, past Lufkin, the road starts to resemble an interstate more and more as it nears Houston. Past Cleveland, it becomes an access-controlled freeway all the way through Houston, until it emerges as a rural four-lane road on the other side of Rosenberg. If you're nervous about having to drive through Houston, fear not; just follow the signs for U.S. Route 59 straight through the city. The speed limit stays at 60 mph through the city, and during non-rush hours, traffic moves quickly. To avoid Houston's worst traffic, plan to cross the city mid-morning or early afternoon; you'll avoid rush hour.

From Marshall to Houston, our route passed through a humid, highly forested region with plentiful lakes and an abundance of greenery. South of Houston, though, and especially past Victoria, the terrain starts to change dramatically. Instead of the rolling hills found throughout northeast Texas, the land becomes flat and dry. Instead of tall pines, scrub brush becomes the common foliage. Further south, you even start to see small cactus line the side of the road.

Signs of a Border

South of Victoria, the Hispanic influence on the region becomes more pronounced. Many of the towns and counties have names derived from the Spanish language, like Refugio, Nueces, and Sarita. Turn on the FM radio near Corpus Christi, and you'll hear popular Tejano music on several of the stations. Family-owned taco stands dot the side of the road in little communities throughout this area.

Continuing south on Highway 77 past Corpus Christi, Robstown and Kingsville are the last two significant communities you'll see for nearly 100 miles. After passing Kingsville, the highway crosses sparsely-populated Kenedy County, which has fewer than 500 total residents. Kenedy County gained national headlines, though, in February 2006 when Vice-President Dick Cheney accidentally shot his hunting partner in the face while visiting the King Ranch here. As you near the village of Sarita, the only settlement in the county, look for the wind turbines being built in the distance, a sign of how windy and flat it is in these parts.

Several miles south of Sarita, after passing a rest area built in the median of U.S. 77, you'll notice that northbound vehicles are lined up at a checkpoint. That's the border patrol checkpoint, designed to screen all northbound traffic for undocumented immigrants and illegal drugs. Although southbound traffic doesn't stop at the checkpoint, cameras posted

Destination: South Padre Island

The drive to South Padre Island can be a little deceiving. Although palm trees dot the landscape south of Raymondville, the drive along Highway 100 toward the island looks like any other road in South Texas – a little bit greener, maybe. But once you reach the town of Port Isabel, you'll know this area caters to tourists. Souvenir shops, restaurants, water parks, even the local Wal-Mart looks festive.

Continuing ahead, you'll cross the Laguna Madre Bay via the Queen Isabella Memorial Bridge, the longest bridge in Texas.

Once arriving in town, you may be surprised at how compact South Padre Island is. As a community, it has fewer than 3,000 residents, many of whom work in the tourism industry. The island is about a third of a mile wide at this point, so nearly every major hotel is located either on the bayfront or on the beachfront. Nearly all hotels have access or a walkway to the beach.

Restaurants are plenty, and after you've spent some time on the beach, you may be ready for something different. The island is one of the few places in the continental United States where tropical birds can be found in the wild, so birdwatching is a popular activity here. The Dolphin and Nature Research Center is worth a look, too, offering dolphin research trips nearly every day for visitors.

There are several other options for enjoying South Padre Island. Numerous companies offer tours of the island and surrounding area. Ask about tours at your hotel; many of them have convenient tour desks in the lobby. The Schlitterbahn Beach Waterpark gives visitors a unique way to enjoy the beach during summer months; admission costs $37 for adults and $29 for kids. The island even hosts an annual fall film festival. Within an hour's drive are four major shopping malls in the Rio Grande Valley, not to mention the potential for a visit to the towns of Matamoros or Nuevo Progreso, Mexico.

South Padre Island is a reasonably-priced destination in one of the few places in America with a real tropical feel. Whether you're looking for a laid-back beach town or one of the wildest Spring Break destinations in the country (generally, in March only), South Padre is a town nearly everyone will enjoy.

along the highway take pictures of all vehicles to document traffic entering the border zone.

The Rio Grande Valley and Tropical Texas

Soon, the highway enters Willacy County, and the first thing you'll notice will be the palm trees lining the median of the expressway. From this point, it's no more than a half hour to Harlingen, the first big town in the Rio Grande Valley. Although it's called a valley, there are no mountains to be seen within 100 miles of here. And contrary to what the name implies, the Rio Grande isn't really that big.   At this point along its riverbed, anyway, the river separating the two countries is not much more than a wide stream.

The Rio Grande Valley is worth stopping for a few days, even if only to witness firsthand the blend of cultures down here. The Valley runs from Brownsville, on the southwest, all the way up through Harlingen and Mc-Allen to the northwest, and includes Rio Grande City, a few miles past Mc-Allen. The main expressway linking the valley is U.S. 83 – the interstates don't come this far south. And although it may be technically be one metropolitan area with over 1.1 million residents, it's actually made up of several small towns, and is really quite rural. The drive from McAllen to Brownsville is every bit of 60 miles, and this 'urban' freeway passes quite a bit of farmland.

One famous tourist area in the Valley is South Padre Island, located 20 miles to the northeast of Brownsville. To get there from the north, take Highway 100 east approximately 25 miles past the town of Port Isabel. You'll cross the Queen Isabella Causeway, the longest bridge in Texas, which takes you right into the resort town of South Padre Island. The island is only about a third of a mile wide at this point, so beachfront hotels are abundant and relatively inexpensive. In addition to resorts, the island boasts numerous recreation opportunities, including a waterpark, fishing, and dolphin watching.

If you're planning on continuing into Mexico, you can cross the Rio Grande on any one of several toll bridges. Nearly a dozen international bridges throughout the Valley carry thousands of people – not to mention cargo – across the border in both directions every day.

Is It Safe to Travel to Mexico?

The news media has reported on drug-related violence in Mexican border towns. Foreigners generally are not the target of this type of violence. Still, the danger is real. Be aware, though, that most violence is limited to larger border cities. For that reason, I strongly recommend you cross the border at the smaller crossings of Los Indios or Nuevo Progreso. Wisely avoid the larger cities of Matamoros, Reynosa, and Nuevo Laredo. Whereas the authorities of Nuevo Progreso will generally go out of their way to help you, the police forces of Reynosa and Nuevo Laredo have a reputation for corruption. If you stick to the route recommended in this chapter, you should be safe.

When in doubt, avoid large cities, especially those near the border. Limit your driving to daylight hours. Most of Mexico is as safe as anywhere in the United States, especially in smaller towns and rural areas. Remember, you hope foreign tourists wouldn't write off the entire U.S.A. just because of rampant inner-city violence. Likewise, rampant inner-city violence in Mexico shouldn't keep you from enjoying the real jewels waiting to be discovered south of the border.

Your trip will be less stressful – and safer – if you avoid the downtown bridges, that is, any bridge in downtown Brownsville or McAllen. The bridges at Los Indios, Nuevo Progreso, and Pharr seem to make for the easiest border crossings, in that order.

Walking into Mexico

If you're just planning to explore a border town instead of continue to the interior of Mexico, don't even bother driving across the Rio Grande. Find one of the numerous parking lots on the U.S. side; most of them charge just a few dollars to leave your car all day. Walking into Mexico is less stressful and lets you see the border towns much more easily; the bridge toll for pedestrians is about 25 cents.

Probably the best border town for those who have never visited Mexico is Nuevo Progreso. Located within easy walking distance of Highway FM 1015 south of Weslaco, Nuevo Progreso provides a little bit of everything. Shopping, restaurants, bars, and hotels are located all along the main street as soon as you cross the bridge into Mexico. You may be surprised to find an abundance of dentists and pharmacies here, too; thousands of Americans cross the border every year to fill prescriptions or have dental work done. Since the price is often a fraction of that in the U.S., it's an attractive option, especially for those on a limited income.

It's possible to buy almost any Mexican product in Nuevo Progreso, from clay pottery to porcelain dolls representing cultures of every state in the country. And don't worry about exchanging your money; American dollars are actually preferred here.

If you decide just to walk through town, be aware that Nuevo Progreso is very compact and designed for pedestrians, but not so much for drivers. From the International Bridge to the farthest edge of town is about seven blocks. And since most businesses for the tourist are on the main street, Calle Juárez, there's little reason to stray much from this area.

Once you've reached the border, our roadtrip is really less than half over. The most spectacular parts are yet to come. If you're nervous about driving in Mexico, though, read on. The next section will give you tips on legal requirements for driving your car in Mexico, as well as tips on driving safely south of the border.

Before Crossing the Border

Important Documents. Even before your Mexico roadtrip, you'll need to take several steps to ensure a smooth entry into the country. Plan on the taking the following documents with you:

Passport	Driver's License
Credit Card	Title to Your Car

If you're still making payments on your car, the border authorities may ask to see a letter from the lienholder, leasing company, or bank granting permission for the car to be driven into Mexico.

If you don't yet have a passport, get one. Mexican officials have traditionally accepted a certified copy of a birth certificate in lieu of a passport (along with valid photo I.D.), but the U.S. government is soon expected to require *all* citizens to present a passport at all entry points, even land crossings. Apply at least two months before your trip; sometimes there are delays, especially before busy travel periods.

Buy insurance. Think seriously about buying auto insurance for your trip to Mexico. Regardless of what your friends may say, your liability coverage from home *does not* cover you once you cross the border. To have coverage, you must buy a special policy from a company licensed to do business in Mexico. Not to worry, though, as most border crossings will sell policies on the spot, and it's even possible to buy insurance by the day.

Buying insurance at the border will usually cost much more than buying a good policy online. Do an online search for "Mexico Insurance," and you'll find dozens of options. When buying, make sure that the policy includes legal assistance in the event of an accident. As a comparison, the liability policy I purchased on my last trip to Mexico cost less than $160 for an entire year. Shop around, and you'll find a good deal.

Although auto insurance is not mandatory for motorists in most parts of Mexico, it's wise to obtain a good policy before making the trip. Normally, drivers without insurance who get into an accident automatically go to jail – regardless of fault – until the details are sorted out. With liability insurance, though, an accident is treated much as it is in the United States, and insurance companies handle matters.

If your car has full coverage back home in the U.S., it's normally easy to add full coverage to your Mexican policy, as well. Be aware, though, that you normally can't add comprehensive or collision coverage to your policy in Mexico unless you're already covered back in the States.

At the Border

It's really quite easy to take your car into Mexico. There are a few steps to take at the border, though, to register your vehicle so you'll be able to drive past the border region into Mexico's interior. On a good day – and at a non-congested border crossing – it may take as little as 20 minutes to complete these steps. When there's a line, though, it can be up to two hours. Plan ahead, take all your documents, and you won't have much of a problem. Be aware that the least congested times at most border stations are early in the morning and mid-afternoon – from 9:00 to 10:00 and 1:00 to 3:00.

Step One: Tourist Card. As soon as you cross the border, there will be a border station marked "Car Permits", "Banjercito", "Tourist Permits", or something similar. Pull into the parking lot and go inside. The first step will be to obtain a *tourist card*, sometimes called a *tourist visa* or *F.M.T.* From this point onward, it will help if you can speak at least a little Spanish, because many of the government workers at the border stations speak little English.

At larger border stations, you'll wait in line at a window similar to those at a bank. At smaller stations, you may actually step into a small office. Whatever the case, present your passport, and then you'll be asked to fill out the actual visa form. Return it to the officer, who will then stamp it. The officer might also stamp your passport. The border officer will grant you a stay of up to 180 days.

Step Two: Pay the Tourist Fee. Mexico charges a fee of about 20 dollars to process a tourist card. At most stations, there will be a bank available to pay this fee. Since the bank will accept either dollars or pesos, don't worry about changing your money just yet. After you pay the fee, the bank teller will stamp your tourist card, showing proof of payment.

Is there no bank available? Or is the bank at the border station closed? If so, don't worry about paying the fee right now. You're allowed to pay it at any time before leaving Mexico. Find a bank a couple hours down the road and pay it there.

Children Traveling to Mexico

If any minors traveling to Mexico with you are not accompanied by both parents, he or she must bring a notarized letter from the parent(s) not traveling with the child. The letter needs to state that the child has permission to travel to Mexico, and it needs to give the names of the adults who *will* be accompanying the child. If one or both of the child's parents are deceased, the appropriate death certificate should be presented.

What You Can Take Into Mexico

Vacationers planning on a roadtrip can generally take their personal belongings into Mexico without any problems. Mexican customs provides an exhaustive list of exactly what can and cannot be taken into the country. Instead of memorizing a list, though, simply be reasonable. Anything that resembles commercial goods will raise suspicions, if you're traveling as a tourist. Anything that resembles an illegal drug, a weapon, or ammunition will disrupt your trip and *will* likely land you into prison. Although pets can be brought into Mexico under certain circumstances, the hassle may be more than it's worth; Fido may be better off staying home.

Step Three: Make Copies. To register your car temporarily in Mexico, you'll have to present your tourist card, passport, vehicle title, driver's license, and credit card. You'll be required to present copies of the first four documents during step four. You can save time by making copies of your license, title, and passport identification page before leaving home. There will be someone, likely in a little office, offering to make copies for a fee, likely between 50 cents and a dollar.

Step Four: Banjercito. Banjercito is the official bank of the Mexican army, and one of their jobs is to register cars driven by foreigners into the country. You may have to wait in quite a line at this step, but when you finish here, you'll be done! Make sure that Banjercito is open when you plan to cross. Although larger, downtown border crossings operate 24 hours a day, smaller crossings, such as Los Indios and Nuevo Progreso, tend to keep 'banker's hours,' and may close as early as 4:00 p.m.

At the Banjercito window, present your tourist card, passport, vehicle title, license, credit card, and all copies to the clerk. Make sure the names on all five of these documents are yours; if they don't match, getting a car permit will become much more difficult, if not impossible. After a few minutes, you'll sign an agreement stating you won't sell the car while in Mexico. You'll also sign a credit card slip authorizing a charge of about $30, the current fee for car permits.

It's important to note that only the owner may import his or her own car into Mexico; you won't be allowed to import someone else's car – whether borrowed or rented. And remember that the credit card must be issued to the same person whose name is on the vehicle's title. If you don't have a major credit card, you'll still be able to get a car permit; you'll just have to leave a bond, or deposit, of several hundred dollars *in cash* as a guarantee that you'll take the car back to the States when the trip is over.

When the clerk is finished processing your papers, he or she will present you with a registration certificate and a hologram. The certificate – which serves as the actual permit – should be kept in the car *at all times* when driving in Mexico. Your car could be impounded if you do not carry the permit when driving. The hologram, which has a small microchip, should be placed on the windshield just below the rearview mirror; it serves as visible evidence that your car has been brought into the country legally.

One of the conditions of your car permit is that you will not let anyone else drive your car while in Mexico, unless you are physically present in the vehicle at the time. So, you can't lend your car to a friend or relative. If you do, the authorities will assume the car is stolen and impound it. There are a few specific instances in which someone else *can* drive the car; they're specifically listed on the back of the car permit certificate.

Step Five: You're Done! Now that you have the car permit and hologram attached to the windshield, you're free to drive all over Mexico. About 25 miles past the border, you'll pass a Mexican border patrol checkpoint. You'll probably be asked to show your papers. If so, present the officer your car permit. You may also be asked for your tourist card or passport.

Step Six: Cancel the Permit. When you leave Mexico, make sure you stop by the Banjercito branch at the border and cancel your car permit. Larger border crossings will have a drive-thru window where you can cancel; smaller crossings may require you to get out of the car and stand in line to cancel your permit. Either way, don't forget this step!

Visitors who forget to cancel their car permits won't be fined automatically, contrary to popular belief. However, if they ever try to obtain a car permit in the future, the computer database *will* flag their names and they will be subject to fines of several hundred dollars. So, by all means, cancel the car permit on your way home!

Currency in Mexico. Don't worry about trying to obtain Mexican pesos before your trip. There are plenty of currency exchanges near the border and within the interior of Mexico; in fact, nearly every bank in the country will be happy to exchange currency upon presentation of a passport or other identification.

At most border crossings, there will be one or more currency exchanges just north of the border. These places usually give a fair exchange rate, normally much better than what you'd find at an airport, or even at your hometown bank. Very few currency exchanges at the border charge a commission on top of the exchange rate; those that do should be avoided.

One of the best ways to obtain local currency, though, is via ATM. The ATM card from your local bank should work just fine in Mexico, and the same PIN number will be valid. Although most banks charge a few dollars for an international transaction, you'll likely get a better exchange rate. To come out ahead, withdraw as much cash as possible at a time, instead of just a few dollars' worth at a time.

Mexico's unit of currency is the peso. The symbol for the peso is $, which is the same as our dollar sign. So when you see a meal at a restaurant that costs $90.00, that's 90 pesos, which is a little less than seven dollars. Bills are available in 20, 50, 100, 200, 500, and 1,000 peso denominations. Coins are issued in 10, 5, 2, and 1 peso values, as well as 10, 20, and 50 cents.

A Primer on Driving in Mexico

After you get your car permit, you'll be excited and ready to embark on a journey few Americans ever get to take. Before charging forward, though, review a few tips on driving in Mexico that will make your trip more enjoyable.

Look out for the speed bumps. They're called *topes* (pronounced TOA-pays) in Mexico, and they're giant speed bumps designed to slow you down to almost a halt when approaching a town or major intersection. Hit one of these *topes* at anything more than about five miles per hour, and you're likely to throw your front end out of alignment or do serious damage to your muffler.

Most of the time, *topes* are announced ahead of time with a sign reading "Zona de Topes" or a yellow sign with two or three bumps. In many small communities throughout the republic, *topes* are used in lieu of traffic signals to slow down vehicles near intersections. You'll also find them when approaching a town or school crossing. Be careful; some of these *topes* are hidden and may take you by surprise!

Obtain a good map. Quality road maps in Mexico are hard to come by. Most road atlases sold in the U.S. relegate Mexico to one page in the back. Those maps of the country are practically useless except, perhaps, for locating major cities or states. Unlike the United States, good road maps are not handed out freely by state tourism boards at rest areas; you'll have to buy one.

My favorite is the comprehensive *Guía Roji* road atlas. It covers the entire Mexican republic, as well as much of Guatemala and Belize. They can be bought online or special-ordered through a bookstore. Often, though, you'll find them sold at gas stations in Mexico, so keep your eyes open for one. The basic atlas runs just under 200 pesos, which may seem expensive, but it's money well spent.

Buying gasoline. Fuel, called *gasolina*, is readily available throughout the country. Don't bother shopping around for the best price, though, as only one gasoline brand – government-controlled *Pemex* – is available. *Pemex* stations don't post their prices, but they don't need to, since the price is set by the government and is the same across the Republic. And all stations are full service.

Gas stations accept cash only, as is the case with most roadside businesses in Mexico. They generally don't accept dollars either, so make sure you have a reserve of pesos on hand. Diesel fuel is available at most stations, and unleaded fuel is available in two grades: *Magna* and *Premium*. *Magna* is the equivalent of regular unleaded gas in the U.S. and is rated 87 octane. *Premium* is high-grade gasoline, rated at 93 octane. I've purchased dozens of tanks of gas in Mexico, and I've had virtually no problems with the fuel quality, contrary to what many people might expect.

If you need a fillup, just tell the attendant *Lleno con Magna, por favor*. Make sure he or she resets the gas pump to zero, instead of adding your total to the last customer's – an old scam. Some attendants may wash your windshield, others may not; give him or her a small tip if you feel it's appropriate. Don't be surprised to be approached by vendors selling everything from chewing gum to pirated CD's while waiting for your gas to be dispensed. Most of the merchandise they sell are convenience items; take a look if you feel like it. If you don't, just say *No, gracias*.

Most *Pemex* stations offer public restroom facilities, but they may not be free, even to customers. Don't be surprised to be charged a couple of pesos to use the gas station restroom. And sadly, my experience has been that price is not proportional to cleanliness.

Don't drive at night. During the day, driving in Mexico is just as safe as driving back home. But at night, things change a little. Few highways utilize reflectors or even reflective paint as lane markers. *Topes* are harder to see at night. Some of the locals drive without taillights or even headlights, foolishly thinking it will save gas. Instead of forging ahead at night, plan on getting a hotel and relaxing. Besides, you'll enjoy more of the scenery during daylight hours.

Toll roads and free roads. Most two-lane highways are free of charge. However, heavily-trafficked routes, especially those connecting major cities, have an alternate four-lane toll road that parallels the two-lane road. The two-lane free road is called the *libre*, and the toll road is called the *cuota*. These toll roads are similar to our interstate highways, except that exits are few and far between. Likewise, gas stations and restaurants are a rarity on rural stretches of the *cuota*.

Toll roads are expensive by American standards; they seem to average about one peso – or almost 10 cents U.S. – per mile. Your toll does include insurance and free towing services, though, should you break down or have an accident while on the expressway. And nearly every toll booth will be adjacent to the Mexican equivalent of a rest area, complete with free restroom services and a convenience store.

If you really want to see towns and villages along the way, though, skip the *cuota*. The slower, two-lane *libre* passes through every town and village on the route. However, I recommend taking the *cuota* under two circumstances. First, when you're getting a little tired of following slow trucks and winding around curves and hills, driving on the fast, four-lane *cuota* can be a relief. Second, when bypassing major cities, definitely opt for the *cuota*. Small towns in Mexico are charming and peaceful; large cities are stressful and generally to be avoided. Be aware, though, that even the *libre* may have an occasional toll bridge; most of those are unavoidable.

Military checkpoints. One of the main responsibilities of the Mexican army is to confiscate drugs and guns, both of which are generally illegal in the country. On highways throughout the republic, the army operates checkpoints. You will be expected to slow down and come to a complete stop. They may ask where you're coming from or where you're going. Respond with *Vengo de...* (I'm coming from...) or *Voy a...* (I'm going to...)

The men, most of whom are teenagers or in their early twenties, may ask you to pull over for a routine search. There's no reason to fear; the young men are normally very professional and polite, and they usually treat foreigners with the utmost respect. For your own protection, never bring illegal drugs, a gun, or even as much as a single bullet into Mexico; doing so will mean going to prison.

Speed limits in Mexico. Speed limits are indicated by a number with a red circle around it, measured in kilometers per hour. On the open road, speed limits are disregarded by most vehicles. For example, on a two-lane straight highway, the speed limit may be 80 kph (about 50 mph), but you may see buses and cars driving at least 70 miles per hour, which is over 110 kph! Very little speed enforcement is seen on the open highways.

In towns, though, speed is a different matter. Local traffic cops often look for speeders and write them tickets. Even without enforcement, though, it may be difficult to speed when a series of *topes* slow traffic to a crawl. Bottom line: use your good judgment and common sense when driving in Mexico.

Restaurants. Typical restaurants along the side of the road are plentiful and reasonably priced. If you're willing to spend the equivalent of ten dollars on a meal, you'll eat very well in all but the most expensive of tourist areas. Few servers speak English, so a little Spanish will go a long way. You won't get the check until you ask for it – *La cuenta, por favor* – and there are no free refills on drinks at most diners in Mexico. A 10% tip for good service is well appreciated and considered generous.

Lodging. All but the smallest of towns will have at least one hotel. Unless you're in a resort area, forget the free breakfast, Wi-Fi, and swimming pool. Most hotel rooms will be simply furnished and feature a television, free parking, private bath, hot water, and possibly a phone. Air conditioning *may* cost extra. The prices will usually be posted at the front desk, but may be negotiable. It's common to let the guest see a room before sealing the deal.

Look for hotels with an enclosed parking lot for guests. Many will actually lock your car in their secure lot overnight.

Remember the three main classes of lodging mentioned in Chapter Seven? The situation is similar in Mexico. At the high end are **American-style Hotels**. Many of these are the chains you've heard of from the States, such as Holiday Inn, Best Western, Howard Johnson, and so forth. These hotels, found in only the largest cities, will give you the surroundings you're used to, but the prices are also the highest.

The mid-tier hotels are **Roadside Hotels**. These are not chains, but locally-owned places. The prices usually range from 250 to 500 pesos a night. You'll usually get a clean, comfortable room at these places. Most of them have a restaurant attached or nearby.

Then there are the **Auto Hotels**. Often found at the edge of towns, their prices are usually quite cheap, with an enclosed curtain to conceal your car. However, these motels sometimes appeal to shady characters and those who have something to hide. Several of these places charge by the hour, if you get the idea.

Credit cards. In most of Mexico, credit cards are not yet widely accepted. They may be accepted at large department stores and in tourist

---

Calling Home from Mexico

Calling a U.S. number from Mexico is easy, but expensive. Making a phone call home may still cost eight pesos per minute (about 70¢ U.S.) or even more. Nearly every town will have a *caseta telefónica* – a payphone center – where it's easy to make phone calls to anywhere in the world. Just give the number to the attendant, who will dial it, then direct you to a private booth where you'll have your conversation. At most *casetas*, payment is made after the call. To dial a U.S. number from Mexico, dial 001, followed by the area code and telephone number.

Of course, e-mail is a cheaper and often more convenient way to stay in touch while south of the border.

---

areas frequented by foreigners, but for the most part, cash is king. Although credit cards are uncommon, ATM machines are found at every bank and nearly every chain convenience store – the most common of which is *Oxxo* – in the country.

Local driving customs. Some two-lane roads, especially in the northern half of Mexico, are especially wide. On these roads, you are expected to slide over to the right when being passed. Likewise, if you see an oncoming vehicle passing a car, you're also expected to slide over to the right. This system actually works quite well and serves to accommodate *three* lanes of traffic on a two-lane road.

In some places, especially the North, if you're following a vehicle displaying a left turn signal, that means it's safe to pass. This custom seems to be fading, especially in the South, and isn't seen as often as in years past. Also, motorists in construction zones are expected to drive *much* slower than Americans are used to – 20 to 30 miles per hour maximum.

If your car breaks down. Mexico's tourism agency supports the Green Angels, who patrol major highways looking for motorists who need help. If you break down on the highway or run out of gas, pull over to the side of the road, open the hood, and wait for help. *Los Ángeles Verdes*, as they are sometimes called, provide free repairs, charging only for parts and gasoline. Many of these *Ángeles* speak at least some English.

Staying out of trouble. For the most part, use the same common sense you do at home. Stay out of questionable areas, especially at night. Avoid bars and cantinas, especially on the weekends. Never drink and drive. Be friendly and polite, and most other people will treat you accordingly. The Mexican people are known for their hospitality and friendliness, especially to strangers.

Traffic cops, or *tránsito*, as their uniforms say, may be paid very little. Some of them live off the bribes they manage to pluck from unsuspecting motorists. To avoid them, try to blend in with other vehicles. Don't give them a reason to stop you. Although they may stop you just to perform a routine check of your paperwork – car permit and license – be polite and don't give them a reason to bother you. Even better, bypass major cities if possible, where most of these *tránsito* cops lurk, and stick to smaller towns.

If you live in a state which issues only one license plate, affix a spare license plate to the front of your car after crossing into Mexico. Traffic police may view the lack of a front plate as suspicious, or at least as a reason to stop you. Putting a temporary plate on the front can keep from drawing attention to yourself. Of course, remove the spare plate before crossing back into the U.S.

Really, with only a few exceptions, driving in Mexico is very similar to driving back in the States. Although some of the customs may be different, the same basic rules apply: Know your surroundings, be a courteous driver, and use common sense.

Heading South

The least congested bridge in the Rio Grande Valley is located at Los Indios, just to the southwest of Harlingen. This border crossing is in a rural area with few businesses nearby, so traffic is practically nonexistent. This road continues straight to the first small city on our route: Valle Hermoso. With all the comforts of a prosperous town, it makes for a convenient first stop before continuing to the interior of Mexico; it's also the last stop before leaving the border zone.

Shortly after Valle Hermoso, the road merges south onto Highway 101, the major thoroughfare leading toward Tampico on the coast and Victoria, the capital of the state of Tamaulipas. After skirting the edge of San Fernando, the roadway quickly leaves the Rio Grande Valley behind in favor of the highest hills we've seen on this trip. The elevation rises at least a few hundred feet, which is high for being so close to the Gulf.

Eventually, we get to a major intersection where we can head to Victoria or to Tampico. We turn left, taking us almost due south, in the direction of Tampico. This route, Highway 180, is the route we will generally follow all the way to the Emerald Coast. But first, we must traverse the flat savannah leading up to the town of Soto La Marina and the river sharing its name.

Soon, the road starts to wind around hills and mountains, passing through the most hauntingly desolate stretch of highway we'll pass this side of the Rio Grande. Although several cars and buses take this road, towns are few and far between. All of a sudden, you've crossed a major milestone; twenty-eight miles after leaving Soto La Marina, you cross the Tropic of Cancer.

As we travel farther into the tropics, the climate slowly becomes warmer and more humid. The town of Aldama, the first town we pass in the tropics, is known for fishing and subterranean rivers that attract cave divers from around the world.

Using the Internet in Mexico

Hotels in Mexico rarely offer free wireless internet – or internet service of any type, for that matter. The easiest way to get online is to visit an internet shop – usually signed *Internet* or *Renta de Computadoras* – and pay by the hour. Most of the time, renting a computer costs less than two dollars an hour, occasionally a little more. I've paid as little as five pesos an hour (about 50¢) and as much as 25 pesos an hour. Of course, printing costs extra.

Good Places to Spend the Night

Here are a few towns in Mexico where I've spent the night en route to other places. These towns are convenient to the major highway and have relatively inexpensive lodging options. They're listed in order from north to south.

Nuevo Progreso – Look for the Las Flores Inn on the south side of town. Restaurant, convenient parking, in a relatively quiet area of this border town.

Valle Hermoso – Several hotels, but the less expensive ones tend to be on the north side of town, before getting to the central business district.

Highway 101 – Look for the large hotel on the right, next to the Pemex station, at the intersection of Highways 101 and 97 – exactly 47 miles south of Valle Hermoso.

Tampico Alto – Just south of Tampico on Highway 180. Two hotels are located across the street from one another. Both have enclosed parking and are within walking distance of several small restaurants.

Cerro Azul – About 80 miles south of Tampico. The Hotel San Carlos sits on a steep hill, but has protected parking and a couple of restaurants nearby.

Alamo – This town has a few lodging options. Restaurants and other services are within walking distance of all hotels.

Nearing Tampico

Arriving at the town of Manuel, you see the first stoplight in many miles. Turn left and continue toward Tampico. As we drive along the first four lane rural highway we've been on in Mexico, the route passes morevillages and settlements, especially as we near the city of Tampico. The highway flattens out, though, signaling our nearness to the Gulf coast. We pass the edges of Altamira, a suburb of Tampico, and the once rural highway becomes a bustling, urban thoroughfare. Instead of heading straight into Tampico, though, we take a bypass around the city's worst congestion. Signaling the bypass is a large fishing boat parked on the right side of the highway.

The bypass starts as a two-lane highway, curving around homes and settlements. The terrain through here is swampy, as our elevation is no more than about 30 feet. As the two-lane bypass ends, we take the ramp to the right, crossing a large river that carries us into the state of Veracruz. This part of the Tampico area is filled with small businesses and industry. After a few miles on this four-lane street, take the exit ramp marked for "Tuxpan".

This new road shifts back down to two lanes as we cross another bridge and pay another toll. As soon as it looks like we're back in the countryside, we pass through another little town, Anahuac. It's slow going through here, as trucks and buses clog this little highway to avoid the city, too. At the fork in the road, veer to the left, climbing a steep hill. Soon, you're back on the main road – Highway 180 – and we turn right, heading south on the federal highway again.

The Hills of Northern Veracruz

Shortly, we hit the southern edge of the Tampico metropolitan area, passing through the town of Tampico Alto. It's a good place to spend the night, as the town has several hotels and restaurants easily accessible from the highway. Continuing south for the next 80 miles, the terrain transitions from a flat coastal plain to rolling hills. By the time you get to Cerro Azul, about 80 miles south of Tampico, we're clearly in a mountainous area. You can look to your left and see practically the whole town, nestled in the valley below. All the while, though, we're no more than a few miles from the Gulf coast.

About eight miles past Cerro Azul, we turn right, then turn left less than a mile later, avoiding the city of Tuxpan in favor of the smaller town of Alamo. Officially, this 'shortcut' is labeled Highway 131, and it takes us on an alternating route between tropical plains and steep hills. Several miles after passing Alamo, we see a sign that reads "Veracruz Cuota". This is the road to take that bypasses the congested oil city of Poza Rica. It's quite a scenic highway, too, as it takes us around the steepest mountains in the region at high speed.

Follow this two-lane *cuota* bypass until it ends, shortly after the toll booth. Then turn left, returning to Mexico 180. You're back in the mountains, and you'll cross several rivers, hills, and streams before getting to the town of Tecolutla and the toll bridge that shares its name. Then, almost exactly ten miles after crossing the bridge, we see a welcome sight on our left – the Gulf of Mexico.

Costa Esmeralda

The plentiful palms you see all around the highway and the hotels you see on both sides of the road are a sure sign the beach is near. You've reached *Costa Esmeralda*, the Emerald Coast, as it's called in English. Highway 180 stays within sight of the beach for the next several miles, all the way to the town of Casitas.

Beachside hotels in this area are inexpensive and range in level from the most basic of roadside inns to the more comfortable and modern. Many of the managers speak English, and a room can sometimes be had for as little as 250 pesos. The little town of Casitas is also a great place to try local seafood – caught that very morning – for very reasonable prices. It's here where our journey into Mexico ends. But this is really only the beginning, for the possibilities are endless if you decide to continue your tropical trek even further. Hang on to your map; it will be your guide to the roadtrip of a lifetime!

Returning to the U.S.A.

When you drive your car across the Rio Grande back into the United States, you'll have to wait in line at the border station – anywhere from five minutes up to three hours, depending on traffic that day. The border patrol inspector will ask for your passports and may ask where you were born and if you're bringing anything back. The inspector may also ask about the purpose of your trip and want to know where you've been. Answer honestly. Your car and luggage may be searched. Remember that you're generally not allowed to bring fresh fruits, vegetables, or meats back into the United States. Even if your vehicle is searched, you'll likely be detained only a few minutes during the actual inspection.

Spanish Primer

Although it's not obligatory to speak Spanish to take a roadtrip to Mexico, it certainly helps. Even if you don't, though, here are a few words and phrases to help you get by:

Basics

por favor [por fah-VOHR]	please
gracias [GRAH-see-ahs]	Thank you
baño [BAH-nyoh]	bathroom, restroom
gratis [GRAH-tees]	free
pasaporte [pah-sah-POR-tay]	passport
un momento [oon moe-MEHN-toe]	one moment

Eating Out

almuerzo [al-MWER-soe]	lunch
desayuno [day-cye-OO-noe]	breakfast
cena [SAY-nah]	dinner
¿Cuánto cuesta? [KWAHN-toe KWAYS-tah]	How much does it cost?
La cuenta [lah KWEN-tah]	the bill, the check
abierto [ah-bee-AIR-toe]	open
cerrado [say-RAH-doe]	closed

On the Road

despacio [des-PAH-see-oe]	slow
cuota [KWOE-tah]	toll, fee, toll road
libre [LEE-bray]	free road
topes [TOE-pays]	speed bumps
la carretera a [la car-reh-TEHR-ah ah]	The highway to
Dónde está... [DOHN-day es-TAH]	Where is...?
mecánico [meh-KAHN-ee-koe]	mechanic
No sirve [no SEER-vay]	It doesn't work.

Lodging

hotel [oh-TELL]	hotel
una habitación [oo-nah ah-bee-tah-see-OHN]	A hotel room
dos camas [dohs KAH-mahs]	two beds
clima [KLEE-mah]	climate, air conditioner

The Cold, Hard Facts About Traveling in Mexico

Every serious roadtripper should take a drive down to Mexico at least once. In the interest of full disclosure, though, travelers should know that it's not always a carefree ride south of the border. There are some key differences you should be aware of:

1. Most roads in Mexico, especially two-lane *libre* highways, are not up to the quality of American highways. Many rural highways are in poor condition and marked by potholes and ruts. Drive much slower on these roads. Although the four-lane *cuotas* are better, some of those aren't that great, either.

2. Under no circumstances should you ever take illegal drugs, guns, or even a single bullet into Mexico. If caught, you *will* go to prison.

3. If you think public restrooms are bad in the United States, just wait until you get to Mexico! Hand sanitizer is a must, as is your own roll of toilet paper. Taking your own paper towels isn't a bad idea, either. Don't throw paper into the toilet, as it may clog the plumbing.

4. Water systems are not as reliable in Mexico, especially in rural areas. It's not unusual for water towers to be shut off at night or at other times. I've heard of areas being without running water for weeks at a time. And, of course, don't drink the tap water; bottled water is plentiful and cheap.

5. Most importantly, use common sense. Travelers who stay out of question-able situations rarely experience any serious problems in Mexico. Although it's very different from what most Americans are used to, a visit to our southern neighbor is filled with treasures at every turn of the road and is well worth any minor inconveniences that you will encounter.

CHAPTER 15

Roadtrip Resources

Each U.S. state and Canadian province operates a tourism department which provides free vacation guides and maps. These free guides highlight places of interest you may find worth a stop along your way. To request free information by mail, visit the following websites, and click on the link that directs you to 'more information', 'vacation guide', or 'free travel guide.' For most states, you can also download information directly from the web or request information by phone.

State Tourism Information

Alabama

    www.800alabama.com   1-800-ALABAMA

Alaska

    www.travelalaska.com

Arizona

    www.arizonaguide.com   1-866-275-5816

Arkansas

    www.arkansas.com

California
       www.visitcalifornia.com   1-877-225-4367

Colorado
       www.colorado.com   1-800-COLORADO

Connecticut
       www.ctvisit.com   1-888-CTVISIT

Delaware
       www.visitdelaware.com   1-866-284-7483

D.C.
       www.washington.org   1-202-789-7000

Florida
       www.visitflorida.com   1-850-488-5607

Georgia
       www.exploregeorgia.org   1-800-VISIT-GA

Hawaii
       www.hawaiitourismauthority.org
                                                  1-808-973-2255

Idaho
       www.visitidaho.org   1-800-VISIT-ID

Illinois
       www.enjoyillinois.com   1-800-2-CONNECT

Indiana
       www.in.gov/visitindiana   1-800-677-9800

Iowa

    www.traveliowa.com   1-888-472-6035

Kansas

    www.travelks.com   1-800-2-KANSAS

Kentucky

    www.kytourism.com   1-800-225-8747

Louisiana

    www.louisianatravel.com

Maine

    www.visitmaine.com   1-888-624-6345

Maryland

    www.visitmaryland.org   1-866-639-3526

Massachusetts

    www.massvacation.com   1-800-227-MASS

Michigan

    www.michigan.org   1-800-644-2489

Minnesota

    www.exploreminnesota.com   1-888-TOURISM

Mississippi

    www.visitmississippi.org   1-866-SEE-MISS

Missouri

    www.visitmo.com   1-800-519-2100

Montana

    www.visitmt.com   1-800-847-4868

Nebraska
    www.visitnebraska.gov   1-877-NEBRASKA

Nevada
    travelnevada.com   1-800-NEVADA-8

New Hampshire
    www.visitnh.gov   1-800-FUN-IN-NH

New Jersey
    www.state.nj.us/travel   1-800-VISIT-NJ

New Mexico
    www.newmexico.org

New York
    www.iloveny.com   1-800-CALL-NYS

North Carolina
    www.visitnc.com   1-800-VISIT-NC

North Dakota
    www.ndtourism.com   1-800-435-5663

Ohio
    consumer.discoverohio.com   1-800-BUCKEYE

Oklahoma
    www.travelok.com   1-800-652-6552

Oregon
    www.traveloregon.com   1-800-547-7842

Pennsylvania
    www.visitpa.com   1-800-VISIT-PA

Rhode Island
>   www.visitrhodeisland.com   1-800-250-7384

South Carolina
>   www.discoversouthcarolina.com   1-866-224-9339

South Dakota
>   www.travelsd.com   1-800-S-DAKOTA

Tennessee
>   www.tnvacation.com   1-615-741-2159

Texas
>   www.traveltex.com   1-800-8888-TEX

Utah
>   www.utah.com   1-800-200-1160

Vermont
>   www.vermontvacation.com   1-800-VERMONT

Virginia
>   www.virginia.org   1-800-VISIT-VA

Washington
>   www.experiencewa.com   1-800-544-1800

West Virginia
>   www.wvtourism.com   1-800-CALL-WVA

Wisconsin
>   www.travelwisconsin.com   1-800-432-8747

Wyoming
>   www.wyomingtourism.org   1-800-225-5996

<u>Canadian Provinces</u>

Alberta
   www.travelalberta.com   1-800-ALBERTA

British Columbia
   www.hellobc.com   1-800-435-5622

Manitoba
   www.travelmanitoba.com   1-800-665-0040

New Brunswick
   www.tourismnewbrunswick.ca   1-800-561-0123

Northwest Territories
   www.gov.nt.ca

Newfoundland & Labrador
   www.newfoundlandlabrador.com   1-800-563-6353

Nova Scotia
   www.novascotia.com   1-800-565-0000

Nunavut
   www.nunavuttourism.com   1-866-NUNAVUT

Ontario
   www.ontariotravel.net   1-800-ONTARIO

Prince Edward Island
   www.tourismpei.com   1-800-463-4-PEI

Quebec
   www.bonjourquebec.com   1-877-BONJOUR

Saskatchewan
   www.sasktourism.com   1-877-2-ESCAPE

Yukon

travelyukon.com   1-800-661-0494

Packing

In addition to the packing list highlighted in Chapter 11, the following websites are excellent resources for travelers looking to pack light.

www.onebag.com - Learn to put everything in one bag.

www.ricksteves.com/plan/tips/packlist.htm - Although this list is tailored to European travel, most of the principles apply to roadtrips, too.

Dining on the Road

www.roadfood.com - The best website for finding local diners on the road. Complemented by the book *Roadfood*, also available for purchase on the site and at bookstores.

www.restaurant.com - A good resource for finding discount gift certificates for independently-owned restaurants across the country. Most $25 gift certificates can be bought for $10 on the site, saving you more than 50%.

www.fatwallet.com - A series of discussion boards for sharing restaurant coupons, and any other type of coupon, for that matter. This site will direct you to sales, coupons, and other travel deals available both on the web and in traditional stores.

Roadtrip Planning

www.roadtripamerica.com - The country's best discussion board for planning a route. Includes great roadtrip ideas and dozens of experienced roadtrippers sharing advice.

maps.google.com – One of the easiest to use online mapping services. Also integrates satellite imagery from Google Earth. Changing a route is as easy as dragging a line to a different road you wish to take.

www.mapquest.com - The granddaddy of mapping services on the web. Mapquest integrates local business information and makes it easy to get door-to-door directions to your next destination.

www.randmcnally.com - Complete with features that integrate seamlessly with Rand McNally's printed road atlas. Also includes turn-by-turn directions and ideas for roadtrips.

Weather Conditions

www.weather.gov - Complete forecasts, current conditions, and meteorological data for anywhere in America. Enter any city and state combination in the country, and complete radar, satellite, and forecast information will be shown immediately.

www.weather.com - The Weather Channel's website. Special links for travel weather. Includes tips for driving in various types of weather.

www.weather.com/outlook/driving/interstate/regional?reg=us – This link at the Weather Channel deserves its own link. At a glance, determine which parts of the country's roads are dangerous for travel.

Gas Prices

www.gasbuddy.com - The most thorough information on gas prices available on the web, submitted by thousands of volunteer participants. Find the cheapest gas prices in a region with an interactive color-coded map.

Comparing Hotel Prices and Quality

www.priceline.com - Usually the cheapest avenue for booking a hotel room. Granted, you won't get to choose your hotel; it will be assigned to you based on your chosen star level and price. Also, you have to wait to see if the hotel accepts your price. Still, the savings can be as much as 50% off the lowest published rate.

www.hotwire.com - Usually a few dollars more expensive than Priceline, but you get to choose the amenities your hotel will have. And there's no waiting to see if your offer is accepted; the price you see *always* gets accepted. Often the best choice when you need a discount hotel room the same day, and you need to book it quickly.

www.betterbidding.com - Web message board where people share their winning bids for Priceline and Hotwire. Takes much of the guesswork out of booking a room on these two websites.

biddingfortravel.yuku.com - Similar to BetterBidding, except this site covers only Priceline.

www.expedia.com - Book hotels, car rentals, and plane tickets.

www.orbitz.com - This site makes it easy to compare prices for plane tickets, as well as hotels and cars.

www.travelocity.com - Another good source for comparing hotel rates and reserving a room online.

www.hotels.com - A useful site for comparing hotel prices in a city and making your reservation.

www.skyauction.com - An auction site for travelers. Bid on stays at resort properties and hotels across the world. There are some excellent deals to be had on this site, if you're willing to do some research and be *very* flexible.

www.tripadvisor.com - The most comprehensive site for user-generated hotel reviews. Practically every hotel, motel, and inn in the United States is reviewed on this site. Some negative reviews should be taken with a grain of salt, but if a location's negative reviews outnumber its positive ones, beware.

Hotel Chains by Classification

High-end Hotels – These hotels cater to business travelers and higher-budget travelers. Expect more luxurious furnishings and public areas. Many of these hotels feature an indoor pool and gym. You'll probably pay extra for breakfast and internet, though.

Clarion Hotels	www.clarionhotel.com
Crowne Plaza	www.crowneplaza.com
Doubletree	doubletree.hilton.com
Embassy Suites	embassysuites.hilton.com
Four Points by Sheraton	www.fourpoints.com
Hilton	www.hilton.com
Holiday Inn	www.holidayinn.com
Hyatt	www.hyatt.com
Hyatt Place	www.hyatt.com/hyatt/place
Marriott	www.marriott.com
Omni	www.omnihotels.com
Radisson	www.radisson.com
Renaissance	www.renaissancehotels.com
Sheraton Hotels	www.sheraton.com

Roadside Chains – These hotels/motels cater to leisure travelers, roadtrippers, and those on a budget. Expect modest, comfortable furnishings. Unless stated otherwise, breakfast and internet service are usually free.

AmericInn	www.americinn.com
America's Best Value Inn	www.americasbestvalueinn.com
Baymont Inn & Suites	www.baymontinns.com

Best Western	www.bestwestern.com
Comfort Inn	www.comfortinn.com
Comfort Suites	www.comfortsuites.com
Country Inns & Suites	www.countryinns.com
Courtyard by Marriott	www.courtyard.com
Days Inn	www.daysinn.com
Drury Inn	wwwc.druryhotels.com
Econo Lodge	www.econolodge.com
Fairfield Inn by Marriott	www.fairfieldinn.com
Hampton Inn (Hilton)	hamptoninn.hilton.com
Hilton Garden Inn	hiltongardeninn.hilton.com
Howard Johnson	www.hojo.com
Jameson Inn	www.jamesoninns.com
Knights Inn	www.knightsinn.com
La Quinta Inn & Suites	www.lq.com
Microtel	www.microtelinn.com
Motel 6	www.motel6.com
Ramada Inn	www.ramada.com
Red Roof Inn	www.redroof.com
Rodeway Inn	www.rodewayinn.com
Sleep Inn	www.sleepinn.com
Travelodge	www.travelodge.com
Wingate Inn	www.wingatehotels.com

Extended-Stay Properties – Lodging at this level usually won't provide a free breakfast, but you will have access to an in-room kitchen, complete with refrigerator and stove, where you can prepare your own meals. Internet access will be available, but you *may* have to pay extra.

Candlewood Suites	www.candlewoodsuites.com
Extended Stay America	www.extendedstayamerica.com
Hawthorn Suites	www.hawthorn.com
Homestead Studio Suites	www.homesteadhotels.com
Homewood Suites	homewoodsuites.hilton.com
Mainstay Suites	www.mainstaysuites.com
Residence Inn by Marriott	www.residenceinn.com

Staybridge Suites   www.staybridgesuites.com
Studio 6   www.staystudio6.com

Speed Limits by State

Each state's speed limits for passenger vehicles on rural interstate highways are as follows:

Alabama	70
Alaska	65 (on major two-lane highways)
Arizona	75
Arkansas	70
California	70 (Handheld phone use prohibited)
Colorado	75
Connecticut	65 (Handheld phone use prohibited)
Delaware	65
D.C.	55 (Handheld phones prohibited; radar detectors illegal)
Florida	70
Georgia	70
Hawaii	60
Idaho	75
Illinois	65
Indiana	70
Iowa	70
Kansas	70
Kentucky	70
Louisiana	70
Maine	65
Maryland	65
Mass.	65
Michigan	70
Minnesota	70 (Nothing may be hung from windshield, e.g. radar detector, GPS)
Mississippi	70
Missouri	70
Montana	75

Nebraska	75
Nevada	75
New Hamp.	65
New Jersey	65 (Handheld phone use prohibited)
New Mexico	75
New York	65 (Handheld phone use prohibited)
N. Carolina	70
N. Dakota	75
Ohio	65
Oklahoma	70 (75 on turnpikes)
Oregon	65
Pennsylvania	65
Rhode Island	65
S. Carolina	70
S. Dakota	75
Tennessee	70
Texas	70 (as high as 80 in parts of rural West Texas)
Utah	75 (as high as 80 on selected sections of I-15)
Vermont	65
Virginia	65 (70 on I-85; radar detectors illegal)
Washington	70 (Handheld phone use prohibited)
W. Virginia	70
Wisconsin	65
Wyoming	75

INDEX

<u>Trip Notes</u>

<u>Trip Notes</u>

Trip Notes

<u>Trip Notes</u>

To obtain additional copies of this book or find out about upcoming works by Jeremy Krug, visit the author's website at www.theroadtripbook.com.

Acero Publishing
Books for the 21ˢᵗ Century

CPSIA information can be obtained at www.ICGtesting.com
Printed in the USA
BVOW021034111012

302765BV00016B/187/P